Neumann Sept. 67

THEORY OF CATEGORIES

PURE AND APPLIED MATHEMATICS

A Series of Monographs and Textbooks

Edited by

PAUL A. SMITH and SAMUEL EILENBERG

Columbia University, New York

I: ARNOLD SOMMERFELD. Partial Differential Equations in Physics. 1949 (Lectures on Theoretical Physics, Volume VI)

II: REINHOLD BAER. Linear Algebra and Projective Geometry. 1952

III: HERBERT BUSEMANN AND PAUL KELLY. Projective Geometry and Projective Metrics. 1953

IV: STEFAN BERGMAN AND M. SCHIFFER. Kernel Functions and Elliptic Differential Equations in Mathematical Physics. 1953

V: RALPH PHILIP BOAS, JR. Entire Functions. 1954

VI: HERBERT BUSEMANN. The Geometry of Geodesics. 1955

VII: CLAUDE CHEVALLEY. Fundamental Concepts of Algebra. 1956

VIII: SZE-TSEN HU. Homotopy Theory. 1959

IX: A. OSTROWSKI. Solution of Equations and Systems of Equations. 1960

X: J. DIEUDONNÉ. Foundations of Modern Analysis. 1960

XI: S. I. GOLDBERG. Curvature and Homology. 1962

XII: SIGURDUR HELGASON. Differential Geometry and Symmetric Spaces. 1962

XIII: T. H. HILDEBRANDT. Introduction to the Theory of Integration. 1963

XIV: SHREERAM ABHYANKAR. Local Analytic Geometry. 1964

XV: RICHARD L. BISHOP AND RICHARD J. CRITTENDEN. Geometry of Manifolds. 1964

XVI: STEVEN A. GAAL. Point Set Topology. 1964

XVII: BARRY MITCHELL. Theory of Categories. 1965

XVIII: ANTHONY P. MORSE. A Theory of Sets. 1965

In preparation:

A. M. OSTROWSKI. Solutions of Equations and Systems of Equations. 2nd Edition.

GUSTAVE CHOQUET. Topology.

JOSÉ LUIS MASSERA AND JUAN JORGE SCHÄFFER. Linear Differential Equations and Function Spaces.

Z. I. BOREVICH AND I. R. SHAFAREVICH. Number Theory.

THEORY OF CATEGORIES

BARRY MITCHELL

1965

ACADEMIC PRESS New York and London

ACADEMIC PRESS INC.
111 Fifth Avenue, New York, New York 10003

United Kingdom Edition published by
ACADEMIC PRESS INC. (LONDON) LTD.
Berkeley Square House, London W.1

LIBRARY OF CONGRESS CATALOG CARD NUMBER: 65-22761

PRINTED IN THE UNITED STATES OF AMERICA.

Preface

A number of sophisticated people tend to disparage category theory as consistently as others disparage certain kinds of classical music. When obliged to speak of a category they do so in an apologetic tone, similar to the way some say, "It was a gift—I've never even played it" when a record of Chopin Nocturnes is discovered in their possession. For this reason I add to the usual prerequisite that the reader have a fair amount of mathematical sophistication, the further prerequisite that he have no other kind.

Functors, categories, natural transformations, and duality were introduced in the early 1940's by Eilenberg and MacLane [10, 11]. Originally, the purpose of these notions was to provide a technique for clarifying certain concepts, such as that of natural isomorphism. Category theory as a field in itself lay relatively dormant during the following ten years. Nevertheless some work was done by MacLane [28, 29], who introduced the important idea of defining kernels, cokernels, direct sums, etc., in terms of universal mapping properties rather than in terms of the elements of the objects involved. MacLane also gave some insight into the nature of the duality principle, illustrating it with the dual nature of the frees and the divisibles in the category of abelian groups (the projectives and injectives, respectively, in that category). Then with the writing of the book "Homological Algebra" by Cartan and Eilenberg [6], it became apparent that most propositions concerning finite diagrams of modules could be proved in a more general type of category and, moreover, that the number of such propositions could be halved through the use of duality. This led to a full-fledged investigation of abelian categories by Buchsbaum [3] (therein called exact categories). Grothendieck's paper [20] soon followed, and in it were introduced the important notions of A.B.5 category and generators for a category. (The latter idea had been touched on by MacLane [29].) Since then the theory has flourished considerably, not only in the direction of generalizing and simplifying much of the already known theorems in homological algebra, but also in its own right, notably through the imbedding theorems and their metatheoretic consequences.

In Chapters I–III and V, I have attempted to lay a unified groundwork for the subject. The other chapters deal with matters of more specific interest. Each chapter has an introduction which gives a summary of the material to follow. I shall therefore be brief in giving a description of the contents.

In Chapter I, certain notions leading to the definition of abelian category are introduced. Chapter II deals with general matters involving diagrams, limits, and functors. In the closing sections there is a discussion of generators, projectives, and small objects. Chapter III contains a number of equivalent formulations of the Grothendieck axiom A.B.5 (herein called C_3) and some of its consequences. In particular the Eckmann and Schopf results on injective envelopes [8] are obtained. Peter Freyd's proof of the group valued imbedding theorem is given in Chapter IV. The resulting metatheorem enables one to prove certain statements about finite diagrams in general abelian categories by chasing diagrams of abelian groups. A theory of adjoint functors which includes a criterion for their existence is developed in Chapter V. Also included here is a theory of projective classes which is due to Eilenberg and Moore [12]. The following chapter is devoted to applications of adjoints. Principal among these are the tensor product, derived and coderived functors for group-valued functors, and the full imbedding theorem. The full imbedding theorem asserts that any small abelian category admits a full, exact imbedding into the category of **R**-modules for some ring **R**. The metatheory of Chapter IV can thus be extended to theorems involving the existence of morphisms in diagrams. Following Yoneda [36], in Chapter VII we develop the theory of Ext in terms of long exact sequences. The exactness of the connected sequence is proved without the use of projectives or injectives. The proof is by Steven Schanuel. Chapter VIII contains Buchsbaum's construction for satellites of additive functors when the domain does not necessarily have projectives [5]. The exactness of the connected sequence for cosatellites of half exact functors is proved in the case where the codomain is a C_3 category. In Chapter IX we obtain results for global dimension in certain categories of diagrams. These include the Hilbert syzygy theorem and some new results on global dimension of matrix rings. Here we find the main application of the projective class theory of Chapter V. Finally, in Chapter X we give a theory of sheaves with values in a category. This is a reorganization of some work done by Gray [19], and gives a further application of the theory of adjoint functors.

We shall be using the language of the Gödel-Bernays set theory as presented in the appendix to Kelley's book "General Topology" [25]. Thus we shall be distinguishing between sets and classes, where by definition a set is a class which is a member of some other class. A detailed knowledge of the theory is not essential. The words *family* and *collection* will be used synonymously with the word *set*.

With regard to terminology, what has previously been called a direct product is herein called a product. In the category of sets, the product of a family is the cartesian product. Generally speaking, if a notion which commutes with products has been called a gadget, then the dual notion has been called a cogadget. In particular what has been known as a direct sum here goes under the name of coproduct. The exceptions to the rule are monomorphism-epimorphism, injective-projective, and pullback-pushout. In these cases euphony has prevailed. In any event the words left and right have been eliminated from the language.

The system of internal references is as follows. Theorem 4.3 of Chapter V is referred to as V, 4.3 if the reference is made outside of Chapter V, and as 4.3 otherwise. The end of each proof is indicated by ∎.

I wish to express gratitude to David Buchsbaum who has given me much assistance over the years, and under whose supervision I have worked out a number of proofs in this book. I have received encouragement from MacLane on a number of occasions, and the material on Ext is roughly as presented in one of his courses during 1959. The value of conversations with Peter Freyd cannot be overestimated, and I have made extensive use of his very elegant work. Conversations with Eilenberg, who has read parts of the manuscript, have helped sharpen up some of the results, and have led to the system of terminology which I have adopted. In particular he has suggested a proof of IX, 7.2 along the lines given here. This has replaced a clumsier proof of an earlier draft, and has led me to make fairly wide use of the projective class theory.

This book has been partially supported by a National Science Foundation Grant at Columbia University.

I particularly wish to thank Miss Linda Schmidt, whose patience and accuracy have minimized the difficulties in the typing of the manuscript.

B. Mitchell

Columbia University, New York

May, 1964

Contents

III. Complete Categories

IV. Group Valued Functors

V. Adjoint Functors

VI. Applications of Adjoint Functors

VII. Extensions

VIII. Satellites

IX. Global Dimension

X. Sheaves

[CHAPTER I]

Preliminaries

Introduction

In this chapter the basic notions and lemmas involving finite diagrams are given. These notions are equalizers, pullbacks, intersections, unions, images, inverse images, kernels, normality, products, and the duals of these. In general, the material is organized in such a way as to lead up to a very economical characterization of abelian categories (20.1) although some of the propositions will not be needed until much later. In the last section we give a discussion of the category of abelian groups, and the technique of diagram chasing is illustrated with the 5 lemma.

1. Definition

A **category** is a class $\mathscr{A}$, together with a class $\mathscr{M}$ which is a disjoint union of the form

$$\mathscr{M} = \bigcup_{(A,B)\in\mathscr{A}\times\mathscr{A}} [A, B]_{\mathscr{A}}.$$

To avoid logical difficulties we postulate that each $[A, B]_{\mathscr{A}}$ is a set (possibly void. When there is danger of no confusion we shall write $[A, B]$ in place of $[A, B]_{\mathscr{A}}$.) Furthermore, for each triple (A, B, C) of members of $\mathscr{A}$ we are to have a function from $[B, C] \times [A, B]$ to $[A, C]$. The image of the pair (β, α) under this function will be called the **composition** of β by α, and will be denoted by $\beta\alpha$. The composition functions are subject to two axioms.

(i) *Associativity:* Whenever the compositions make sense we have $(\gamma\beta)\alpha = \gamma(\beta\alpha)$.

(ii) *Existence of identities:* For each $A \in \mathscr{A}$ we have an element $1_A \in [A, A]$ such that $1_A\alpha = \alpha$ and $\beta 1_A = \beta$ whenever the compositions make sense.

The members of $\mathscr{A}$ are called **objects** and the members of $\mathscr{M}$ are called **morphisms**. If $\alpha \in [A, B]$ we shall call A the **domain** of α and B the

codomain, and we shall say "α is a morphism from A to B." This last statement is represented symbolically by "$\alpha : A \to B$," or sometimes "$A \xrightarrow{\alpha} B$." When there is no need to name the morphism in question, we shall simply write $A \to B$.

Observe that 1_A can be the only identity for A, for if e is another we must have $e = e1_A = 1_A$. We sometimes write $1_A : A = A$ in the case of identity morphisms.

If $\mathscr{A}$ is a set, then the category will be called **small.** In this case $\mathscr{M}$, being a union of sets indexed over a set, is also a set.

We shall commit a common notational inconsistency in denoting the above category by the underlying class $\mathscr{A}$.

2. The Nonobjective Approach

Reluctant as we are to introduce any abstraction into the theory, we must remark that there is an alternative definition for category which dispenses with the notion of objects. A category can be defined as a class $\mathscr{M}$, together with a binary operation on $\mathscr{M}$, called **composition**, which is not always defined (that is, a function from a subclass of $\mathscr{M} \times \mathscr{M}$ to $\mathscr{M}$). The image of the pair (β, α) under this operation is denoted by $\beta\alpha$ (if defined). An element $e \in \mathscr{M}$ is called an **identity** if $e\alpha = \alpha$ and $\beta e = \beta$ whenever the compositions are defined. We assume the following axioms:

(1) If either $(\gamma\beta)\alpha$ or $\gamma(\beta\alpha)$ is defined, then the other is defined, and they are equal.
(2) If $\gamma\beta$ and $\beta\alpha$ are defined and β is an identity, then $\gamma\alpha$ is defined.
(3) Given $\alpha \in \mathscr{M}$, there are identities e_L and e_R in $\mathscr{M}$ such that $e_L\alpha$ and αe_R are defined (and hence equal α).
(4) For any pair of identities e_L and e_R, the class $\{\alpha \in \mathscr{M} \mid (e_L\alpha)e_R \text{ is defined}\}$ is a set.

Clearly our first definition of category gives us a category of the second type. Conversely, given a class $\mathscr{M}$ satisfying the postulates (1) to (4), we proceed to show how this can be associated with a category of the first type. We index the class of identities in $\mathscr{M}$ by a class $\mathscr{A}$, denoting the identity corresponding to $A \in \mathscr{A}$ by 1_A. Now if $\alpha \in \mathscr{M}$, then there can be only one identity such that $\alpha 1_A$ is defined. For if $1_{A'}$ is another, then we have $\alpha 1_{A'} = (\alpha 1_A)1_{A'}$, and so by (1) the composition $1_A 1_{A'}$ is defined. Since both are identities we must then have $1_A = 1_{A'}$. The unique $A \in \mathscr{A}$ such that $\alpha 1_A$ is defined is called the **domain** of α. Similarly, the unique $B \in \mathscr{A}$ such that $1_B\alpha$ is defined is called the **codomain** of α. We denote by $[A, B]$ the class of members of $\mathscr{M}$ with domain A and codomain B. Then $[A, B]$ is a set by (4), and by (3) $\mathscr{M}$ is the disjoint union $\bigcup [A, B]$.

Next we show that $\beta\alpha$ is defined if and only if the codomain of α is the domain of β. Suppose that $\beta\alpha$ is defined, and let B be the codomain of α. Then $\beta(1_B\alpha)$ is defined, and so $\beta 1_B$ is defined by (1). In other words, B is the domain of β. Conversely, if the codomain of α is the same as the domain of β, then $\beta\alpha$ is defined by (2).

Therefore composition can be regarded as a union of functions of the type $[B, C] \times [A, B] \to \mathcal{M}$. We must show, finally, that the image of such a function is in $[A, C]$. That is, we must show that if $\beta\alpha$ is defined, then the domain of $\beta\alpha$ is the domain of α, and the codomain of $\beta\alpha$ is the codomain of β. But this follows easily from (1).

3. Examples

1. The category $\mathcal{S}$ whose class of objects is the class of all sets, where $[A, B]_{\mathcal{S}}$ is the class of all functions from A to B, is called the **category of sets.** It is not small.

2. A similar definition applies to the category $\mathcal{T}$ of all **topological spaces**, where the morphisms from space A to space B are the continuous functions from A to B.

3. The category $\mathcal{S}_0$ of **sets with base point** is the category whose objects are ordered pairs (A, a) where A is a set and $a \in A$. A morphism from (A, a) to (B, b) is a function f from A to B such that $f(a) = b$.

4. Replacing sets by topological spaces and functions by continuous functions in example 3 we obtain the category $\mathcal{T}_0$ of **topological spaces with base point.**

5. If $\mathcal{M}$ has only one identity (so that composition is always defined), we call the category a **semigroup** and we replace the word "composition" by "multiplication." Hence an alternative word for "category" would be "semigroupoid"—a semigroup where multiplication is not always defined. If $\beta\alpha = \alpha\beta$ for every pair of morphisms in a semigroup, then the semigroup is called **abelian**. In this case composition is usually called addition, and $\alpha + \beta$ is written in place of $\alpha\beta$. Furthermore, the identity is called **zero** and is denoted by 0.

6. We shall say that a category $\mathcal{A}'$ is a **subcategory** of a category $\mathcal{A}$ under the following conditions:

   (i) $\mathcal{A}' \subset \mathcal{A}$.
   (ii) $[A, B]_{\mathcal{A}'} \subset [A, B]_{\mathcal{A}}$ for all $(A, B) \in \mathcal{A}' \times \mathcal{A}'$.
   (iii) The composition of any two morphisms in $\mathcal{A}'$ is the same as their composition in $\mathcal{A}$.
   (iv) 1_A is the same in $\mathcal{A}'$ as in $\mathcal{A}$ for all $A \in \mathcal{A}'$.

   If furthermore $[A, B]_{\mathcal{A}'} = [A, B]_{\mathcal{A}}$ for all $(A, B) \in \mathcal{A}' \times \mathcal{A}'$ we say that $\mathcal{A}'$ is a **full** subcategory of $\mathcal{A}$.

7. An **ordered class** is a category $\mathcal{A}$ with at most one morphism from an object to any other object. If A and B are objects in an ordered class and

if there is a morphism from A to B we write $A \leqslant B$ and we say that A **precedes** B or that B **follows** A. Hence $A \leqslant A$ for all objects A, and if $A \leqslant B$ and $B \leqslant C$, then $A \leqslant C$. If $A \leqslant B$ and $A \neq B$, then we write $A < B$. Conversely any class possessing a relation which satisfies these two properties may be considered as an ordered class. If for any pair of objects in $\mathscr{A}$ there is an object C which follows both of them, then we call $\mathscr{A}$ a **directed class**. $\mathscr{A}$ is a **linearly ordered class** if $A \leqslant B$ and $B \leqslant A$ implies $A = B$, and if for every pair A, B it is true either that $A \leqslant B$ or $B \leqslant A$. An **ordered subclass** of the ordered class $\mathscr{A}$ is a full subcategory of $\mathscr{A}$. We call $\mathscr{A}$ **inductive** if every linearly ordered subclass $\mathscr{L}$ of $\mathscr{A}$ has an upper bound in $\mathscr{A}$ (that is, a member $X \in \mathscr{A}$ such that $L \leqslant X$ for each $L \in \mathscr{L}$). A **maximal member** M of an ordered class $\mathscr{A}$ is one such that for each $A \in \mathscr{A}$ the relation $M \leqslant A$ implies $A \leqslant M$. If $\mathscr{A}$ is a small category, then the word class is replaced by the word set in each of the above definitions. We shall be using the following form of **Zorn's lemma**:

If $\mathscr{A}$ is an inductive ordered set, then $\mathscr{A}$ has a maximal member.

8. Let $\mathscr{A}$ be a category, and for each $(A, B) \in \mathscr{A} \times \mathscr{A}$ suppose that $[A, B]_{\mathscr{A}}$ is divided into equivalence classes. Denoting the equivalence class of α by $[\alpha]$, suppose further that whenever $[\alpha] = [\alpha']$ we have $[f\alpha] = [f\alpha']$ and $[\alpha g] = [\alpha' g]$ when the compositions make sense. Then we can form a new category $\mathscr{A}''$ called the **quotient category** of $\mathscr{A}$ with respect to the given equivalence relation. The objects of $\mathscr{A}''$ are the same as the objects of $\mathscr{A}$, and the set of morphisms $[A, B]_{\mathscr{A}''}$ is defined as the set of equivalence classes of $[A, B]_{\mathscr{A}}$. Composition is defined by the rule $[\beta][\alpha] = [\beta\alpha]$.

4. Duality

The **dual category** of a category $\mathscr{A}$, denoted by $\mathscr{A}^*$, has the same class of objects as $\mathscr{A}$, and is such that

$$[A, B]_{\mathscr{A}} = [B, A]_{\mathscr{A}^*}.$$

The composition $\beta\alpha$ in $\mathscr{A}^*$ is defined as the composition $\alpha\beta$ in $\mathscr{A}$. It will be convenient notationally to represent an object $A \in \mathscr{A}$ by A^* when it is considered as an object of the dual category. Clearly $(\mathscr{A}^*)^* = \mathscr{A}$, and consequently every theorem about categories actually embodies two theorems. If statement p is true for category $\mathscr{A}$, then there is a dual statement p^* which will be true for $\mathscr{A}^*$. If the assumptions on $\mathscr{A}$ used to prove p hold also in $\mathscr{A}^*$, then p^* is true for $(\mathscr{A}^*)^* = \mathscr{A}$. We have not bothered to write out the dual statements for most of the theorems.

5. Special Morphisms

A morphism $\theta : A \to B$ is called a **coretraction** if there is a morphism $\theta' : B \to A$ such that $\theta'\theta = 1_A$. We shall say that A is a **retract** of B in this case. If $\theta : A \to B$ and $\pi : B \to C$ are coretractions, then $\pi\theta$ is a coretraction. On the other hand, if $\pi\theta$ is a coretraction, then θ is a coretraction, but not necessarily π. Dually we say that θ is a **retraction** if there is a morphism $\theta'' : B \to A$ such that $\theta\theta'' = 1_B$. If θ is both a retraction and a coretraction, then we call it an **isomorphism**. In this case we have

$$\theta' = \theta' 1_B = \theta'(\theta\theta'') = (\theta'\theta)\theta'' = 1_A\theta'' = \theta''.$$

We call $\theta' = \theta''$ the **inverse** of θ and we denote it by θ^{-1}. Then by definition we have $(\theta^{-1})^{-1} = \theta$. A semigroup in which every morphism is an isomorphism is called a **group**. In the case of abelian groups we use the additive notation for inverses, writing $-\theta$ in place of θ^{-1}.

If $\theta \in [A, B]_{\mathscr{A}}$ is a retraction and $\mathscr{A}''$ is a quotient category of $\mathscr{A}$, then $[\theta]$ is a retraction in $\mathscr{A}''$. However, if $\mathscr{A}'$ is a subcategory of $\mathscr{A}$ and $\theta \in [A, B]_{\mathscr{A}'}$ is a retraction in $\mathscr{A}$, it does not necessarily follow that θ is a retraction in $\mathscr{A}'$ unless $\mathscr{A}'$ is a full subcategory of $\mathscr{A}$.

We shall say "A is isomorphic to B" if there is an isomorphism from A to B. It must be kept in mind, however, that there may be many isomorphisms from A to B, and that the above statement will usually be used with reference to a specific isomorphism $\theta : A \to B$. The notation $\theta : A \approx B$ will often be used to express the fact that θ is an isomorphism. If θ and π are isomorphisms and $\pi\theta$ is defined, then $\pi\theta$ is an isomorphism with inverse $\theta^{-1}\pi^{-1}$. Also every object is isomorphic to itself by means of its identity morphism. Hence the relation "is isomorphic to" is an equivalence relation.

A morphism whose codomain is the same as its domain is called an **endomorphism.** The set $[A, A]$ of endomorphisms on A is a semigroup, and is sometimes denoted by $\mathrm{End}(A)$, or $\mathrm{End}_{\mathscr{A}}(A)$ when there is more than one category in question. An endomorphism which is an isomorphism is called an **automorphism**. The set of automorphisms of A is a group and is denoted by $\mathrm{Aut}(A)$, or $\mathrm{Aut}_{\mathscr{A}}(A)$.

A morphism $\alpha \in [A, B]$ is called a **monomorphism** if $\alpha f = \alpha g$ implies that $f = g$ for all pairs of morphisms f, g with codomain A. If α is a monomorphism in $\mathscr{A}$, then it will be a monomorphism in any subcategory. However, a morphism may be a monomorphism in a subcategory without being a monomorphism in $\mathscr{A}$. Moreover it is not necessarily true that if α is a monomorphism in $\mathscr{A}$, then $[\alpha]$ is a monomorphism in a quotient category of $\mathscr{A}$. If α and β are monomorphisms and if $\beta\alpha$ is defined, then $\beta\alpha$ is a monomorphism. On the other hand, if $\beta\alpha$ is a monomorphism, then α is a monomorphism, but not necessarily β.

A morphism α is called an **epimorphism** if $f\alpha = g\alpha$ implies that $f = g$. The notion of epimorphism is dual to that of monomorphism in the sense that α is an epimorphism in $\mathscr{A}$ if and only if it is a monomorphism in $\mathscr{A}^*$. Thus if α and β are epimorphisms and $\alpha\beta$ is defined, then $\alpha\beta$ is an epimorphism, and if $\alpha\beta$ is an epimorphism, then α is an epimorphism but not necessarily β.

A coretraction is necessarily a monomorphism and a retraction is an epimorphism. Thus an isomorphism is both a monomorphism and an epimorphism. Nevertheless a morphism can be at once a monomorphism and an epimorphism but fail to be an isomorphism (exercise 1). We shall call a category **balanced** if every morphism which is both a monomorphism and an epimorphism is also an isomorphism.

Proposition 5.1. *If $\alpha : A \to B$ is a coretraction and is also an epimorphism, then it is an isomorphism.*

Proof. Letting $\beta\alpha = 1_A$ we have

$$(\alpha\beta)\alpha = \alpha(\beta\alpha) = \alpha 1_A = \alpha = 1_B \alpha$$

and consequently $\alpha\beta = 1_B$ since α is an epimorphism. This shows that α is an isomorphism. ▌

The dual proposition reads as follows.

Proposition 5.1*. *If $\alpha : B \to A$ is a retraction and is also a monomorphism, then it is an isomorphism.* ▌

If $\alpha : A' \to A$ is a monomorphism, we shall call A' a **subobject** of A, and we shall refer to α as the **inclusion** of A' in A. Sometimes we shall write $\alpha : A' \subset A$, or simply $A' \subset A$ when we want to indicate that A' is a subobject of A, and we shall say that A' is **contained** in A, or that A **contains** A'. However, it is important to remember that in general there is more than one monomorphism from A' to A, and that whenever we speak of A' as a subobject of A we shall be referring to a specific monomorphism α. In this loose language, the statement that the composition of two monomorphisms is a monomorphism becomes: If A is a subobject of B and B is a subobject of C, then A is a subobject of C. If the monomorphism $\alpha : A' \to A$ is not an isomorphism, we shall call A' a **proper** subobject of A. The composition of a monomorphism $\alpha : A' \to A$ with a morphism $f : A \to B$ is often denoted by $f|A'$ and is called the **restriction** of f to A'.

If $\alpha_1 : A_1 \to A$ and $\alpha_2 : A_2 \to A$ are monomorphisms, we shall write $\alpha_1 \leqslant \alpha_2$ if there is a morphism $\gamma : A_1 \to A_2$ such that $\alpha_2\gamma = \alpha_1$. If γ exists, then it is unique, and is also a monomorphism. If also $\alpha_2 \leqslant \alpha_1$ so that there is a morphism $\delta : A_2 \to A_1$ such that $\alpha_2 = \alpha_1\delta$, then we have

$$\alpha_2\gamma\delta = \alpha_1\delta = \alpha_2 = \alpha_2 1_{A_2}.$$

Hence since α_2 is a monomorphism we have $\gamma\delta = 1_{A_2}$. Similarly, $\delta\gamma = 1_{A_1}$, and so γ is an isomorphism with inverse δ. We shall then say that A_1 and A_2 are **isomorphic subobjects** of A. However, A_1 and A_2 may be isomorphic objects without being isomorphic subobjects of A. More precisely, there may be an isomorphism $\gamma : A_1 \approx A_2$, without it being true that $\alpha_2\gamma$ is the same as α_1. If $\alpha_3 : A_3 \to A$ is another monomorphism, and $\alpha_1 \leqslant \alpha_2 \leqslant \alpha_3$, then $\alpha_1 \leqslant \alpha_3$. Hence the class of subobjects of A (or, rather, monomorphisms into A) is an ordered class with the property that two subobjects precede each other if and only if they are isomorphic subobjects.

A class $\mathscr{C}$ of subobjects of A will be called a **representative class** of subobjects for A if every subobject of A is isomorphic as a subobject to some member of $\mathscr{C}$. More generally, if every member of $\mathscr{C}$ has a certain property p, then $\mathscr{C}$ is called a **representative class for** p if every subobject of A which has property p is isomorphic as a subobject to some member of $\mathscr{C}$. If every $A \in \mathscr{A}$ has a representative class of subobjects which is a set, then $\mathscr{A}$ is called a **locally small** category.

Dually, if $\alpha : A \to A'$ is an epimorphism, we call A' a **quotient object** of A. If $\alpha_1 : A \to A_1$ and $\alpha_2 : A \to A_2$ are epimorphisms we write $\alpha_1 \leqslant \alpha_2$ if there is a morphism $\gamma : A_2 \to A_1$ such that $\gamma\alpha_2 = \alpha_1$. That is, $\alpha_1 \leqslant \alpha_2$ in $\mathscr{A}$ if and only if $\alpha_1 \leqslant \alpha_2$ as monomorphisms in $\mathscr{A}^*$. We shall say that $\mathscr{A}$ is **colocally small** if $\mathscr{A}^*$ is locally small.

If $\mathscr{A}$ is locally small, it does not necessarily follow that a subcategory $\mathscr{A}'$ is locally small. The reason is twofold. In the first place there may be monomorphisms in $\mathscr{A}'$ which are not monomorphisms in $\mathscr{A}$, and in the second place two monomorphisms may be isomorphic in $\mathscr{A}$ but not in $\mathscr{A}'$.

6. Equalizers

We call a diagram of the form

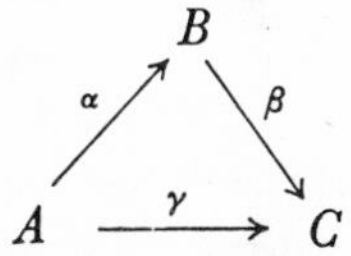

commutative if $\beta\alpha = \gamma$, and we shall say in this case that the morphism γ **factors through** B. Likewise a diagram of the form

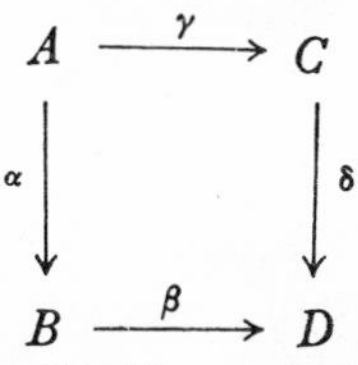

(1)

is commutative if $\beta\alpha = \delta\gamma$. In II, §1 we shall give a general definition of diagram and commutativity, but the above two types and various simple combinations thereof will be all that we need for the present.

If (1) is commutative and β is a coretraction, say $\beta'\beta = 1_B$, then

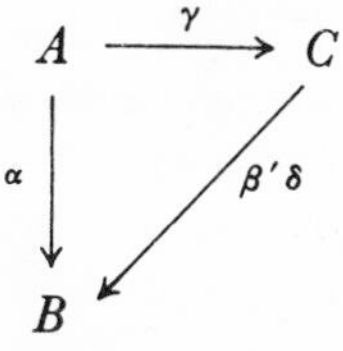

is commutative. Furthermore if β and γ are both isomorphisms, then

$$\begin{array}{ccc} A & \xleftarrow{\gamma^{-1}} & C \\ {\scriptstyle\alpha}\downarrow & & \downarrow{\scriptstyle\delta} \\ B & \xleftarrow[\beta^{-1}]{} & D \end{array}$$

is commutative.

Given two morphisms $\alpha, \beta : A \to B$, we say that $u : K \to A$ is an **equalizer** for α and β if $\alpha u = \beta u$, and if whenever $u' : K' \to A$ is such that $\alpha u' = \beta u'$ there is a unique morphism $\gamma : K' \to K$ making the diagram

$$\begin{array}{ccc} & K' & \\ {\scriptstyle\gamma}\swarrow & & \searrow{\scriptstyle u'} \\ K & \xrightarrow{u} & A \end{array} \tag{2}$$

commutative.

Proposition 6.1. *If u is an equalizer for α and β, then u is a monomorphism. Any two equalizers for α and β are isomorphic subobjects of A.*

Proof. Suppose that $\gamma_1, \gamma_2 : K' \to K$ are such that $u\gamma_1 = u\gamma_2$. Then γ_1 and γ_2 are factorizations through K of the morphism $u\gamma_1 = u\gamma_2 : K' \to A$. Furthermore we have $\alpha(u\gamma_1) = (\alpha u)\gamma_1 = (\beta u)\gamma_1 = \beta(u\gamma_1)$. But then by definition of equalizer, the factorization of $u\gamma_1$ through K must be unique; that is, $\gamma_1 = \gamma_2$. This proves that u is a monomorphism.

Now suppose that $u' : K' \to A$ in (2) is also an equalizer for α and β. Then we have a morphism $\gamma' : K \to K'$ such that $u'\gamma' = u$. Hence $u\gamma\gamma' = u'\gamma' = u = u1_K$. Since u is a monomorphism, it follows that $\gamma\gamma' = 1_K$. Similarly $\gamma'\gamma = 1_{K'}$, and so γ is an isomorphism with inverse γ'. ▮

Thus in some sense we can talk about "the" equalizer of two morphisms. The equalizer of α and β will sometimes be denoted $\mathrm{Equ}(\alpha, \beta)$, and an unnamed morphism $\mathrm{Equ}(\alpha, \beta) \to A$ will refer to the morphism u above. We shall not be inconvenienced too much by the fact that $\mathrm{Equ}(\alpha, \beta)$ can stand for any one of a class of isomorphic subobjects of A. If $\mathrm{Equ}(\alpha, \beta)$ exists for all pairs of morphisms in $\mathscr{A}$ with the same domain and the same codomain, then we shall simply say that $\mathscr{A}$ **has** equalizers. Observe that $\alpha = \beta$ if and only if 1_A is the equalizer of α and β.

Dually we say that $B \to \mathrm{Coequ}(\alpha, \beta)$ is the **coequalizer** of α and β if it is the equalizer of these two morphisms in the dual category. Hence if $\mathscr{A}^*$ has equalizers, then $\mathscr{A}$ has coequalizers. The statement of 6.1* is left to the reader.

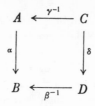

7. Pullbacks, Pushouts

Given two morphisms $\alpha_1 : A_1 \to A$ and $\alpha_2 : A_2 \to A$ with a common co-domain, a commutative diagram

$$\begin{array}{ccc} P & \xrightarrow{\beta_2} & A_2 \\ {\scriptstyle\beta_1}\downarrow & & \downarrow{\scriptstyle\alpha_2} \\ A_1 & \xrightarrow[\alpha_1]{} & A \end{array} \tag{1}$$

is called a **pullback** for α_1 and α_2 if for every pair of morphisms $\beta_1' : P' \to A_1$ and $\beta_2' : P' \to A_2$ such that $\alpha_1\beta_1' = \alpha_2\beta_2'$, there exists a unique morphism $\gamma : P' \to P$ such that $\beta_1' = \beta_1\gamma$ and $\beta_2' = \beta_2\gamma$. If P' is also a pullback, then there must exist a morphism $\gamma' : P \to P'$ such that $\beta_1 = \beta_1'\gamma'$ and $\beta_2 = \beta_2'\gamma'$. Then we have $\beta_1\gamma\gamma' = \beta_1'\gamma' = \beta_1 = \beta_1 1_P$ and similarly $\beta_2\gamma\gamma' = \beta_2 1_P$. Therefore, by uniqueness of factorizations through the pullback we have $\gamma\gamma' = 1_P$ and $\gamma'\gamma = 1_{P'}$.

Proposition 7.1. *Relative to the pullback diagram* (1), *if α_1 is a monomorphism, then so is β_2.*

Proof. Suppose that $\beta_2 f = \beta_2 g$. Then $\alpha_1\beta_1 f = \alpha_2\beta_2 f = \alpha_2\beta_2 g = \alpha_1\beta_1 g$, and so since α_1 is a monomorphism we must have $\beta_1 f = \beta_1 g$. Therefore by uniqueness of factorizations through the pullback we have $f = g$. This shows that β_2 is a monomorphism. ▌

It is not true in general that if α_1 is an epimorphism then so is β_2. However this will be a true statement in abelian categories (20.2).

Proposition 7.2. *If each square in the diagram*

$$\begin{array}{ccccc} P & \longrightarrow & Q & \longrightarrow & B' \\ \downarrow & & \downarrow & & \downarrow \\ A & \longrightarrow & I & \longrightarrow & B \end{array} \tag{2}$$

is a pullback and $B' \to B$ is a monomorphism, then the outer rectangle is a pullback.

Proof. Given morphisms $X \to A$ and $X \to B'$ such that

$$X \to A \to I \to B \;=\; X \to B' \to B,$$

we must find a unique morphism $X \to P$ such that $X \to P \to A = X \to A$ and $X \to P \to Q \to B' = X \to B'$. Now since the right-hand square is a pullback we have a morphism $X \to Q$ such that $X \to Q \to I = X \to A \to I$ and

$$X \to Q \to B' \;=\; X \to B'.$$

Then since the left-hand square is a pullback we have a morphism $X \to P$ such that $X \to P \to A = X \to A$ and $X \to P \to Q = X \to Q$. The morphism $X \to P$ then satisfies the required conditions. By two applications of 7.1 we see that $P \to A$ is a monomorphism, and from this follows the uniqueness of the morphism $X \to P$. ▮

The dual of a pullback is called a **pushout**. Thus a pushout diagram is obtained by reversing the direction of all arrows in the diagram (1). Propositions 7.1* and 7.2* are left to the formulation of the reader.

8. Intersections

Let $\{u_i : A_i \to A\}_{i \in I}$ be a family (set) of subobjects of A. We shall call a morphism $u : A' \to A$ the **intersection** of the family if for each $i \in I$ we can write $u = u_i v_i$ for some morphism $v_i : A' \to A_i$ (necessarily unique) and furthermore if every morphism $B \to A$ which factors through each u_i factors uniquely through u. From the uniqueness condition one shows easily that u is a monomorphism, and that any two intersections for the same family are isomorphic subobjects of A. We shall denote A' by $\bigcap_{i \in I} A_i$, or simply by $\bigcap A_i$ when there is no doubt as to the index set. Consider a union of sets $I = \bigcup_{\lambda \in \Lambda} I_\lambda$. If $\bigcap_{i \in I_\lambda} A_i$ is defined for each $\lambda \in \Lambda$ and if $\bigcap_{\lambda \in \Lambda} \left(\bigcap_{i \in I_\lambda} A_i \right)$ is defined, then $\bigcap_{i \in I} A_i$ is defined and we have

$$\bigcap_{\lambda \in \Lambda} \left(\bigcap_{i \in I_\lambda} A_i \right) = \bigcap_{i \in I} A_i. \tag{1}$$

For a finite family $A_1, A_2, \ldots, A_n$ of subobjects we often write $\bigcap_{i=1}^{n} A_i$ or $A_1 \cap A_2 \cap A_3 \cap \ldots \cap A_n$ for the intersection. Observe that the intersection of the empty class of subobjects of A is A itself. If the intersection of the family A_i exists, then it is the largest subobject of A which precedes each of the A_i. However, a subobject may have this maximal property without the intersection existing. If the intersection exists for every set of subobjects of every object in $\mathscr{A}$, we shall say that $\mathscr{A}$ **has intersections**. If intersections exist only for finite sets of subobjects then we shall say that $\mathscr{A}$ **has finite intersections**.

Proposition 8.1. *If $A_1 \to A_2$ and $A_2 \to A$ are monomorphisms in a category $\mathscr{A}$, then the diagram*

$$\begin{array}{ccc} P & \longrightarrow & A_2 \\ \downarrow & & \downarrow \\ A_1 & \longrightarrow & A \end{array}$$

is a pullback diagram if and only if $P \to A_2 \to A = P \to A_1 \to A$ *is the intersection of* A_1 *and* A_2*. Hence if* $\mathscr{A}$ *has pullbacks then* $\mathscr{A}$ *has finite intersections.*

Proof. That the diagram is a pullback if and only if it is an intersection follows immediately from the definitions of pullback and intersection. If $\mathscr{A}$ has pullbacks, then using (1) the intersection of n subobjects may be obtained inductively by the formula

$$\bigcap_{i=1}^{n} A_i = \left(\bigcap_{i=1}^{n-1} A\right) \cap A_n. \qquad \blacksquare$$

We reserve no special notation for the dual notion of the **cointersection** of a family of quotient objects.

9. Unions

Consider a diagram

$$\begin{array}{ccc} A' & & B' \\ \downarrow & & \downarrow \\ A & \xrightarrow{f} & B \end{array} \tag{1}$$

where f is any morphism and the vertical morphisms are monomorphisms. Then we say that the subobject A' is **carried into** the subobject B' by f if there exists a morphism $A' \to B'$ (necessarily unique) making (1) commutative.

The **union** of a family $\{A_i\}_{i \in I}$ of subobjects of an object A is defined as a subobject A' of A which is preceded by each of the A_i, and which has the following property: If $f: A \to B$ and each A_i is carried into some subobject B' by f, then A' is also carried into B' by f. By taking $f = 1_A$ we see that if each A_i precedes some subobject A_1 of A, then A' must also precede A_1. In particular any other subobject of A which behaves as a union for the above family must be isomorphic as a subobject to A'. The object A' will be denoted by $\bigcup_{i \in I} A_i$.

Remark that the union is in no sense dual to the intersection, although in exact categories a relationship exists between the union and the cointersection (15.2). An associativity formula analogous to (1) of the previous section applies to unions, as well as the notational remarks made there. Observe again that while the union of a family of subobjects is necessarily the smallest subobject which contains every member of the family, nevertheless an object may exist having this minimal property without being the union. If the union exists for every set of subobjects of any object in $\mathscr{A}$, we shall say that $\mathscr{A}$ **has unions**.

Proposition 9.1. *Suppose that* $\alpha, \beta : A \to B$ *in a category which has equalizers, and suppose that for each member* A_i *of a family of subobjects of* A *we have* $\alpha | A_i = \beta | A_i$*. Then if the union exists we have* $\alpha | \bigcup A_i = \beta | \bigcup A_i$.

Proof. Letting K be the equalizer of the two morphisms $\alpha|\bigcup A_i$ and $\beta|\bigcup A_i$, we see that each A_i is a subobject of K. Hence $\bigcup A_i$ is a subobject of K, and so $K = \bigcup A_i$. ∎

10. Images

The **image** of a morphism $f: A \to B$ is defined as the smallest subobject of B which f factors through. That is, a monomorphism $u: I \to B$ is the image of f iff $f = uf'$ for some $f': A \to I$, and if u precedes any other monomorphism into B with the same property. The object I will sometimes be denoted by $\mathrm{Im}(f)$. If every morphism in a category has an image, then we shall say that the category **has images**. If, moreover, the morphism f' is always an epimorphism, we say that $\mathscr{A}$ has **epimorphic images**. If $\mathscr{A}$ has intersections and is locally small, then $\mathscr{A}$ has images. In fact, given a morphism f, we can find a representative set for the class of subobjects of the codomain which f factors through. The intersection of such a set of subobjects clearly serves as an image for f. If f is a monomorphism, then f is its own image.

Proposition 10.1. *Let $f: A \to B$ in a category with equalizers and let $A \xrightarrow{f'} I \to B$ be the factorization of f through its image. Then f' is an epimorphism.*

Proof. Suppose that $\alpha f' = \beta f'$. Then f' (and hence f) factors through $\mathrm{Equ}(\alpha, \beta)$, and the latter is a subobject of I. But by the definition of image we must then have $I = \mathrm{Equ}(\alpha, \beta)$. Therefore $\alpha = \beta$, and so f' is an epimorphism. ∎

Proposition 10.2. *Let $f: A \to B$ in a balanced category, and suppose that f has an image. If f can be factored as $A \xrightarrow{f'} I \xrightarrow{u} B$ with f' an epimorphism and u a monomorphism, then u is the image of f.*

Proof. By definition of $\mathrm{Im}(f)$ we know that f' factors through $\mathrm{Im}(f)$. But then since f' is an epimorphism, the inclusion of $\mathrm{Im}(f)$ in I is an epimorphism. Therefore since the category is balanced this inclusion must be an isomorphism. ∎

If $f: A \to B$ and $A' \to A$ is a monomorphism, we shall denote the image of the composition $A' \to A \xrightarrow{f} B$ by $f(A')$. Then using the fact that the composition of two epimorphisms is an epimorphism, we have the following corollary of 10.2.

Corollary 10.3. *Let $\mathscr{A}$ be a balanced category with epimorphic images. If $f: A \to B$, $g: B \to C$, and A' is a subobject of A, then $g(f(A')) = gf(A')$.* ∎

We call an epimorphism $A \to I$ the **coimage** of a morphism f if it is the image of f in the dual category. In this case we denote the object I by $\mathrm{Coim}(f)$. In exact categories it will turn out that $\mathrm{Coim}(f)$ and $\mathrm{Im}(f)$ are isomorphic, but in general there is no relation between these two objects.

11. Inverse Images

If $f: A \to B$ and B' is a subobject of B, then the **inverse image** of B' by f is the pullback diagram

$$\begin{array}{ccc} P & \longrightarrow & B' \\ \downarrow & & \downarrow \\ A & \xrightarrow{f} & B \end{array} \qquad (1)$$

The object P is usually denoted by $f^{-1}(B')$. Then by 7.1, $f^{-1}(B')$ is a subobject of A. It is the largest subobject of A which is carried into B' by f. However, the existence of such a maximal subobject does not guarantee the existence of the inverse image.

Suppose that in the diagram (1) the morphism $P \to B'$ factors through a subobject B_1 of B'. Then it is easy to see that P is also the inverse image of B_1. In particular if I is a subobject of B which f factors through (such as $\mathrm{Im}(f)$) and the intersection $I \cap B'$ is defined, then $f^{-1}(I \cap B')$ is defined and equals $f^{-1}(B')$.

Proposition 11.1. *Let $f: A \to B$, and consider inclusions $A_1 \subset A_2 \subset A$ and $B_1 \subset B_2 \subset B$. Then the following relations hold whenever both sides are defined:*

(i) $f(A_1) \subset f(A_2)$
(ii) $f^{-1}(B_1) \subset f^{-1}(B_2)$
(iii) $A_1 \subset f^{-1}(f(A_1))$
(iv) $B_1 \supset f(f^{-1}(B_1))$
(v) $f(A_1) = f(f^{-1}(f(A_1)))$
(vi) $f^{-1}(B_1) = f^{-1}(f(f^{-1}(B_1)))$.

Proof. Statements (i) to (iv) are trivial consequences of the definitions of image and inverse image. To prove (v), apply (i) to statement (iii) to obtain $f(A_1) \subset f(f^{-1}(f(A_1)))$, and then apply (iv) to the object $f(A_1)$ to obtain $f(A_1) \supset f(f^{-1}(f(A_1)))$. Statement (vi) follows similarly. ▮

Proposition 11.2. *Let $f: A \to B$ in a category with images and inverse images, and let $\{A_i\}$ be a family of subobjects of A for which $\bigcup A_i$ is defined. Then $\bigcup f(A_i)$ is defined and equals $f(\bigcup A_i)$.*

Proof. Consider a morphism $g: B \to C$ and suppose that each $f(A_i)$ is carried by g into some subobject C' of C. Then each A_i is carried by gf into C', and so by definition of union, $\bigcup A_i$ is carried by gf into C'. Hence $\bigcup A_i$ is carried by f into $g^{-1}(C')$, and so $f(\bigcup A_i)$ is a subobject of $g^{-1}(C')$. But this means that $f(\bigcup A_i)$ is carried by g into C'. Since by 11.1, $f(\bigcup A_i)$ contains each of the $f(A_i)$, this shows that $f(\bigcup A_i)$ is the union of the family $\{f(A_i)\}$. ▮

The proof of the following analogous proposition is left to the reader.

Proposition 11.3. *Let $f : A \to B$ in a category with inverse images, and let $\{B_i\}$ be a family of subobjects of B for which the intersection $\bigcap B_i$ is defined. Then $\bigcap f^{-1}(B_i)$ is defined and is equal to $f^{-1}(\bigcap B_i)$.* ∎

If $f : A \to B$ is a monomorphism and if A' is a subobject of A, then it is trivial to see that $f^{-1}(f(A')) = A'$. However, if f is an epimorphism and B' is a subobject of B we will have to put some hypothesis on the category before we can prove $f(f^{-1}(B')) = B'$ (see 16.4). In the case where f is an isomorphism, the inverse image of B' is the same as the image of B' under the morphism f^{-1}, hence there is no ambiguity in notation.

12. Zero Objects

An object 0 is called a **null object** for $\mathscr{A}$ if $[A, 0]$ has precisely one element for each $A \in \mathscr{A}$. If $0'$ is another null object, then $[0, 0']$ and $[0', 0]$ each have one morphism, say θ and θ', respectively. Then $\theta'\theta$ is the unique morphism in $[0, 0]$, hence must be 1_0. Likewise $\theta\theta' = 1_{0'}$. Thus any two null objects are isomorphic. In the dual category 0 becomes a **conull object**. We say that 0 is a **zero object** for $\mathscr{A}$ if it is at once a null object and a conull object. In this case we will call a morphism $A \to B$ a **zero morphism** if it factors through 0. Each set $[A, B]$ has precisely one zero morphism, which we denote sometimes by 0_{AB}, but more often simply by 0. The composition of a zero morphism with any other morphism is a zero morphism. On the other hand, suppose that $\mathscr{A}$ is a category (with or without a zero object) such that each set $[A, B]$ has a distinguished element e_{AB} with the property that the composition of a distinguished morphism with any other morphism is again a distinguished morphism. Then one shows that there can be at most one such class of distinguished morphisms, and that a zero object can be adjoined to $\mathscr{A}$ so that the distinguished morphisms become zero morphisms and so that $\mathscr{A}$ remains essentially unchanged (exercise 6).

13. Kernels

Let $\mathscr{A}$ be a category with a zero object, and let $\alpha : A \to B$. We will call a morphism $u : K \to A$ the **kernel** of α if $\alpha u = 0$, and if for every morphism $u' : K' \to A$ such that $\alpha u' = 0$ we have a unique morphism $\gamma : K' \to K$ such that $u\gamma = u'$. Equivalently, the kernel of α is given by the pullback diagram

$$\begin{array}{ccc} K & \longrightarrow & 0 \\ {\scriptstyle u}\downarrow & & \downarrow \\ A & \longrightarrow & B \end{array}$$

In other words $K = \alpha^{-1}(0)$, so that in particular u must be a monomorphism, and any two kernels must be isomorphic subobjects of A. The object K is frequently denoted by $\mathrm{Ker}(\alpha)$. If α is a monomorphism then $\mathrm{Ker}(\alpha) = 0$, but the converse is not true in general (cf. exercise 9*). If $\mathrm{Ker}(\beta\alpha)$ and $\mathrm{Ker}(\alpha)$ are defined, then $\mathrm{Ker}(\alpha) \subset \mathrm{Ker}(\beta\alpha)$. If β is a monomorphism, then

$$\mathrm{Ker}(\alpha) = \mathrm{Ker}(\beta\alpha)$$

in the sense that if either side is defined then so is the other and they are equal. Also if either of $\mathrm{Equ}(\alpha, 0)$ and $\mathrm{Ker}(\alpha)$ are defined then so is the other and they are equal, so that in particular if $\mathscr{A}$ has equalizers then $\mathscr{A}$ has kernels. Frequently we will want to know if a morphism u is the kernel of some morphism α, knowing in advance that $\alpha u = 0$ and that u is a monomorphism. In such a case it suffices to test for the existence of the morphism γ. Uniqueness will be automatic since u is a monomorphism.

A morphism $B \to \mathrm{Coker}(\alpha)$ is called the **cokernel** of α if it is the kernel of α in the dual category. When speaking of kernels and cokernels we will always be implying tacitly that the category in question has a zero, for otherwise the terms make no sense.

Proposition 13.1. *Consider a commutative diagram*

$$\begin{array}{ccccc} K & \xrightarrow{\gamma} & P & \xrightarrow{\beta_2} & A_2 \\ \| & & \downarrow{\scriptstyle \beta_1} & & \downarrow{\scriptstyle \alpha_2} \\ K & \xrightarrow{u} & A_1 & \xrightarrow{\alpha_1} & A \end{array}$$

where the right-hand square is a pullback, u is the kernel of α_1, and γ is the morphism into the pullback induced by the two morphisms $u : K \to A_1$ and $0 : K \to A_2$. Then γ is the kernel of β_2.

Proof. First observe that since $\beta_1\gamma = u$ and u is a monomorphism, γ must be a monomorphism. Also, $\beta_2\gamma = 0$ by construction of γ. Now let $v : X \to P$ such that $\beta_2 v = 0$. Then $0 = \alpha_2\beta_2 v = \alpha_1\beta_1 v$, and so since u is the kernel of α_1 we must have a morphism $w : X \to K$ such that $uw = \beta_1 v$. We then see that $\gamma w = v$ since each of these morphisms gives the same thing when composed with both β_1 and β_2. This proves that γ is the kernel of β_2. ∎

Proposition 13.2. *Consider a diagram*

$$\begin{array}{ccc} A' & \longrightarrow & A \\ & & \downarrow \\ B' & \longrightarrow & B \end{array} \qquad (1)$$

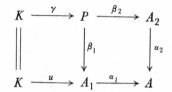

where $B' \to B$ is the kernel of some morphism $B \to B''$. Then the diagram can be extended to a pullback if and only if $A' \to A$ is the kernel of the composition $A \to B \to B''$.

Proof. Suppose that $A' \to A$ is the kernel $A \to B \to B''$. Then $A' \to A \to B \to B''$ is 0, and so since $B' \to B$ is the kernel of $B \to B''$ we get a unique morphism $A' \to B'$ making (1) commutative. Suppose that $X \to A \to B = X \to B' \to B$. Then $X \to A \to B \to B''$ is zero, hence there is a unique morphism $X \to A'$ such that $X \to A' \to A = X \to A$. Then also

$$X \to A' \to B' \to B = X \to A' \to A \to B = X \to B' \to B,$$

and so since $B' \to B$ is a monomorphism it follows that $X \to A' \to B' = X \to B'$. This proves that (1) is a pullback. The converse is left to the reader. ▮

Proposition 13.3. *Let $u : K \to A$ be the kernel of $\alpha : A \to B$ and let $p : A \to C$ be the cokernel of u. Then u is the kernel of p.*

Proof. Consider the diagram

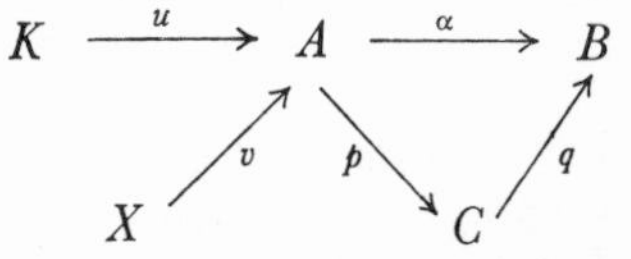

where v is any morphism such that $pv = 0$ and q is defined by virtue of the fact that $\alpha u = 0$ and p is the cokernel of u. Then $\alpha v = qpv = 0$, and so since u is the kernel of α there is a morphism $\gamma : X \to K$ such that $u\gamma = v$. Since u is a monomorphism and $pu = 0$ it follows that u is the kernel of p. ▮

14. Normality

If $A' \to A$ is the kernel of some morphism then we call A' a **normal** subobject of A. If every monomorphism in a category is normal then we say that the category is **normal**.

The following is an immediate consequence of 13.2.

Proposition 14.1. *A normal category with kernels has inverse images, and in particular, finite intersections.* ▮

Dually, if $A \to A''$ is the cokernel of some morphism, then we call A'' a **conormal** quotient object of A, and if every epimorphism in a category is conormal then we say that the category is a **conormal** category.

Proposition 14.2. *Let $\mathscr{A}$ be a normal category with cokernels. Then there is a univalent function from the class of equivalence classes of subobjects of an object A to the class of equivalence classes of quotient objects of A. In particular, if $\mathscr{A}$ is colocally small, then it is locally small. If $\mathscr{A}$ is normal and conormal and has kernels and cokernels, then the* *above function is a one to one correspondence between the (equivalence classes of) sub-objects of A and the (equivalence classes of) quotient objects of A.*

Proof. The function in question is the one which assigns to every monomorphism u its cokernel. Proposition 13.3 assures that if we take the kernel of the cokernel we get back to u, hence the assignment is univalent. The inverse function in the case where $\mathscr{A}$ is conormal and has kernels is the one which assigns to each epimorphism its kernel. ▮

Proposition 14.3. *Let $\alpha : A \to B$ be a monomorphism with cokernel 0 in a normal category. Then α is an isomorphism. Hence a normal category is balanced.*

Proof. By normality α is the kernel of its cokernel (13.3). But since the cokernel is $B \to 0$, a kernel for it is 1_B. From this it follows that α must be an isomorphism. ▮

Lemma 14.4. *Let $\mathscr{A}$ be any category with zero. Let $\alpha : A \to B$ be any morphism, and suppose that $p : B \to C$ is its cokernel. Finally suppose that $v : I \to B$ is the kernel of p. Then there is a unique morphism $q : A \to I$ such that $vq = \alpha$. If $\mathscr{A}$ has cokernels and is normal, then v is the image of α. If, further, $\mathscr{A}$ has equalizers, then q is the coimage of α.*

Proof. The existence and uniqueness of q follow since $p\alpha = 0$ and I is the kernel of p. Suppose that $\mathscr{A}$ has cokernels and is normal and let $B' \to B$ be a subobject of B through which α factors. Consider the following commutative diagram

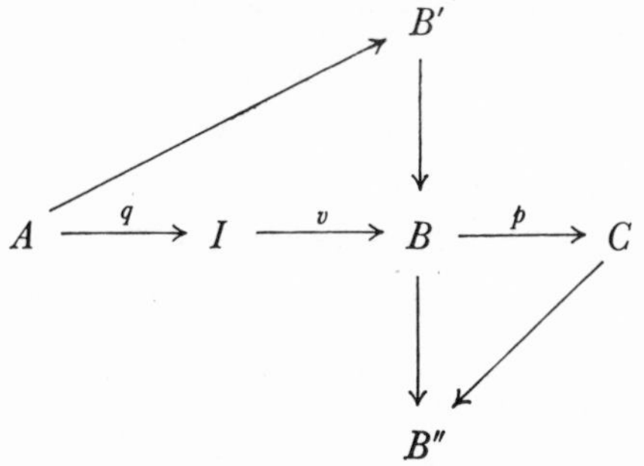

where $B \to B''$ is the cokernel of $B' \to B$ (and hence $B' \to B$ is the kernel of $B \to B''$), and $C \to B''$ is defined since the composition $A \to B \to B''$ is zero. Then $I \to B \to B'' = I \to B \to C \to B'' = 0$ and so v can be factored through $B' \to B$. This shows that v is the image of α.

If $\mathscr{A}$ has equalizers, then by 10.1, q is an epimorphism. Consider any factorization $A \xrightarrow{q'} I' \xrightarrow{v'} B$ of α with q' an epimorphism. Then $pv' = 0$, and so there is an induced morphism $I' \to I$. Using the fact that v is a monomorphism it follows that I precedes I' as a quotient object of A. This shows that q is the coimage of α. ▮

15. Exact Categories

Let $\mathscr{A}$ be a normal and conormal category with kernels and cokernels. We shall call $\mathscr{A}$ an **exact** category if every morphism $\alpha : A \to B$ can be written as a composition $A \xrightarrow{q} I \xrightarrow{v} B$ where q is an epimorphism and v is a monomorphism. Let $K \xrightarrow{u} A$ be the kernel of q and $B \xrightarrow{p} C$ be the cokernel of v. Then u is also the kernel of α and p is the cokernel of α. Furthermore, by normality and conormality it follows that v is the kernel of p and q is the cokernel of u. Then by 14.4, v is the image of α, and dually q is the coimage of α. Furthermore, 14.4 tells us that a normal and conormal category with cokernels and equalizers is an exact category. Observe the self-dual nature of the axioms for an exact category; $\mathscr{A}$ is exact if and only if $\mathscr{A}^*$ is exact.

A sequence of morphisms

$$\cdots \to A_{i-1} \xrightarrow{\alpha_{i-1}} A_i \xrightarrow{\alpha_i} A_{i+1} \xrightarrow{\alpha_{i+1}} A_{i+2} \cdots$$

in an exact category is called an **exact sequence** if $\operatorname{Ker}(\alpha_{i+1}) = \operatorname{Im}(\alpha_i)$ as subobjects of A_{i+1} for every i. If, for every i, the weaker condition $\alpha_{i+1}\alpha_i = 0$ is satisfied (or equivalently, $\operatorname{Im}(\alpha_i) \subset \operatorname{Ker}(\alpha_{i+1})$), then the sequence is said to be of **order two**.

Proposition 15.1. *The following statements are true in an exact category* $\mathscr{A}$:

1. $A \xrightarrow{\alpha} B \xrightarrow{\beta} C$ *is exact in* $\mathscr{A}$ *if and only if* $A^* \xleftarrow{\alpha} B^* \xleftarrow{\beta} C^*$ *is exact in* $\mathscr{A}^*$.
2. $0 \to A \xrightarrow{\alpha} B$ *is exact if and only if* α *is a monomorphism.*
3. $A \to B \to 0$ *is exact if and only if* α *is an epimorphism.*
4. $0 \to A \xrightarrow{\alpha} B \to 0$ *is exact if and only if* α *is an isomorphism.*

Proof. 1. Consider

$$A \xrightarrow{q} I \xrightarrow{v} B \xrightarrow{r} J \xrightarrow{w} C$$

where v is the image of α and w is the image of β. Then r is the coimage of β. If $A \to B \to C$ is exact, then v is the kernel of β and hence also the kernel of r. Therefore r is the cokernel of v and hence also the cokernel of α. In the dual category r then becomes the kernel of α as well as the image of β, and so $A^* \leftarrow B^* \leftarrow C^*$ is exact.

2. If α is a monomorphism then its kernel is 0, and so clearly $0 \to A \to B$ is exact. Conversely, if $0 \to A \to B$ is exact, then α has kernel 0. Let $A \xrightarrow{q} I \xrightarrow{v} B$ be a factorization of α as an epimorphism followed by a monomorphism. Then q is

the cokernel of the kernel of α. Since the latter is 0, q must be an isomorphism. But then $\alpha = vq$ must be a monomorphism.

3. Follows from 1 and 2.
4. Since a normal category is balanced, 4 follows from 2 and 3. ▮

It follows from 15.1 that, in an exact category, a sequence

$$0 \to A \xrightarrow{\alpha} B \xrightarrow{\beta} C \to 0 \tag{1}$$

is exact if and only if α is a monomorphism, β is an epimorphism, and α is the kernel of β (or equivalently, β is the cokernel of α). An exact sequence of the type (1) will be called a **short exact sequence.** We shall frequently denote C by B/A. An undesignated morphism $B \to B/A$ will be understood to be β. Given a diagram of the form

$$\begin{array}{ccccccccc} 0 & \longrightarrow & A & \longrightarrow & B & \longrightarrow & B/A & \longrightarrow & 0 \\ & & & & \downarrow & & & & \\ 0 & \longrightarrow & A' & \longrightarrow & B' & \longrightarrow & B'/A' & \longrightarrow & 0 \end{array}$$

then there is a morphism $A \to A'$ making the diagram commutative if and only if there is a morphism $B/A \to B'/A'$ making the diagram commutative. In particular, taking $B = B'$ with 1_B for $B \to B'$, we see that A precedes A' as a subobject of B if and only if B/A' precedes B/A as a quotient object of B.

Proposition 15.2. *Let $\{A_i\}$ be a set of subobjects of A in an exact category, and suppose A/A' is the cointersection of the family of quotient objects A/A_i. Then A' is the union of the family $\{A_i\}$.*

Proof. Consider a morphism $f: A \to B$ and a subobject B' of B such that each A_i is carried into B' by f. Then for each i we have a morphism $A/A_i \to B/B'$ such that $A \to B \to B/B' = A \to A/A_i \to B/B'$. Consequently, since A/A' is the cointersection we have a morphism $A/A' \to B/B'$ such that

$$A \to A/A' \to B/B' = A \to B \to B/B'.$$

But this implies that A' is carried into B' by f. Now since each A/A_i is preceded by A/A', it follows that each A_i precedes A'. Therefore A' is the union of the family $\{A_i\}$. ▮

Corollary 15.3. *An exact category has finite unions.*

Proof. By 14.1* an exact category has finite cointersections. Therefore the result follows from 15.2. ▮

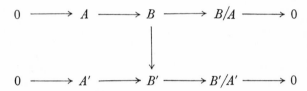

16. The 9 Lemma

Proposition 16.1 (The 9 Lemma). *Given a commutative diagram*

$$\begin{array}{ccccccccc}
 & & 0 & & 0 & & 0 & & \\
 & & \downarrow & & \downarrow & & \downarrow & & \\
 & & A' & & A & & A'' & & \\
 & & \downarrow & & \downarrow & & \downarrow & & \\
0 & \longrightarrow & B' & \longrightarrow & B & \longrightarrow & B'' & \longrightarrow & 0 \\
 & & \downarrow & & \downarrow & & \downarrow & & \\
0 & \longrightarrow & C' & \longrightarrow & C & \longrightarrow & C'' & \longrightarrow & 0 \\
 & & \downarrow & & \downarrow & & \downarrow & & \\
 & & 0 & & 0 & & 0 & &
\end{array}$$

in an exact category where all the rows and columns are exact, then there are morphisms $A' \to A$ *and* $A \to A''$ *keeping the diagram commutative. Furthermore, the sequence* $0 \to A' \to A \to A'' \to 0$ *is exact.*

Proof. We have seen the existence of the morphisms $A' \to A$ and $A \to A''$ in the preceding section. Now since $A' \to B' \to B$ is a monomorphism it follows that $A' \to A$ must also be a monomorphism. To prove the exactness assertion we first show that

$$0 \to A' \to A \to B'' \to C'' \to 0$$

is exact, where $A \to B''$ is the composition $A \to B \to B''$. Now

$$A' \to A \to B'' = A' \to B' \to B \to B'' = 0.$$

Suppose that $X \to A$ is such that $X \to A \to B \to B'' = 0$. Then we have a morphism $X \to B'$ such that $X \to B' \to B = X \to A \to B$. Also

$$X \to B' \to C' \to C = X \to B' \to B \to C = X \to A \to B \to C = 0.$$

Since $C' \to C$ is a monomorphism we then have $X \to B' \to C' = 0$. Therefore we have a morphism $X \to A'$ such that $X \to A' \to B' = X \to B'$. Then

$$X \to A' \to A \to B = X \to A' \to B' \to B = X \to B' \to B = X \to A \to B.$$

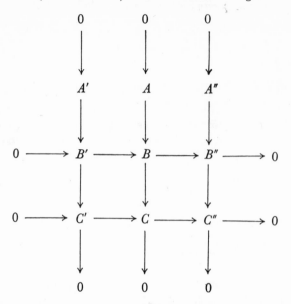

Since $A \to B$ is a monomorphism this means that $X \to A' \to A = X \to A$. Consequently we have shown that $A' \to A$ is the kernel of $A \to B''$, or, in other words, that $0 \to A' \to A \to B''$ is exact. By duality it follows that $A \to B'' \to C'' \to 0$ is exact. Now since $A'' \to B''$ is the kernel of $B'' \to C''$ we see that the factorization of $A \to B''$ through its image is just $A \to A'' \to B''$. Exactness of

$$0 \to A' \to A \to A'' \to 0$$

now follows. ▌

Corollary 16.2 (First Noether Isomorphism Theorem). *Let $B \subset A_1 \subset A_2$ in an exact category. Then we have a commutative diagram with exact rows*

$$\begin{array}{ccccccccc}
0 & \longrightarrow & A_2 & \longrightarrow & A_1 & \longrightarrow & A_1/A_2 & \longrightarrow & 0 \\
 & & \downarrow & & \downarrow & & \| & & \\
0 & \longrightarrow & A_2/B & \longrightarrow & A_1/B & \longrightarrow & A_1/A_2 & \longrightarrow & 0
\end{array}$$

(In other words A_2/B is a subobject of A_1/B, and $(A_1/B)/(A_2/B) = A_1/A_2$).

Proof. The proof follows immediately from 16.1* applied to the diagram

$$\begin{array}{ccccccccc}
 & & 0 & & 0 & & 0 & & \\
 & & \downarrow & & \downarrow & & \downarrow & & \\
0 & \longrightarrow & B & = & B & \longrightarrow & 0 & \longrightarrow & 0 \\
 & & \downarrow & & \downarrow & & \downarrow & & \\
0 & \longrightarrow & A_2 & \longrightarrow & A_1 & \longrightarrow & A_1/A_2 & \longrightarrow & 0 \\
 & & \downarrow & & \downarrow & & \| & & \\
 & & A_2/B & & A_1/B & & A_1/A_2 & & \\
 & & \downarrow & & \downarrow & & \downarrow & & \\
 & & 0 & & 0 & & 0 & &
\end{array}$$

▌

Corollary 16.3. *Consider a pullback diagram in an exact category*

$$\begin{array}{ccc}
B' & \longrightarrow & C' \\
\downarrow & & \downarrow \\
B & \longrightarrow & C
\end{array}$$

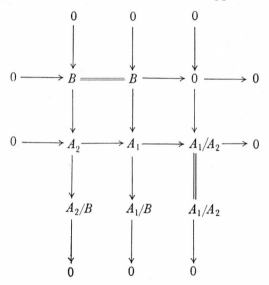

where $B \to C$ is an epimorphism and $C' \to C$ is a monomorphism. Then this can be extended to a commutative diagram

$$
\begin{array}{ccccccccc}
 & & & & 0 & & 0 & & \\
 & & & & \downarrow & & \downarrow & & \\
0 & \longrightarrow & A & \longrightarrow & B' & \longrightarrow & C' & \longrightarrow & 0 \\
 & & \| & & \downarrow & & \downarrow & & \\
0 & \longrightarrow & A & \longrightarrow & B & \longrightarrow & C & \longrightarrow & 0 \\
 & & & & \downarrow & & \downarrow & & \\
 & & & & C'' & = & C'' & & \\
 & & & & \downarrow & & \downarrow & & \\
 & & & & 0 & & 0 & &
\end{array}
$$

with exact rows and columns.

Proof. Let $C \to C''$ be the cokernel of $C' \to C$ and $A \to B$ the kernel of $B \to C$. Then by 13.2, $B' \to B$ is the kernel of $B \to C \to C''$, and since the latter is an epimorphism we have exactness of the columns. Exactness of the top row then follows from 16.1. ▮

Corollary 16.4. *Let $f: A \to B$ in an exact category, and let I be the image of f. If B' is a subobject of B we have an epimorphism*

$$f^{-1}(B') \to I \cap B'$$

and an exact sequence

$$0 \to f^{-1}(B') \to A \to I/I \cap B' \to 0.$$

Proof. By 7.2 we have a pullback diagram

$$
\begin{array}{ccc}
f^{-1}(B') & \longrightarrow & I \cap B' \\
\downarrow & & \downarrow \\
A & \longrightarrow & I
\end{array}
\qquad (1)
$$

Both our results then follow by applying 16.3 to (1). ▮

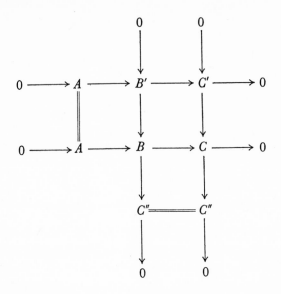

Proposition 16.5. *In an exact category consider the diagram*

$$\begin{array}{ccccccccc} & & 0 & & 0 & & 0 & & \\ & & \downarrow & & \downarrow & & \downarrow & & \\ 0 & \longrightarrow & A' & \longrightarrow & A & \longrightarrow & A'' & \longrightarrow & 0 \\ & & \downarrow & II & \downarrow & I & \downarrow & & \\ 0 & \longrightarrow & B' & \longrightarrow & B & \longrightarrow & B'' & \longrightarrow & 0 \\ & & \downarrow & III & \downarrow & IV & \downarrow & & \\ 0 & \longrightarrow & C' & \longrightarrow & C & \longrightarrow & C'' & \longrightarrow & 0 \\ & & \downarrow & & \downarrow & & \downarrow & & \\ & & 0 & & 0 & & 0 & & \end{array} \qquad (2)$$

where the middle row and middle column are exact. Then the diagram is commutative with exact rows and columns if and only if II is a pullback, IV is a pushout, and I and III are factorizations of $A \to B \to B''$ *and* $B' \to B \to C$ *through their respective images.*

Proof. Suppose that (2) is commutative with exact rows and columns. Then $A \to A''$ being an epimorphism and $A'' \to B''$ being a monomorphism we must have I as described. Likewise III is as described. Now $A' \to B'$ is the kernel of $B' \to C'$, and so since $C' \to C$ is a monomorphism it is also the kernel of $B' \to C' \to C = B' \to B \to C$. Therefore by 13.2, II is a pullback. Dually IV is a pushout.

Conversely, given the middle row and column exact, construct II as the pullback, IV as the pushout, and I and III as factorizations through images. We show that the top row is exact. The left column will be exact by symmetry, and the bottom row and right column will be exact by duality. By 13.2 we know that $A' \to A$ is the kernel of $A \to B \to B'' = A \to A'' \to B''$, and so since $A'' \to B''$ is a monomorphism it is also the kernel of $A \to A''$. Therefore since $A \to A''$ is an epimorphism the top row is exact. ▌

The pullback of two subobjects $A_1, A_2 \subset A$ is $A_1 \cap A_2$. Also by 15.2 the pushout of two quotient objects A/A_1 and A/A_2 is $A/A_1 \cup A_2$. Hence:

Corollary 16.6. *If A_1 and A_2 are subobjects of A in an exact category, then we have a commutative diagram with exact rows and columns*

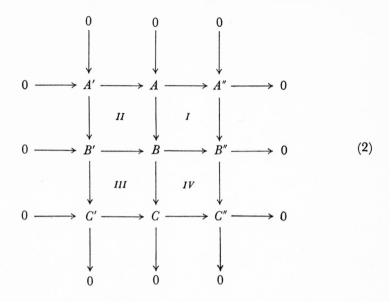

$$\begin{array}{ccccccccc}
 & & 0 & & 0 & & 0 & & \\
 & & \downarrow & & \downarrow & & \downarrow & & \\
0 & \longrightarrow & A_1 \cap A_2 & \longrightarrow & A_2 & \longrightarrow & A_2/A_1 \cap A_2 & \rightarrow & 0 \\
 & & \downarrow & & \downarrow & & \downarrow & & \\
0 & \longrightarrow & A_1 & \longrightarrow & A & \longrightarrow & A/A_1 & \longrightarrow & 0 \\
 & & \downarrow & & \downarrow & & \downarrow & & \\
0 & \longrightarrow & A_1/A_1 \cap A_2 & \rightarrow & A/A_2 & \longrightarrow & A/A_1 \cup A_2 & \rightarrow & 0 \\
 & & \downarrow & & \downarrow & & \downarrow & & \\
 & & 0 & & 0 & & 0 & &
\end{array} \tag{3}$$

▮

Corollary 16.7 (Second Noether Isomorphism Theorem). *If A_1 and A_2 are subobjects of A in an exact category, then we have a commutative diagram with exact rows*

$$\begin{array}{ccccccccc}
0 & \longrightarrow & A_1 \cap A_2 & \longrightarrow & A_2 & \longrightarrow & A_2/A_1 \cap A_2 & \longrightarrow & 0 \\
 & & \downarrow & & \downarrow & & \| & & \\
0 & \longrightarrow & A_1 & \longrightarrow & A_1 \cup A_2 & \longrightarrow & A_1 \cup A_2/A_1 & \rightarrow & 0
\end{array}$$

Proof. This follows by replacing A by $A_1 \cup A_2$ in (3). ▮

Corollary 16.8. *In an exact category consider exact sequences $0 \to A \to B \to C \to 0$ and $0 \to B' \to B \to B'' \to 0$. Then $B' \to B \to C$ is an epimorphism if and only if $A \to B \to B''$ is an epimorphism. Dually, the same is true of monomorphisms. Consequently $B' \to B \to C$ is an isomorphism if and only if $A \to B \to B''$ is an isomorphism.*

Proof. Form the diagram (2) according to 16.5. If $B' \to B \to C$ is an epimorphism, then $C' \to C$ is an epimorphism and so $C'' = 0$. But then this means that $A'' \to B''$ is an epimorphism, and hence $A \to B \to B''$ is an epimorphism. ▮

17. Products

Let $\{A_i\}_{i \in I}$ be a set of objects in an arbitrary category $\mathscr{A}$. A **product** for the family is a family of morphisms $\{p_i : A \to A_i\}_{i \in I}$ with the property that for any family $\{\alpha_i : A' \to A_i\}_{i \in I}$ there is a unique morphism $\alpha : A' \to A$ such that $p_i \alpha = \alpha_i$ for all $i \in I$. Hence for all $A' \in \mathscr{A}$ the set of morphisms $[A', A]$ is in one to one correspondence with the cartesian product of sets $\mathop{\times}\limits_{i \in I} [A', A_i]$. If the family $\{\alpha_i\}$ above is also a product, then one shows as usual that α is an isomorphism.

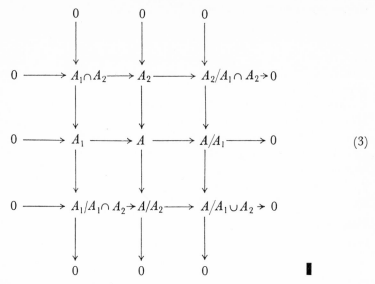

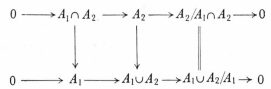

The object A will be denoted by $\bigtimes_{i \in I} A_i$, or simply $\bigtimes A_i$. For a finite family of objects $A_1, A_2, \ldots, A_n$ the product will sometimes be denoted $\bigtimes_{i=1}^{n} A_i$ or $A_1 \times A_2 \times \ldots \times A_n$. An object is a null object for $\mathscr{A}$ if and only if it serves as a product for the empty family. Also a product of null objects is again a null object.

The morphisms p_i are called the **projection** morphisms from the product. If i is a fixed index in I, and if there is a morphism $f_j : A_i \to A_j$ for all $j \in I$ such that $j \neq i$, then we can take $f_i = 1_{A_i}$ to obtain a morphism $f : A_i \to A$ such that $p_i f = 1_{A_i}$. This shows that p_i is a retraction. In particular, this will always be true when $\mathscr{A}$ has a zero object. In this case we can define morphisms $u_i : A_i \to A$, called the **injection** morphisms into the product, such that $p_j u_i \to \delta_{ij}$, where $\delta_{ij} = 0$ for $i \neq j$ and $\delta_{ii} = 1_{A_i}$.

Proposition 17.1. *Consider a product $A_1 \times A_2$ with injections u_1, u_2 and projections p_1, p_2 in a category with zero. Then u_1 is the kernel of p_2.*

Proof. Let $\alpha : A' \to A_1 \times A_2$ be such that $p_2 \alpha = 0$. Define $\alpha_1 : A' \to A_1$ by $\alpha_1 = p_1 \alpha$. Then $u_1 \alpha_1 = \alpha$, since both morphisms give the same thing when composed with the projection morphisms. Since u_1 is a monomorphism and $p_2 u_1 = 0$, this shows that u_1 is the kernel of p_2. ∎

It is not true in general that p_2 is the cokernel of u_1, although of course this is true in a conormal category.

Let $\{A_i\}_{i \in I}$ be any family, and let $I = \bigcup_{\lambda \in \Lambda} I_\lambda$ be a disjoint union of sets. Suppose that the product $A_\lambda = \bigtimes_{i \in I_\lambda} A_i$ is defined with projections $\{p_i\}_{i \in I_\lambda}$ for all λ, and suppose further that $\bigtimes_{\lambda \in \Lambda} A_\lambda$ is defined with projections $\{p_\lambda\}_{\lambda \in \Lambda}$. Then the family of morphisms $\{p_i p_\lambda | i \in I, \lambda \in \Lambda\}$ gives $\bigtimes_{\lambda \in \Lambda} A_\lambda$ the structure of a product for $\{A_i\}_{i \in I}$.

Let $\{A_i\}_{i \in I}$ be any set of objects and suppose that J is a subset of I. Then if $\bigtimes_{i \in J} A_i$ and $\bigtimes_{i \in I} A_i$ are both defined, we have a morphism

$$p_{JI} : \bigtimes_{i \in I} A_i \to \bigtimes_{i \in J} A_i$$

which is such that if we compose with the jth projection from $\bigtimes_{i \in J} A_i$ we obtain the jth projection from $\bigtimes_{i \in I} A_i$. If $\mathscr{A}$ has a zero object then p_J is an epimorphism. In fact p_{JI} can be interpreted as one of the projection morphisms p_λ relative to a suitable decomposition of the set I as in the preceding paragraph.

Consider a family of morphisms $\{f_i : A_i \to B_i\}_{i \in I}$. Then these define a morphism

$$\bigtimes_{i \in I} f_i : \bigtimes_{i \in I} A_i \to \bigtimes_{i \in I} B_i.$$

This is the unique morphism such that for each $i \in I$ the diagram

$$\begin{array}{ccc} \mathsf{X}\, A_i & \longrightarrow & \mathsf{X}\, B_i \\ \downarrow & & \downarrow \\ A_i & \xrightarrow{f_i} & B_i \end{array}$$

is commutative. Observe the relations

$$\underset{i\in I}{\mathsf{X}}\, g_i \underset{i\in I}{\mathsf{X}}\, f_i = \underset{i\in I}{\mathsf{X}}\, (g_i f_i), \qquad \underset{i\in I}{\mathsf{X}}\, 1_{A_i} = 1$$

which are valid whenever the products involved are defined and the compositions make sense.

The **coproduct** of the family $\{A_i\}_{i\in I}$ is defined dually to the product. Thus the coproduct is a family of morphisms $\{u_i : A_i \to A\}$ called **injections**, such that for each family of morphisms $\{\alpha_i : A_i \to A'\}_{i\in I}$ we have a unique morphism $\alpha : A \to A'$ with $\alpha u_i = \alpha_i$ for all $i \in I$. The object A will be denoted by $\bigoplus_{i\in I} A_i$. For a finite family alternative notations will be $\bigoplus_{i=1}^{n} A_i$ and $A_1 \oplus A_2 \oplus \dots \oplus A_n$. If $\mathscr{A}$ has a zero object then we can define **projections** $p_i : A \to A_i$ such that $p_j u_i = \delta_{ij}$.

Proposition 17.2. *If $\mathscr{A}$ has images, inverse images, and coproducts, then $\mathscr{A}$ has unions. In fact if $\{A_i\}$ is a family of subobjects of A, then their union is given by the image of the morphism $f : \bigoplus A_i \to A$ such that for each i, fu_i is the inclusion of A_i in A.*

Proof. Considering the A_i as subobjects of $\bigoplus A_i$ by means of the injections, it is trivial to verify that their union is $\bigoplus A_i$. Consequently our result follows from 11.2. ▌

Suppose that for all $i \in I$ we have $A_i = A$. In this case we denote the product of the family by A^I and the coproduct by ${}^I A$. We have the **diagonal** morphism $\Delta : A \to A^I$ defined by $p_i \Delta = 1_A$ for all $i \in I$, and dually the **codiagonal** morphism $\nabla : {}^I A \to A$ defined by $\nabla u_i = 1_A$ for all $i \in I$. Then Δ is necessarily a monomorphism and ∇ is necessarily an epimorphism.

In a general category $\mathscr{A}$, a morphism f from a coproduct $\bigoplus_{j\in J} A_j$ to a product $\underset{i\in I}{\mathsf{X}}\, B^i$ is completely determined by its **coordinate morphisms** $f_{ij} = p_i{}^j f u$, where u_j is the jth injection into the coproduct and p_i is the ith projection from the product. Hence $\left[\bigoplus_{j\in J} A_j, \underset{i\in I}{\mathsf{X}}\, B_i\right]$ is in one to one correspondence with the set of all $I \times J$ matrices of the form (f_{ij}) where $f_{ij} \in [A_j, B_i]$. We shall frequently denote such a morphism by its corresponding matrix. In particular when $\mathscr{A}$

has a zero object, we have the morphism $\delta = (\delta_{ij}) : \bigoplus_{i \in I} A_i \to \mathsf{X}_{i \in I} A_i$. If δ is an isomorphism then we call $\bigoplus_{i \in I} A_i$ a **biproduct**.

Proposition 17.3. *The following statements are equivalent in a category* $\mathscr{A}$.

(a) $\mathscr{A}$ *has finite intersections and finite products.*
(b) $\mathscr{A}$ *has equalizers and finite products.*
The above statements imply
(c) $\mathscr{A}$ *has pullbacks.*

and are equivalent to (c) *if* $\mathscr{A}$ *has a null object.*

Proof. To prove the proposition we first prove three lemmas which give us more detailed information.

Lemma 17.4. *Consider two morphisms* $\alpha, \beta : A \to B$ *in an arbitrary category. Then the diagram*

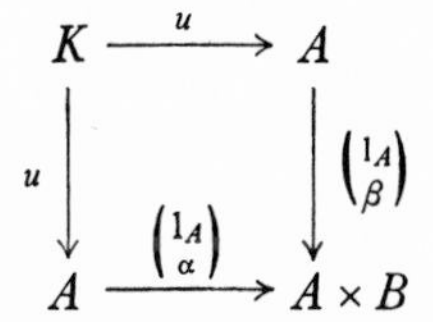

(1)

is an intersection if and only if u is the equalizer of α *and* β.

Proof. We have used the word intersection rather than pullback since the morphisms $\begin{pmatrix} 1_A \\ \alpha \end{pmatrix}$ and $\begin{pmatrix} 1_A \\ \beta \end{pmatrix}$ are necessarily monomorphisms. Now in order that (1) be commutative we must have $\alpha u = \beta u$. From this the lemma easily follows. ▌

The proofs of the following two lemmas are straightforward and are left to the reader.

Lemma 17.5. *Given two morphisms* $\alpha_1 : A_1 \to A$ *and* $\alpha_2 : A_2 \to A$, *consider the diagram*

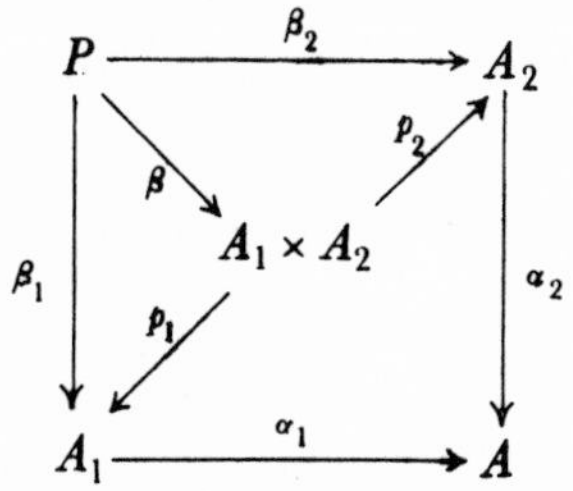

where p_1 *and* p_2 *are projections from the product and* $\beta_i = p_i\beta$ *for* $i = 1, 2$. *Then the square is a pullback diagram if and only if* β *is the equalizer of the two morphisms* $\alpha_1 p_1$ *and* $\alpha_2 p_2$. ▮

Lemma 17.6. *Let* 0 *be a null object for a category and let* A_1 *and* A_2 *be any objects. Then the diagram*

$$\begin{array}{ccc} P & \xrightarrow{p_2} & A_2 \\ {\scriptstyle p_1}\downarrow & & \downarrow \\ A_1 & \longrightarrow & 0 \end{array}$$

is a pullback if and only if P *is the product of* A_1 *and* A_2 *with projections* p_1 *and* p_2. ▮

Returning now to the proof of 17.3, we have (a)⇒(b) by 17.4 and (b)⇒(c) by 17.5. Also since (c) implies that $\mathscr{A}$ has finite intersections (8.1) we have (b)⇒(a). If $\mathscr{A}$ has a null object, then (c)⇒(a) follows from 17.6. ▮

18. Additive Categories

A **semiadditive** category is a category $\mathscr{A}$ together with an abelian semigroup structure on each of its morphism sets, subject to the following conditions:

(i) The composition functions $[B, C] \times [A, B] \to [A\ C]$ are bilinear. That is, if $\alpha, \beta \in [A, B]$ and $\gamma \in [B, C]$, then $\gamma(\alpha + \beta) = \gamma\alpha + \gamma\beta$, and if $\gamma \in [A, B]$ and $\alpha, \beta \in [B, C]$ then $(\alpha + \beta)\gamma = \alpha\gamma + \beta\gamma$.

(ii) The zero elements of the semigroups behave as zero morphisms.

That is $\alpha 0 = 0$ and $0\alpha = 0$ whenever the compositions make sense. (Observe that the 0 on the right-hand side of the equations is not in general the same as the 0 on the left-hand side).

Condition (ii) together with exercise 6 tells us that we can always assume that a semiadditive category has a zero object.

If, further, each set $[A, B]$ is an abelian group, then we call $\mathscr{A}$ an **additive** category. In this case condition (ii) follows from condition (i), for we have $\alpha 0 = \alpha(0 + 0) = \alpha 0 + \alpha 0$, and so subtracting $\alpha 0$ from both sides we obtain $0 = \alpha 0$. Also

$$\alpha(-\beta) + \alpha\beta = \alpha((-\beta) + \beta) = \alpha 0 = 0$$

so that $\alpha(-\beta) = -(\alpha\beta)$. Similarly $(-\alpha)\beta = -(\alpha\beta)$ and $(-\alpha)(-\beta) = \alpha\beta$. The kernel of a difference $\alpha - \beta$ is the same as the equalizer of the two morphisms α and β. Hence an additive category has kernels if and only if it has equalizers. A morphism is a monomorphism in an additive category if and only if its kernel is 0.

A **ring** is an additive category **R** which has only one object. The dual category **R*** is called the **opposite ring**. If **R** = **R***, then **R** is called a **commutative** ring. A commutative ring in which every nonzero morphism is a monomorphism (and hence also an epimorphism) is called an **integral domain**. A ring in which every nonzero morphism is an isomorphism is called a **division ring**, and a commutative division ring is called a **field**.

Proposition 18.1. *Let $A_1, A_2, \ldots, A_n$ be a finite collection of objects in a semiadditive category. Then a family of morphisms $\{u_i : A_i \to A\}$ is a coproduct for the family if and only if there is a family of morphisms $\{p_i : A \to A_i\}$ such that $p_i u_j = \delta_{ij}$ and $\sum_{k=1}^{n} u_k p_k = 1_A$.*

Proof. Suppose first that A is the coproduct. Then we know that the morphisms p_i exist satisfying the relations $p_i u_j = \delta_{ij}$. Now we have for each i

$$\left(\sum_{k=1}^{n} u_k p_k\right) u_i = \sum_{k=1}^{n} (u_k p_k u_i) = \sum_{k=1}^{n} u_k \delta_{ki} = u_i = 1_A u_i.$$

Hence, by definition of coproduct, we must have $\sum_{k=1}^{n} u_k p_k = 1_A$.

Conversely, suppose that we are given morphisms p_i satisfying the given conditions, and let $f_i : A_i \to A'$ for $1 \leqslant i \leqslant n$. Define $f = \sum_{k=1}^{n} f_k p_k$. Then we have

$$fu_i = \sum_{k=1}^{n} f_k p_k u_i = f_i.$$

Furthermore, if f' is another morphism satisfying the conditions $f' u_i = f_i$ for all i, then we have

$$f' = f' 1_A = f' \sum_{k=1}^{n} u_k p_k = \sum_{k=1}^{n} f' u_k p_k = \sum_{k=1}^{n} f_k p_k = f.$$

Hence f is unique, and so A is the coproduct. ∎

Remark. In the case $n = 2$, the conditions $p_2 u_1 = 0$ and $p_1 u_2 = 0$ follow from the conditions $p_1 u_1 = 0$, $p_2 u_2 = 0$, and $u_1 p_1 + u_2 p_2 = 1_A$.

Corollary 18.2. *In a semiadditive category every finite product (coproduct) is a biproduct.* ∎

Let

$$f = (f_{jk}) : \bigoplus_{k \in K} A_k \to \bigoplus_{j \in J} B_j$$

and

$$g = (g_{ij}) : \bigoplus_{j \in J} B_j \to \bigoplus_{i \in I} C_i$$

in a semiadditive category where I, J, and K are finite sets, and we have written $\oplus$ in place of $\times$ in the codomains by virtue of 18.2. Let $h = gf$. Then we have

$$h_{ik} = p_i^C g f u_k^A = p_i^C g \left(\sum_{j \in J} u_j^B p_j^B \right) f u_k^A$$
$$= \sum_{j \in J} (p_i^C g u_j^B)(p_j^B f u_k^A) = \sum_{j \in J} g_{ij} f_{jk}.$$

That is, the matrix corresponding to the composition gf is the product of matrices $(g_{ij})(f_{ij})$. In particular, for a finite set I, $[{}^I A, {}^I A]$ is isomorphic to the ring of $I \times I$ matrices over the ring $[A, A]$.

Lemma 18.3. *In a semiadditive category the sum $\alpha + \beta$ of two morphisms $\alpha, \beta : A \to B$ is given by any of the three compositions*

$$A \xrightarrow{\Delta} A \oplus A \xrightarrow{(\alpha,\beta)} B \tag{1}$$

$$A \xrightarrow{\binom{\alpha}{\beta}} B \oplus B \xrightarrow{\nabla} B \tag{2}$$

$$A \xrightarrow{\Delta} A \oplus A \xrightarrow{\begin{pmatrix}\alpha & 0\\ 0 & \beta\end{pmatrix}} B \oplus B \xrightarrow{\nabla} B. \tag{3}$$

Proof. Writing $\Delta = \begin{pmatrix}1_A\\ 1_A\end{pmatrix}$ and $\nabla = (1_A, 1_A)$ the results follow from a few trivial matrix multiplications. ∎

Observe that the middle morphism of (3) is the same as the morphism $\alpha \oplus \beta$ defined in §17.

The following proposition was first observed in part by MacLane [29]. The proof given here was devised by Eckmann, Hilton, and Eilenberg.

Proposition 18.4. *Suppose that $\mathscr{A}$ is a category with biproducts of the form $A \oplus A$ for all $A \in \mathscr{A}$. Then $\mathscr{A}$ has a unique semiadditive structure. If, further, $\mathscr{A}$ is balanced, then it is additive.*

Proof. For $\alpha, \beta : A \to B$ define $\alpha + \beta$ as the composition (1). This definition is forced on us by 18.3; hence we already have our uniqueness assertion. Also define $\alpha \times \beta$ as the composition (2). Letting p_1 be the first projection from $A \oplus A$ we have $(\alpha, 0) = \alpha p_1$, and from this we see that $\alpha + 0 = \alpha$. Similarly $0 + \alpha = \alpha$, and dually $\alpha \times 0 = \alpha$ and $0 \times \alpha = \alpha$.

Next let $\gamma : B \to B'$. Then we have $\gamma(\alpha, \beta) = (\gamma\alpha, \gamma\beta)$ and from this follows the equation

$$\gamma(\alpha + \beta) = (\gamma\alpha) + (\gamma\beta). \tag{4}$$

Dually, if $\rho : A' \to A$ we have

$$(\alpha \times \beta)\rho = (\alpha\rho) \times (\beta\rho). \tag{5}$$

Finally, let x, y, z, w be any four morphisms from A to B. Then we have

$$(x+z)\times(y+w) = \nabla\left(\begin{pmatrix} x & z \\ y & w\end{pmatrix}\Delta\right) = \left(\nabla\begin{pmatrix} x & z \\ y & w\end{pmatrix}\right)\Delta = (x\times y)+(z\times w).$$

Setting z and y zero we get $x+w = x\times w$, hence $+ = \times$. Setting x and w zero we then have $z+y = y+z$. Setting y zero we have

$$(x+z)+w = x+(z+w).$$

Therefore $+$ makes $[A, B]$ an abelian semigroup, and bilinearity of composition follows from (4) and (5).

Now suppose that $\mathscr{A}$ is balanced, and consider the morphism

$$\theta : A \oplus A \rightarrow A \oplus A$$

given by the matrix $\begin{pmatrix} 1 & 1 \\ 0 & 1\end{pmatrix}$. If $\alpha, \alpha' : A \oplus A \rightarrow B$ are such that $\alpha\theta = \alpha'\theta$, then expressing α and α' as matrices it is a simple matter to verify that $\alpha = \alpha'$. Hence θ is an epimorphism. Dually θ is a monomorphism and so, since $\mathscr{A}$ is balanced, θ is an isomorphism. Writing $\theta^{-1} = \begin{pmatrix} a & b \\ c & d\end{pmatrix}$, the relation $\theta^{-1}\theta = \begin{pmatrix} 1 & 0 \\ 0 & 1\end{pmatrix}$ yields $1 + b = 0$. Then for any morphism $x : A \rightarrow B$ we have

$$x + xb = x1 + xb = x(1+b) = x0 = 0$$

and so xb is an additive inverse for x. ∎

An endomorphism $\theta : A \rightarrow A$ is called **idempotent** if $\theta\theta = \theta$. If θ is idempotent in an additive category, then $1_A - \theta$ is also idempotent.

Proposition 18.5. *Consider a coretraction $u_1 : A_1 \rightarrow A$ in an additive category, and suppose that $p_1 u_1 = 1_{A_1}$. Then $\theta = u_1 p_1$ is idempotent, and u_1 is the kernel of $1_A - \theta$. On the other hand, if $\theta : A \rightarrow A$ is idempotent and $u_1 : A_1 \rightarrow A$ and $u_2 : A_2 \rightarrow A$ are the kernels of $1_A - \theta$ and θ, respectively, then A is the coproduct of u_1 and u_2.*

Proof. If $p_1 u_1 = 1_{A_1}$, then we have

$$\theta\theta = u_1 p_1 u_1 p_1 = u_1 1_{A_1} p_1 = u_1 p_1 = \theta.$$

Also if $(1_A - \theta)\alpha = 0$, then we have $u_1(p_1\alpha) = \theta\alpha = \alpha$, and so since u_1 is a monomorphism and $(1_A - \theta)u_1 = u_1 - u_1 p_1 u_1 = 0$, we see that u_1 is the kernel of $1_A - \theta$.

Now suppose that θ is idempotent and u_1 and u_2 are the kernels of $1_A - \theta$ and θ. Since $(1_A - \theta)\theta = 0$, there is a morphism $p_1 : A \rightarrow A_1$ such that $u_1 p_1 = \theta$. Then we have $u_1 p_1 u_1 = \theta u_1 = u_1$, and so $p_1 u_1 = 1_{A_1}$ since u_1 is a monomorphism. Likewise we have $p_2 : A \rightarrow A_2$ such that $u_2 p_2 = 1_A - \theta$, and $p_2 u_2 = 1_{A_2}$. Then since $u_1 p_1 + u_2 p_2 = \theta + (1_A - \theta) = 1_A$, we see from the remark following 18.1 that A is the coproduct of u_1 and u_2. ∎

19. Exact Additive Categories

In an exact category $\mathscr{A}$ we shall say that a short exact sequence

$$0 \longrightarrow A \xrightarrow{\alpha} B \xrightarrow{\beta} C \longrightarrow 0 \tag{1}$$

splits if β is a retraction.

Proposition 19.1. *If in an exact additive category the exact sequence* (1) *splits, say* $\beta\gamma = 1_C$, *then* B *is the coproduct of* α *and* γ. *Furthermore* $\rho : B \to A$ *can be chosen such that* β *and* ρ *are the projections from the coproduct.*

Proof. This follows immediately from 18.5. ▌

Corollary 19.2. *In an exact additive category, if*

$$A \xrightarrow{\alpha} B \xrightarrow{\beta} C$$

$$A \xleftarrow{\rho} B \xleftarrow{\gamma} C$$

are exact sequences such that $\rho\alpha = 1_A$ *and* $\beta\gamma = 1_C$, *then* B *is the coproduct of* A *and* C *with injections* α *and* γ *and projections* β *and* ρ.

Proof. Since β is a retraction, it is an epimorphism. Similarly α is a monomorphism, and so the sequence $0 \to A \to B \to C \to 0$ is exact. Consequently by 19.1, α and γ are the injections of a coproduct and β is one of the projections. The relations $\rho\alpha = 1_A$ and $\rho\nu = 0$ show that ρ is the other projection. ▌

Proposition 19.3. *Let* $u_1 : A_1 \to A$ *and* $u_2 : A_2 \to A$ *be monomorphisms in an exact category* $\mathscr{A}$. *If* A *is the coproduct of* A_1 *and* A_2 *with injections* u_1 *and* u_2, *then* $A_1 \cap A_2 = 0$ *and* $A_1 \cup A_2 = A$. *On the other hand assuming further that* $\mathscr{A}$ *is additive, if* $A_1 \cap A_2 = 0$ *and* $A_1 \cup A_2 = A$, *then* A *is the coproduct of* A_1 *and* A_2.

Proof. We refer to the diagram (3) of 16.6. If A is the coproduct, then by 17.1* we can take $A/A_2 = A_1$, so that $A_1 \to A \to A/A_2$ becomes the identity morphism on A_1. From this it follows that $A_1 \cap A_2 = 0$ and $A_1 \cup A_2 = A$.

Now suppose that $\mathscr{A}$ is exact and additive, and that $A_1 \cap A_2 = 0$ and $A_1 \cup A_2 = A$. Then by 16.6 $A_1 \to A \to A/A_2$ is an isomorphism. Consequently it follows from 19.1 that A is the coproduct of A_1 and the kernel of $A \to A/A_2$; that is, A is the coproduct of A_1 and A_2. ▌

Proposition 19.4. *Consider an order two sequence*

$$A_1 \xrightarrow{d_1} A_2 \xrightarrow{d_2} A_3 \tag{2}$$

in an exact additive category, and suppose that there are morphisms $s_1 : A_2 \to A_1$ *and* $s_2 : A_3 \to A_2$ *such that* $d_1 s_1 + s_2 d_2 = 1_{A_2}$. *Then* (2) *is exact.*

Proof. Let $A_1 \overset{p}{\to} I \overset{u}{\to} A_2$ be the factorization of d_1 through its image. We have $0 = d_2 d_1 = d_2 u p$, and so $d_2 u = 0$ since p is an epimorphism. Now if $d_2 \alpha = 0$, then

$$\alpha = (d_1 s_1 + s_2 d_2)\alpha = u p s_1 \alpha.$$

This shows that u is the kernel of d_2 and so (2) is exact. ▮

20. Abelian Categories

An **abelian category** is an exact additive category with finite products. The following theorem is due to Peter Freyd.

Theorem 20.1. *The following statements are equivalent:*

(a) *$\mathscr{A}$ is an abelian category.*
(b) *$\mathscr{A}$ has kernels, cokernels, finite products, finite coproducts, and is normal and conormal.*
(c) *$\mathscr{A}$ has pushouts and pullbacks and is normal and conormal.*

Proof. (a) $\Rightarrow$ (b) This is immediate from the definition of exact category and the fact that finite products and coproducts coincide in an additive category.

(b) $\Rightarrow$ (c) By 14.1, $\mathscr{A}$ has finite intersections, and so by 17.3 $\mathscr{A}$ has pullbacks. Dually $\mathscr{A}$ has pushouts.

(c) $\Rightarrow$ (a) By 17.3 and 17.3*, $\mathscr{A}$ has finite products, finite coproducts, equalizers, and coequalizers. Hence, by 14.4, $\mathscr{A}$ is exact. To show that $\mathscr{A}$ is additive, by 18.4 it suffices to show that the morphism $\delta : A \oplus B \to A \times B$ is an isomorphism for any pair of objects $A, B \in \mathscr{A}$. Let K and K' be defined by the exact sequence

$$0 \to K \to A \oplus B \overset{\delta}{\to} A \times B \to K' \to 0.$$

Then $K \to A \oplus B \to A = K \to A \oplus B \to A \times B \to A = 0$, and so K is a subobject of B in $A \oplus B$. Similarly K is a subobject of A, and so $K = 0$ by 19.3. By duality $K' = 0$. Consequently, by 15.1, δ is an isomorphism. ▮

Consider a pullback diagram

$$\begin{array}{ccc} P & \xrightarrow{\beta_2} & A_2 \\ {\scriptstyle\beta_1}\downarrow & & \downarrow{\scriptstyle\alpha_2} \\ A_1 & \xrightarrow{\alpha_1} & A \end{array} \qquad (1)$$

In 7.1 we saw that if α_1 is a monomorphism then β_2 is a monomorphism. In 16.3 it was proved among other things that, in an exact category, if α_1 is an epimorphism and α_2 is a monomorphism then β_2 is an epimorphism. The following important proposition tells us that in an abelian category the latter statement is true without the assumption that α_2 be a monomorphism.

Proposition 20.2. *If* (1) *is a pullback diagram in an abelian category and if* α_1 *is an epimorphism, then* β_2 *is an epimorphism.*

Proof. Consider the diagram

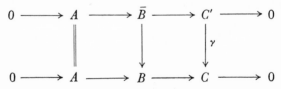

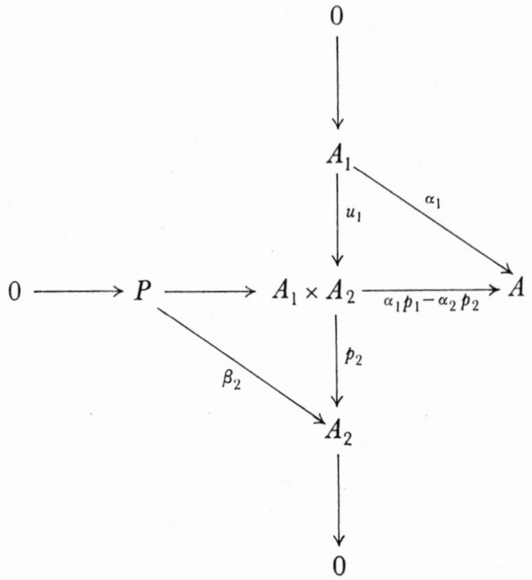

where u_1 is the first injection into the product, p_2 is the second projection from the product, and exactness of the row defines the pullback P by 17.5. Then the triangles are commutative, and so since α_1 is an epimorphism the same must be true of $\alpha_1 p_1 - \alpha_2 p_2$. Therefore by 16.8, we see that β_2 is an epimorphism. ▌

Combining 20.2 and 13.1 we have

Corollary 20.3. *In an abelian category, an exact sequence* $0 \to A \to B \to C \to 0$ *and a morphism* $\gamma : C' \to C$ *can be put into a commutative diagram*

$$\begin{array}{ccccccccc} 0 & \longrightarrow & A & \longrightarrow & \bar{B} & \longrightarrow & C' & \longrightarrow & 0 \\ & & \| & & \downarrow & & \downarrow \gamma & & \\ 0 & \longrightarrow & A & \longrightarrow & B & \longrightarrow & C & \longrightarrow & 0 \end{array}$$

where the top row is exact and the right square is a pullback. ▌

21. The Category of Abelian Groups $\mathscr{G}$

This is the category whose class of objects is the class of all abelian groups. The morphisms from group A to group B are the additive functions from A to

B; that is, functions $f: A \to B$ such that $f(a+b) = f(a) + f(b)$ for all $a, b \in A$. The set $[A, B]$ becomes an abelian group if we define $f+g$ by the rule $(f+g)(a) = f(a) + g(a)$ for all $a \in A$. An identity for A is the morphism 1_A defined by $1_A(a) = a$ for all $a \in A$. Then composition given by the usual composition of functions is bilinear, and $\mathscr{G}$ is an additive category.

Let $f: A \to B$ be any morphism of groups, and let $K = \{a \in A \mid f(a) = 0\}$. Then K is closed under subtraction in A, hence has an induced abelian group structure such that the inclusion function $u: K \to A$ defined by $u(k) = k$ is a group morphism. It is easy to verify that u is a kernel for f. Now we can put an equivalence relation on B by defining $b \sim b'$ if and only if $b - b' = f(a)$ for some $a \in A$. Denoting the resulting set of equivalence classes by K' and the equivalence class of b by $[b]$, we define a group structure on K' by the rule $[b_1] + [b_2] = [b_1 + b_2]$. Then the function $p: B \to K'$ given by $p(b) = [b]$ is a morphism of groups. Again it is easy to check that p is a cokernel for f.

A group morphism is a monomorphism if and only if it is univalent, an epimorphism if and only if it is onto, and an isomorphism if and only if it is a one to one correspondence. If f is a monomorphism, then it is easy to see that f is a kernel for p. Similarly, if f is an epimorphism then it is a cokernel for u. In other words $\mathscr{G}$ is normal and conormal and so by 14.4 $\mathscr{G}$ is exact. Explicitly, the decomposition of f into an epimorphism followed by a monomorphism is given by $A \xrightarrow{q} I \xrightarrow{v} B$ where $I = \{f(a) \mid a \in A\}$, q is defined by $q(a) = f(a)$, and v is defined by $v(b) = b$.

If $\{A_i\}_{i \in I}$ is any set of abelian groups, then a product is given by the cartesian product $\underset{i \in I}{\times} A_i$ with addition defined by the rule $(a_i) + (b_i) = (a_i + b_i)$. The projection $p_k : \underset{i \in I}{\times} A_i \to A_k$ is given by $p_k((a_i)) = a_k$. In particular this shows that $\mathscr{G}$ is an abelian category. A coproduct for the above family is obtained by taking the subgroup of $\underset{i \in I}{\times} A_i$ consisting of all those elements (a_i) such that $a_k = 0$ for all but a finite number of $k \in I$. The injection u_k from A_k to the coproduct is given by $u_k(a) = (a_i)$ where $a_i = 0$ for $i \neq k$ and $a_k = a$.

The simple characterizations of monomorphisms and epimorphisms in $\mathscr{G}$ enable us to handle diagrams in this category with comparative ease. Let us prove, for example, the "5 lemma."

Proposition 21.1. *Suppose that the following diagram is commutative and has exact rows in* $\mathscr{G}$*:*

$$\begin{array}{ccccccccc}
A_1 & \xrightarrow{\alpha_1} & A_2 & \xrightarrow{\alpha_2} & A_3 & \xrightarrow{\alpha_3} & A_4 & \xrightarrow{\alpha_4} & A_5 \\
\downarrow{\scriptstyle \gamma_1} & & \downarrow{\scriptstyle \gamma_2} & & \downarrow{\scriptstyle \gamma_3} & & \downarrow{\scriptstyle \gamma_4} & & \downarrow{\scriptstyle \gamma_5} \\
B_1 & \xrightarrow{\beta_1} & B_2 & \xrightarrow{\beta_2} & B_3 & \xrightarrow{\beta_3} & B_4 & \xrightarrow{\beta_4} & B_5
\end{array}$$

(i) *If* γ_1 *is an epimorphism and* γ_2 *and* γ_4 *are monomorphisms, then* γ_3 *is a monomorphism.*

(ii) *If* γ_5 *is a monomorphism and* γ_2 *and* γ_4 *are epimorphisms, then* γ_3 *is an epimorphism.*

(iii) *If* γ_1 *is an epimorphism,* γ_5 *is a monomorphism, and* γ_2 *and* γ_4 *are isomorphisms, then* γ_3 *is an isomorphism.*

Proof. (i) To show that γ_3 is a monomorphism we must prove that if $a \in A_3$ and $\gamma_3(a) = 0$, then $a = 0$. Now if $\gamma_3(a) = 0$, then $0 = \beta_3(\gamma_3(a)) = \gamma_4(\alpha_3(a))$. Since γ_4 is a monomorphism this means that $\alpha_3(a) = 0$. By exactness of the top row we then have $a = \alpha_2(a')$ for some $a' \in A_2$. Then

$$\beta_2(\gamma_2(a')) = \gamma_3(\alpha_2(a')) = \gamma_3(a) = 0.$$

Hence, by exactness of the bottom row we can find $b \in B_1$ such that $\gamma_2(a') = \beta_1(b)$. Since γ_1 is an epimorphism we can write $b = \gamma_1(a'')$ for some $a'' \in A_1$. Then $\gamma_2(\alpha_1(a'')) = \beta_1(\gamma_1(a'')) = \beta_1(b) = \gamma_2(a')$, and so since γ_2 is a monomorphism we have $\alpha_1(a'') = a'$. Hence $a = \alpha_2(a') = \alpha_2(\alpha_1(a'')) = 0$ by exactness (order two) of the top row.

(ii) This is the dual of statement (i). However we cannot say that (ii) follows from (i) by duality, since we have proved (i) only for the category $\mathcal{G}$. If we apply duality we are no longer in the category of abelian groups. Statement (ii) is proved by the same type of "diagram chasing" used to prove (i).

(iii) This follows by combining (i) and (ii). ▮

We could have assumed a weaker hypothesis in 21.1 than that the rows be exact. In some instances we used kernel $\subset$ image and in other instances we used image $\subset$ kernel. Likewise it is informative to prove the 9 lemma (16.1) for $\mathcal{G}$ by diagram chasing and to list precisely the exactness conditions needed.

Of course the 5 lemma is true in any abelian category (in fact, in any exact category, see exercise 14). Usually, however, it is not as easy to prove a statement in a general abelian category as it is to prove it in the category $\mathcal{G}$ where we can always chase diagrams. In Chapter IV we shall prove a theorem which tells us that any general enough statement about a finite diagram which is true in the category of abelian groups is also true in any abelian category.

Exercises

1. In the categories $\mathcal{S}, \mathcal{T}, \mathcal{S}_0, \mathcal{T}_0$ (examples 1–4, §3) a morphism is a monomorphism if and only if it is a univalent function, and an epimorphism if and only if it is onto. All four categories are locally small, colocally small, have equalizers, coequalizers, intersections, cointersections, unions, counions, images, coimages, pushouts, pullbacks, products (cartesian products), and coproducts (disjoint unions, with base points identified in the cases of $\mathcal{S}_0$ and $\mathcal{T}_0$). $\mathcal{S}$ and $\mathcal{S}_0$ are balanced, but not $\mathcal{T}$ and $\mathcal{T}_0$. In $\mathcal{S}$ and $\mathcal{T}$ any set with precisely one element is a null object, and the empty set ø is a conull object. $\mathscr{S}_0$ and $\mathscr{T}_0$ are categories with zero, and have kernels and cokernels. $\mathscr{S}_0$ is normal, but $\mathscr{T}_0$ is neither normal nor conormal. However, the full subcategory of $\mathscr{T}_0$ consisting of all compact Hausdorff spaces is normal, and moreover is balanced.

2. In the category of all Hausdorff spaces a morphism can be an epimorphism without being onto as a function. In fact, in order that a continuous function $f: X \to Y$ be an epimorphism it suffices that $f(X)$ be a dense subspace of Y.

3. Let I denote the closed unit interval of real numbers. Define two morphisms $\alpha, \beta : A \to B$ in $\mathscr{T}$ to be equivalent if there is a continuous function $h : A \times I \to B$ such that $h(a, 0) = \alpha(a)$ and $h(a, 1) = \beta(a)$ for all $a \in A$. Then this is an equivalence relation which behaves in the right way with respect to composition so as to define a quotient category of $\mathscr{T}$.

4. Consider $f: A \to B$ in any category, and let $\{A_i\}$ be a set of subobjects of A. If $\bigcup A_i$ and $\bigcup f(A_i)$ are defined, then so is $f(\bigcup A_i)$ and we have $\bigcup f(A_i) = f(\bigcup A_i)$. Likewise if $\{B_i\}$ is a set of subobjects of B and if $\bigcap B_i$ and $\bigcap f^{-1}(B_i)$ are defined, then so is $f^{-1}(\bigcap B_i)$ and we have $\bigcap f^{-1}(B_i) = f^{-1}(\bigcap B_i)$. (Cf. 11.2 and 11.3).

5. In 11.1 it suffices to assume that $f^{-1}(f(A_1))$ exists in (v) and that $f(f^{-1}(B_1))$ exists in (vi).

6. If $\mathscr{A}$ has a set of distinguished morphisms in the sense of §12, then a zero object can be adjoined without changing any of the pullbacks, products, unions, etc., that already exist.

7. Proposition 7.2 is true if the assumption that $B' \to B$ be a monomorphism is removed.

8. If $A_i \to A$ is the kernel of $A \to A_i''$ for each i, then $A' \to A$ is the intersection of the A_i's if and only if it is the kernel of the morphism $A \to \times A_i''$. Hence a normal category with products and kernels has intersections.

9. In a normal category with equalizers, a morphism is an epimorphism if and only if its cokernel is 0.

10. If $f: A \to B$ is an epimorphism and $B' \to B$ is a subobject in a normal and conormal category with kernels and cokernels, then $f(f^{-1}(B')) = B'$ (use 13.2 and 14.4).

11. For any category $\mathscr{A}$ define a category Add($\mathscr{A}$) as follows. The objects of Add($\mathscr{A}$) are the same as the objects of $\mathscr{A}$. The set of morphisms from A to B in Add($\mathscr{A}$) is the free abelian group generated by the elements of $[A, B]_{\mathscr{A}}$; that is, the set of all finite formal linear combinations of the form $\sum_i n_i\alpha_i$ where n_i is an integer and $\alpha_i \in [A, B]_{\mathscr{A}}$. Composition in Add($\mathscr{A}$) is defined by the rule

$$\left(\sum_i n_i\alpha_i\right)\left(\sum_j m_j\beta_j\right) = \sum_{(i,j)} (n_im_j)(\alpha_i\beta_j).$$

Then Add($\mathscr{A}$) is an additive category which contains $\mathscr{A}$ as a subcategory. If $\mathscr{A}$ is a category with zero, then denoting the zero morphism from A to B by 0_{AB} we can factor $[A, B]_{\text{Add}(\mathscr{A})}$ by the subgroup generated by 0_{AB}, and in this way we obtain a quotient category $\overline{\text{Add}(\mathscr{A})}$ of Add($\mathscr{A}$) which is additive, contains $\mathscr{A}$ as a subcategory, and has the same set of zero morphisms as $\mathscr{A}$.

12. In any category $\mathscr{A}$ with zero we can define a sequence $A \xrightarrow{\alpha} B \xrightarrow{\beta} C$ to be coexact if the cokernel of α is the same as the coimage of β. If $\mathscr{A}$ is a normal category with kernels and coequalizers and if the above sequence is coexact, then it is exact (use 10.1* and 14.4).

13. Let $\mathscr{H}$ be the category of not necessarily abelian groups. A morphism $\varphi : M \to G$ of groups is a function from M to G such that $\varphi(m_1 m_2) = \varphi(m_1)\varphi(m_2)$ for all $m_1, m_2 \in M$. Then φ is a monomorphism if and only if it is a univalent function, but in such a case it is the kernel of some morphism if and only if A is a normal subgroup of B. $\mathscr{H}$ has kernels, images, equalizers, unions, intersections, pullbacks, and products.

Less trivially φ is an epimorphism if and only if it is onto as a function. (Suppose that φ is not onto, and let $H = \varphi(M)$. If G/H has just two cosets, then H must be a normal subgroup of G, and so it is clear in this case that φ is not an epimorphism. Otherwise there is a permutation γ of G/H whose only fixed point is H. Let $\pi : G \to G/H$ be the obvious function and choose $\theta : G/H \to G$ such that $\pi\theta = 1$. Let $\tau : G \to H$ be such that $x = \tau(x)\theta\pi(x)$ for all $x \in G$ and define $\lambda : G \to G$ by $\lambda(x) = \tau(x)\theta\gamma\pi(x)$. Then λ is a permutation of G. Let P be the group of permutations of G, and let $\alpha, \beta : G \to P$ be defined by $\alpha(g)(x) = gx$ for $g, x \in G$ and $\beta(g) = \lambda^{-1}\alpha(g)\lambda$. Then α and β are morphisms of groups, and $\alpha(g) = \beta(g)$ if and only if $g \in H$. Hence $\alpha\varphi = \beta\varphi$. This proof is due to Eilenberg and Moore.) $\mathscr{H}$ is conormal and has cokernels, coimages, coequalizers, co-unions, cointersections, pushouts, and coproducts (free products). By exercise 12* a sequence in $\mathscr{H}$ is coexact if it is exact.

Discuss also the category of finite groups.

14. Prove the 5 lemma (21.1) as follows in an exact category. In proving part (i) replace A_1 by Im(α_1) and B_1 by Im(β_1) and show that the induced morphism $\text{Im}(\alpha_1) \to \text{Im}(\beta_1)$ is an isomorphism. Then by 16.2 the induced morphism $\text{Im}(\alpha_2) \to \text{Im}(\beta_2)$ is a monomorphism. Hence we may assume that α_2, β_2, and γ_2 are all monomorphisms. From the fact that γ_4 is a monomorphism it then follows that γ_3 is a monomorphism. Part (ii) now follows by duality.

15. In an exact additive category, if A, B_1, and B_2 are subobjects of C and $A \cup B_1$, $A \cup B_2$ are coproducts, and if $(A \cup B_1) \cap (A \cup B_2) = A$, then $A \cup B_1 \cup B_2$ is a coproduct.

16. Prove the following proposition in an exact additive category. Consider a commutative diagram

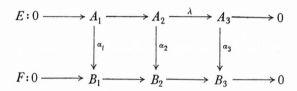

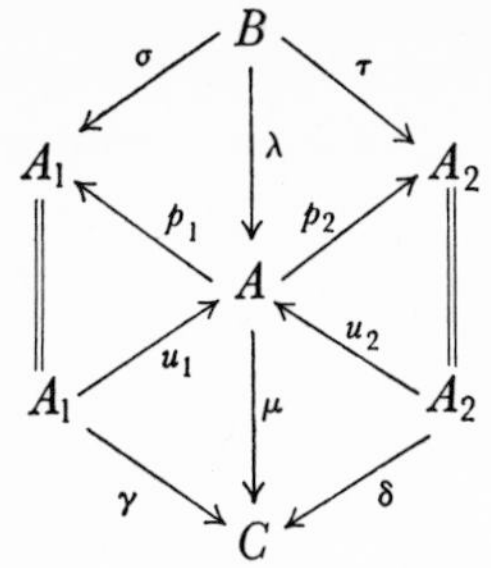

where $\mu\lambda = 0$ and the diagonals are exact. Then $u_1 p_1 + u_2 p_2 = 1_A$; that is, A is the coproduct of A_1 and A_2. Furthermore $\gamma\sigma + \delta\tau = 0$.

17. In an abelian category if one of two morphisms $\alpha_1 : A_1 \to A$ and $\alpha_2 : A_2 \to A$ is an epimorphism, then the corresponding pullback diagram is also a pushout diagram (use 20.2).

18. Let $\mathscr{A}$ be any abelian category. Let $\mathscr{E}$ be the class of short exact sequences in $\mathscr{A}$. A morphism $\alpha : E \to F$ of short exact sequences is a commutative diagram

$$\begin{array}{ccccccccc} E: 0 & \longrightarrow & A_1 & \longrightarrow & A_2 & \xrightarrow{\lambda} & A_3 & \longrightarrow & 0 \\ & & \downarrow{\scriptstyle \alpha_1} & & \downarrow{\scriptstyle \alpha_2} & & \downarrow{\scriptstyle \alpha_3} & & \\ F: 0 & \longrightarrow & B_1 & \longrightarrow & B_2 & \longrightarrow & B_3 & \longrightarrow & 0 \end{array}$$

Then $\mathscr{E}$ is an additive category. The kernel of α is the sequence

$$K : 0 \to K_1 \to K_2 \to \lambda(K_2) \to 0$$

where $K_1 = \operatorname{Ker}(\alpha_1)$ and $K_2 = \operatorname{Ker}(\alpha_2)$. The cokernel K' is given by the dual construction. Hence α is a monomorphism (epimorphism) if and only if α_2 is a monomorphism (epimorphism), and so α is a monomorphism and an epimorphism if and only if α_2 is an isomorphism. Let I' be the cokernel of $K \to E$ and I the kernel of $F \to K'$. Then the induced morphism $I' \to I$ is a monomorphism and an epimorphism. If $\mathscr{A}$ has (infinite) products or coproducts, then so has $\mathscr{E}$.

19. Let $\{A_i \subset A\}_{i \in I}$ be a family of subobjects in $\mathscr{G}$. Show that $\bigcup_{i \in I} A_i$ is the set of elements in A of the form $\sum_{i \in I} a_i$ where $a_i \in A_i$ for all $i \in I$, and $a_i = 0$ for all but a finite number of i.

20. Prove the following proposition in the category $\mathscr{G}$. Consider the commutative diagram with exact rows

$$\begin{array}{ccccccc} & & A' & \xrightarrow{\alpha_1} & A & \xrightarrow{\alpha_2} & A'' & \longrightarrow & 0 \\ & & \downarrow{\scriptstyle d'} & & \downarrow{\scriptstyle d} & & \downarrow{\scriptstyle d''} & & \\ 0 & \longrightarrow & B' & \xrightarrow{\beta_1} & B & \xrightarrow{\beta_2} & B'' & & \end{array}$$

Then the induced sequences

$$\mathrm{Ker}(d') \to \mathrm{Ker}(d) \to \mathrm{Ker}(d'')$$

and

$$\mathrm{Coker}(d') \to \mathrm{Coker}(d) \to \mathrm{Coker}(d'')$$

are exact. Define a function $\delta : \mathrm{Ker}(d'') \to \mathrm{Coker}(d')$ as follows. For $x \in \mathrm{Ker}(d'')$ let $\alpha_2(y) = x$. Then $\beta_2 d(y) = 0$, so $d(y) = \beta_1(z)$ for some $z \in B'$. Define $\delta(x) = [z] \in \mathrm{Coker}(d')$. Then δ is well defined morphism of groups, and the sequence

$$\mathrm{Ker}(d) \to \mathrm{Ker}(d'') \xrightarrow{\delta} \mathrm{Coker}(d') \to \mathrm{Coker}(d)$$

is exact.

21. Consider the exact sequence

$$0 \to A \xrightarrow{\alpha} B \xrightarrow{\beta} C \to 0$$

in an exact category. Then β is a retraction if and only if α is a coretraction. (Use 16.8).

22. Let $\theta : A \oplus B \to A \oplus B$ be an idempotent of the form $\begin{pmatrix} f, & h \\ 0, & g \end{pmatrix}$ in an additive category with kernels and finite products. Then f and g are idempotents, and so we can find factorizations of f and g of the form

$$A \xrightarrow{f_1} A_1 \xrightarrow{f_2} A$$

$$B \xrightarrow{g_1} B_2 \xrightarrow{g_2} B$$

such that $f_1 f_2 = 1$ and $g_1 g_2 = 1$. Find morphisms $\mu : A \oplus B \to A_1 \oplus B_1$ and $\lambda : A_1 \oplus B_1 \to A \oplus B$ such that $\lambda\mu = \theta$ and $\mu\lambda = 1$. Hence show that if $[A, B] = 0$ in such a category, then any retract of $A \oplus B$ is isomorphic to an object of the form $A_1 \oplus B_1$ where A_1 is a retract of A and B_1 is a retract of B.

[CHAPTER II]

Diagrams and Functors

Introduction

We begin by giving a formal definition of the terms diagram scheme and diagram (due to Grothendieck [20]). It is pointed out that the diagrams in a category over a given scheme themselves form a category, but a detailed examination of diagram categories is postponed until §12 where the notions of functor and functor category are studied. At that time it will be shown that a diagram can be regarded simply as a functor from an appropriate category.

In §2 we introduce the notion of limit for a diagram. This generalizes the older notion of inverse limit for an inverse system, and embraces inverse limits, products, pullbacks, and intersections as special cases. Necessary and sufficient conditions for the existence of limits in a category are given.

Sections 3 and 4 are devoted mainly to examples and the classification of certain types of functors according to the notions they preserve. In §5 we show how the set valued morphism functors (group-valued in the case of additive categories) can be used to characterize limits in a category. This is followed by an analysis of limit preserving functors. Then in §7 we examine faithful functors. It is seen that the main feature of faithful functors is that they preserve unpleasant situations.

After some exposition on functors of several variables and natural equivalences and a section on equivalences of categories, in §§11 and 12 we turn to the study of functor categories. In general it is shown that the category of functors from a category $\mathscr{A}$ to a category $\mathscr{B}$ inherits the properties of $\mathscr{B}$. The main result here is that the functor from a diagram category $[\Sigma, \mathscr{B}]$ to $\mathscr{B}$ which assigns to each diagram its limit is a limit preserving monofunctor. In §13 we study categories of additive functors, and in particular **R**-modules. The last three sections are devoted to the special types of objects which will be needed in the sequel; namely, generators, projectives, and small objects. Each of these can be defined in terms of the preservation properties of the morphism functors associated with them.

1. Diagrams

A **diagram scheme** Σ is a triple (I, M, d) where I is a set whose elements are called **vertices**, M is a set whose elements are called **arrows**, and d is a function from M to $I \times I$. If $m \in M$ and $d(m) = (i, j)$, then we call i the **origin** of m and j the **extremity**. A **diagram** in a category $\mathscr{A}$ over the scheme Σ is a function D which assigns to each vertex $i \in I$ an object $D_i \in \mathscr{A}$, and to each arrow m with origin i and extremity j a morphism $D(m) \in [D_i, D_j]$. If I and M are finite sets then we call Σ a **finite** scheme and D a **finite** diagram.

Let $[\Sigma, \mathscr{A}]$ denote the class of all diagrams in $\mathscr{A}$ over Σ. We make this into a category by defining a **morphism** f from diagram D to diagram D' as a family of morphisms $\{f_i : D_i \to D_i'\}_{i \in I}$ in $\mathscr{A}$ such that for each $m \in M$ with $d(m) = (i, j)$ we have $f_j D(m) = D'(m) f_i$. Composition defined by $(gf)_i = g_i f_i$ is clearly associative, and 1_D is given by the relation $(1_D)_i = 1_{D_i}$.

A **composite arrow** in Σ is a finite sequence $c = m_p m_{p-1} \ldots m_2 m_1$ of arrows such that the origin of m_{k+1} is the extremity of m_k for $1 \leqslant k \leqslant p-1$. The **length** of the composite arrow c is p. The origin of m_1 is called the **origin** of c, and the extremity of m_p is called the **extremity** of c. If $b = m_s m_{s-1} \ldots m_2 m_1$ and $a = m_p m_{p-1} \ldots m_{s+2} m_{s+1}$, we shall write $c = ab$. If D is a diagram over Σ we define $D(c) = D(m_p) D(m_{p-1}) \ldots D(m_2) D(m_1)$.

Let Σ_0 be the diagram scheme with the same vertices as Σ, and whose arrows are those of Σ together with one new arrow from i to i, called the **identity arrow** at i and denoted by 1_i, for all vertices i. Let $\sim$ be an equivalence relation on the set of all composite arrows of Σ_0. We call $\sim$ a **commutativity relation** if the following conditions hold:

(i) Equivalent composite arrows have the same origin and the same extremity. (The common origin and extremity of the members of an equivalence class are called the **origin** and the **extremity** of the class.)

(ii) If $c \sim c'$ and ca is defined, then $ca \sim c'a$. Likewise if bc is defined then $bc \sim bc'$.

(iii) $c1_i \sim c$ and $1_j c \sim c$ whenever the left-hand expression make sense.

Corresponding to a commutativity relation $\sim$ and a category $\mathscr{A}$ we let $[\Sigma/\sim, \mathscr{A}]$ be the full subcategory of $[\Sigma, \mathscr{A}]$ whose objects are diagrams D in $\mathscr{A}$ over Σ such that $D(c) = D(c')$ for $c \sim c'$, where $D(1_i)$ is defined as 1_{D_i}.

The smallest commutativity relation for Σ is that which identifies two composite arrows in Σ_0 if and only if they become the same after removing all identity arrows from their decompositions. In this case we have $[\Sigma, \mathscr{A}] = [\Sigma/\sim, \mathscr{A}]$. The largest commutativity relation for Σ is that which identifies any two composite arrows in Σ_0 which have the same origin and the same extremity. In this case the objects of $[\Sigma/\sim, \mathscr{A}]$ are called **commutative diagrams** in $\mathscr{A}$ over Σ. Note that if D is a commutative diagram in $\mathscr{A}$ over Σ, and m is an arrow such that $d(m) = (i, i)$, then $D(m) = 1_{D_i}$.

Let $\Sigma = (I, M, d)$ and $\Sigma' = (I', M', d')$ be two diagram schemes. We define the **product scheme** $\Sigma \times \Sigma'$ as the scheme whose vertex set is $I \times I'$ and whose arrow set is $(M \times I') \cup (I \times M')$. An arrow of the form (m, i') has origin (i, i') and extremity (j, i') where $d(m) = (i, j)$. Similarly an arrow of the form (i, m') has origin (i, i') and extremity (i, j') where $d'(m') = (i', j')$. If Σ, Σ', and Σ'' are any three schemes, then we have an isomorphism between $(\Sigma \times \Sigma') \times \Sigma''$ and $\Sigma \times (\Sigma' \times \Sigma'')$; that is, a one to one correspondence between their vertices and arrows which preserves origins and extremities.

For example, if Σ is the scheme represented by $1 \rightarrow 2$ (that is, Σ has two vertices and one arrow) then $\Sigma \times \Sigma$ is represented by the square

$$\begin{array}{ccc} (1,1) & \longrightarrow & (2,1) \\ \downarrow & & \downarrow \\ (1,2) & \longrightarrow & (2,2) \end{array}$$

Similarly, if we draw $(\Sigma \times \Sigma) \times \Sigma$ we obtain a cubical configuration. We define inductively $\Sigma^n = \Sigma^{n-1} \times \Sigma$, and we call Σ^n the **n-cube scheme**.

The following proposition concerning commutativity of diagrams over the 3-cube is fundamental in the study of categories.

Proposition 1.1. *Consider a diagram over the 3-cube:*

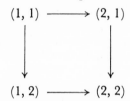

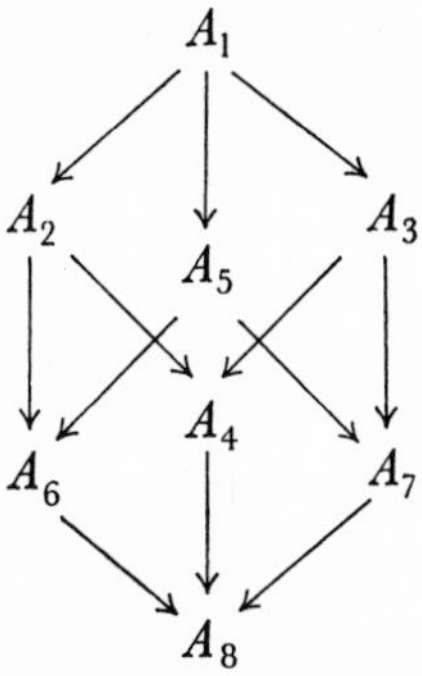

If $A_1 \rightarrow A_5$ is an epimorphism and all faces of the cube are commutative save possibly the face involving A_5, A_6, A_7, A_8, then this face is also commutative.

Proof. Denote the morphism from A_i to A_j by f_{ij}. Then we have

$$\begin{aligned} f_{78}f_{57}f_{15} &= f_{78}f_{37}f_{13} \\ &= f_{48}f_{34}f_{13} \\ &= f_{48}f_{24}f_{12} \\ &= f_{68}f_{26}f_{12} \\ &= f_{68}f_{56}f_{15}. \end{aligned}$$

Therefore since f_{15} is an epimorphism we have $f_{78}f_{57} = f_{68}f_{56}$ as required. ▮

2. Limits

If D is a diagram in $\mathscr{A}$ over $\Sigma = (I, M, d)$ we call a family of morphisms $\{X \to D_i\}_{i \in I}$ a **compatible** family for D if for every arrow $m \in M$ the diagram

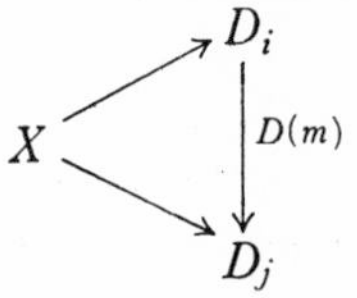

is commutative. The family is called a **limit** for D if it is compatible, and if for every compatible family $\{Y \to D_i\}_{i \in I}$ there is a unique morphism $Y \to X$ such that for each $i \in I$ we have $Y \to X \to D_i = Y \to D_i$. If $\{Y \to D_i\}_{i \in I}$ is also a limit for D, then $Y \to X$ is an isomorphism.

We have the following trivialities.

Proposition 2.1. *If $\{X \to D_i\}$ is a limit for D and if $\theta : Y \to X$ is an isomorphism, then $\{Y \xrightarrow{\theta} X \to D_i\}$ is a limit for D.* ▮

Proposition 2.2. *Let $\theta : D \to D'$ be an isomorphism in $[\Sigma, \mathscr{A}]$ (that is, for each i, $\theta_i : D_i \to D'_i$ is an isomorphism in $\mathscr{A}$). If $\{X \to D_i\}$ is a limit for D, then $\{X \to D_i \xrightarrow{\theta_i} D'_i\}$ is a limit for D'.* ▮

We say that a category $\mathscr{A}$ is **Σ-complete** if every diagram in $\mathscr{A}$ over Σ has a limit. If $\mathscr{A}$ is Σ-complete for all diagram schemes Σ, then $\mathscr{A}$ is called **complete**. If $\mathscr{A}$ is Σ-complete for all finite diagram schemes Σ, then $\mathscr{A}$ is called **finitely complete**.

Proposition 2.3. *If $\mathscr{A}$ is finitely complete, then $\mathscr{A}$ has pullbacks. If $\mathscr{A}$ is complete, then $\mathscr{A}$ has intersections and products.*

Proof. The limit of the diagram

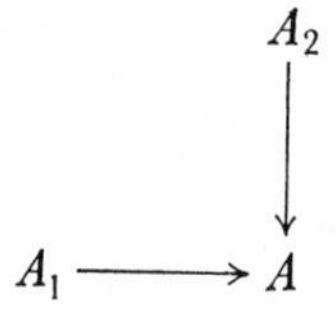

is the pullback. The intersection of a family $\{A_i\}_{i \in I}$ of subobjects of A is given by the limit of the following diagram D. The scheme of D has vertex set $I \cup \{p\}$ where p is some element not in I, and has an arrow from i to p for each $i \in I$. Then $D_i = A_i$, $D_p = A$, and if m is the arrow from i to p we take $D(m)$ as the inclusion of A_i in A. Finally, the product of a family of objects $\{A_i\}_{i \in I}$ is the limit of the diagram D over the scheme whose vertex set is I and whose arrow set is empty, defined by $D_i = A_i$ for all $i \in I$. ▮

Let D be a diagram in $\mathscr{A}$ over $\Sigma = (I, M, d)$. In looking for a limit for D we may always assume that Σ has the property that if i is any vertex, then there is an arrow whose extremity is not i. For if this is not the case, we can construct a new scheme Σ' which has this property. The vertices of Σ' are the vertices of Σ together with one new vertex v. The arrows of Σ' are the arrows of Σ together with an arrow α from i to v and an arrow β from v to i. We extend D to a diagram D' over Σ' by defining $D'_v = D_i$, $D(\alpha) = 1_{D_i} = D(\beta)$. Clearly the restriction to D of a limit for D' will be a limit for D.

Now define $P = \underset{i \in I}{\times} D_i$, and let $p_i : P \to D_i$ denote the ith projection. Also for $m \in M$ let $q_m : P^M \to P$ denote the mth projection. Let $\mu : P \to P^M$ be defined as follows. If $m \in M$ and $d(m) = (j, k)$, then for $i \neq k$ let $p_i q_m \mu = p_i$, and let $p_k q_m \mu = D(m) p_j$. Then we have the following theorem, due to Freyd.

Theorem 2.4. *Let D be a diagram over a scheme Σ which is such that no vertex is the extremity of all arrows, and let $\mu : P \to P^M$ be as defined above. Then μ is a monomorphism. Furthermore, letting $\Delta : P \to P^M$ be the diagonal morphism, if the diagram*

$$\begin{array}{ccc} L & \xrightarrow{\bar{\mu}} & P \\ {\scriptstyle \bar{\Delta}}\downarrow & & \downarrow{\scriptstyle \Delta} \\ P & \xrightarrow{\mu} & P^M \end{array} \qquad (1)$$

is a pullback (intersection), then a limit for D is given by the family $\{p_i \bar{\Delta}\}_{i \in I}$. Thus if $\mathscr{A}$ has products and finite intersections then $\mathscr{A}$ is complete.

Conversely, if $\{\gamma_i : L \to D_i\}$ is a limit for D and if $\gamma : L \to P$ is the morphism induced by this family, then replacing each of $\bar{\Delta}$ and $\bar{\mu}$ by γ in (1) we obtain a pullback diagram.

Proof. We first prove that μ is a monomorphism. Suppose that $\mu\alpha = \mu\beta$. For $i \in I$ choose an arrow m which does not have extremity i. Then we have

$$p_i \alpha = p_i q_m \mu \alpha = p_i q_m \mu \beta = p_i \beta$$

and since this can be done for each $i \in I$ we must have $\alpha = \beta$. Therefore μ is a monomorphism.

Next we show that $\bar{\Delta} = \bar{\mu}$. Again given $i \in I$ let m be an arrow which does not have extremity i. Then

$$p_i \bar{\Delta} = p_i q_m \mu \bar{\Delta} = p_i q_m \Delta \bar{\mu} = p_i \bar{\mu}$$

and so $\bar{\Delta} = \bar{\mu}$.

Now we show that $\{p_i \bar{\Delta}\}_{i \in I}$ is a compatible family. Consider an arrow $m \in M$ with $d(m) = (j, k)$. Then

$$D(m) p_j \bar{\Delta} = p_k q_m \mu \bar{\Delta} = p_k q_m \Delta \bar{\mu} = p_k \bar{\mu} = p_k \bar{\Delta}$$

as required.

Finally, we show that $\{p_i\bar{\Delta}\}_{i\in I}$ is the limit. Let $\{f_i : X \to D_i\}_{i\in I}$ be a compatible family. Then we have an induced morphism $f : X \to P$. For $m \in M$ with $d(m) = (j, k)$ we have for $i \neq k$

$$p_i q_m \mu f = p_i f = p_i q_m \Delta f,$$

and for $i = k$, using the fact that the family is compatible,

$$p_k q_m \mu f = D(m) p_j f = D(m) f_j = f_k = p_k q_m \Delta f.$$

Therefore $\Delta f = \mu f$, and so there is a unique morphism $f' : X \to L$ such that $\bar{\Delta} f' = f$, or in other words, such that $p_i \bar{\Delta} f' = f_i$ for all $i \in I$. This shows that $\{p_i \bar{\Delta}\}_{i\in I}$ is the limit for D.

Conversely assume that $\{\gamma_i : L \to D_i\}$ is the limit and replace $\bar{\Delta}$ and $\bar{\mu}$ by the induced morphism $\gamma : L \to P$ in (1). Then as we showed for f above we have $\Delta\gamma = \mu\gamma$. Now if $f : X \to P$ and $g : X \to P$ are such that $\mu f = \Delta g$, then replacing $\bar{\Delta}$ and $\bar{\mu}$ by f and g respectively in the above, we see that $f = g$ and that $\{p_i f\}_{i\in I}$ is a compatible family. Consequently it follows from the definition of limit that there is a unique morphism $f' : X \to L$ such that $\gamma f' = f$. This shows that the diagram is a pullback. ∎

Corollary 2.5. *Suppose that $\mathscr{A}$ is either additive or normal. Then $\mathscr{A}$ is complete if and only if it has kernels and products.*

Proof. If $\mathscr{A}$ is complete, then since kernels and products are special cases of limits, $\mathscr{A}$ must have kernels and products. Conversely, suppose that $\mathscr{A}$ is additive and has kernels and products. Then $\mathscr{A}$ has equalizers and so by I, 17.3, $\mathscr{A}$ has finite intersections. Likewise, if $\mathscr{A}$ is normal then by I, 14.1, $\mathscr{A}$ has finite intersections. Hence in either case it follows from 2.4 that $\mathscr{A}$ is complete. ∎

If D is a finite diagram in 2.4 then P and P^M will be finite products. Hence we have

Corollary 2.6. *A category is finitely complete if and only if it has finite intersections and finite products.* ∎

The dual notions of **cocompatible family, colimit, Σ-cocomplete category**, **finitely cocomplete category**, and **cocomplete category** are left to the reader. Combining 2.6 and 2.6* with I, 20.1, we then have:

Corollary 2.7. *A category is abelian if and only if it is finitely complete and finitely cocomplete and is normal and conormal.* ∎

We see now that an abelian category is complete (cocomplete) if and only if it has products (coproducts). In particular the category of abelian groups $\mathscr{G}$ is complete and cocomplete.

Proposition 2.8. *Let $\mathscr{A}$ be a category with images and inverse images, and let $\{D_i \to L\}$ be the colimit for a diagram D in $\mathscr{A}$. If $\{f_i : D_i \to A\}$ is a cocompatible system for D and if $f : L \to A$ is the induced morphism, then $\bigcup \operatorname{Im}(f_i)$ is defined and is the same as $\operatorname{Im}(f)$.*

Proof. Let $g: A \to B$, and let B' be a subobject of B such that $\mathrm{Im}(f_i)$ is carried into B' by g for each i. Then the compositions $D_i \to \mathrm{Im}(f_i) \to B'$ form a co-compatible system for D, and we get an induced morphism $L \to B'$. Furthermore, due to the uniqueness of morphisms induced on limits we must have $L \to B' \to B = L \xrightarrow{f} A \xrightarrow{g} B$. Hence f factors through $g^{-1}(B')$, and consequently $\mathrm{Im}(f) \subset g^{-1}(B')$. But then since $g^{-1}(B')$ is carried into B' by g, the same must be true of $\mathrm{Im}(f)$. Since it is clear that $\mathrm{Im}(f_i) \subset \mathrm{Im}(f)$ for each i, it follows that $\mathrm{Im}(f) = \bigcup \mathrm{Im}(f_i)$. ▮

Proposition 2.9. *Let $\mathscr{A}$ be a category with products and finite intersections and let D be a diagram in $\mathscr{A}$ over a scheme (I, M, d). Then a limit for D is given by the family of compositions*

$$\bigcap_{m \in M} \mathrm{Equ}(p_k, D(m)p_j) \subset \bigtimes_{h \in I} D_h \xrightarrow{p_i} D_i \tag{2}$$

where $d(m) = (j, k)$, and p_i represents the ith projection from the product.

Proof. It follows easily from the definitions of equalizer and intersection that the family (2) is compatible. Now let $\{f_i : A \to D_i\}_{i \in I}$ be any other compatible family. Then there is a unique morphism $f: A \to \bigtimes D_h$ such that $p_i f = f_i$ for each i, and the condition that the family $\{f_i\}$ be compatible is precisely the condition that f factor through the subobject $\bigcap_{m \in M} \mathrm{Equ}(p_k, D(m)p_j)$. This proves that (2) is the limit. ▮

In an additive category the subobject $\mathrm{Equ}(p_k, D(m)p_j)$ is the same as $\mathrm{Ker}(p_k - D(m)p_j)$. Therefore if we apply duality to 2.9 and use I, 15.2, we obtain

Corollary 2.10. *Let $\mathscr{A}$ be a cocomplete abelian category, and let D be a diagram in $\mathscr{A}$ over (I, M, d). Then a colimit for D is given by the family of compositions*

$$D_i \xrightarrow{u_i} \bigoplus_{h \in I} D_h \longrightarrow \bigoplus_{h \in I} D_h / \bigcup_{m \in M} \mathrm{Im}(u_k - u_j D(m))$$

where $d(m) = (k, j)$ and u_i is the ith injection into the coproduct. ▮

Let I be a directed set, and consider the diagram scheme whose set of vertices is I and which has precisely one arrow from i to j if $i \leqslant j$ and no arrows from i to j otherwise. A commutative diagram D in $\mathscr{A}$ over this scheme is called a **direct system** in $\mathscr{A}$ over I. Commutativity of the diagram requires that if $i \leqslant j$ then there is only one morphism from D_i to D_j in the diagram, and so there is no ambiguity in denoting it by π_{ij}. Then we must have $\pi_{jk}\pi_{ij} = \pi_{ik}$ for $i \leqslant j \leqslant k$, and $\pi_{ii} = 1_{D_i}$ for all $i \in I$. The colimit $\{D_i \to L\}_{i \in I}$ for D is called the **direct limit** for D, and the object L is denoted by $\varinjlim_{i \in I} D_i$. The above direct system

D will be denoted by $\{D_i, \pi\}_{i\in I}$, and the limit morphism $D_i \to L$ will be denoted by π_i. If $D_i = A$ for all $i \in I$ and $\pi_{ij} = 1_A$ whenever $i \leqslant j$, then it is trivial to verify that $\{1_A : A \to D_i\}_{i\in I}$ is the direct limit of D.

Recall that a subset J of a directed set I is called a **cofinal** subset of I if for every element $i \in I$ there is an element $j \in J$ such that $i \leqslant j$. If the ordered subset J is cofinal then J is itself a directed set. Thus if D is a direct system in $\mathscr{A}$ over I, then the restriction of D to J is a direct system in $\mathscr{A}$ over J. The set of all elements which follow a given element is an example of such a set J. We then have the following proposition, whose proof is left to the reader.

Proposition 2.11. *Let D be a direct system in $\mathscr{A}$ over I and let J be a cofinal subset of I. If $\{\pi_i : D_i \to L\}_{i\in I}$ is a direct limit for D, then $\{\pi_i : D_i \to L\}_{i\in J}$ is a direct limit for the restriction of D to J.* ∎

In other words, the direct limit of a system is determined by the values of the system on any cofinal subset. In particular, if $\mathscr{A}$ has a zero object and if $D_i = 0$ for all i in a cofinal subset of I, then $\varinjlim_{i\in I} D_i = 0$.

We consider two examples of direct limits.

1. Let $\{A_\lambda\}_{\lambda\in\Lambda}$ be any set of objects in a category, and suppose that for any finite subset $F \subset \Lambda$ the coproduct $\bigoplus_{\lambda\in F} A_\lambda$ is defined. Let I be the set of all finite subsets of Λ, and for $F, G \in I$ define $F \leqslant G$ if and only if $F \subset G$. Then for $F \leqslant G$ we have the obvious morphism $u_{FG} : \bigoplus_{\lambda\in F} A_\lambda \to \bigoplus_{\lambda\in G} A_\lambda$ whose dual is described in I, §17, and in this way we obtain a direct system in $\mathscr{A}$ over I. The direct limit exists if and only if $\bigoplus_{\lambda\in\Lambda} A_\lambda$ exists, in which case they are equal. Hence if a category has direct limits and finite coproducts, then it has coproducts. In particular an abelian category is cocomplete if and only if it has direct limits.

2. Let $\{u_i : A_i \to A\}_{i\in I}$ be a set of subobjects. Define $i \leqslant j$ if and only if $u_i \leqslant u_j$. We will say that the family is a **direct family of subobjects** if I becomes a directed set under this ordering. Then taking for π_{ij} the inclusion morphism $A_i \to A_j$ we obtain a direct system over I. Supposing that the direct limit exists, we have the morphism $u : \varinjlim_{i\in I} A_i \to A$ induced by the compatible family $\{u_i\}$. In general u is not a monomorphism. That is, the direct limit of a direct family of subobjects is not necessarily a subobject. The most that can be said is that if $\mathscr{A}$ has images and inverse images, then $\mathrm{Im}(u) = \bigcup_{i\in I} A_i$ (2.8). In the following chapter we shall find conditions on a cocomplete abelian category which are necessary and sufficient in order that u be always a monomorphism.

An **inverse system** in $\mathscr{A}$ over I is a system of objects and morphisms which is a direct system in $\mathscr{A}^*$. Hence an inverse system is a family of objects $\{D_i\}_{i\in I}$

and a family of morphisms $\{\pi_{ij} : D_j \to D_i\}_{i \leqslant j}$ such that for $i \leqslant j \leqslant k$ we have $\pi_{ij}\pi_{jk} = \pi_{ik}$, and $\pi_{ii} = 1_{D_i}$ for all $i \in I$. In this case the limit is called the **inverse limit** of D and is denoted by $\lim\limits_{\overleftarrow{i \in I}} D_i$.

3. Functors

Let $\mathscr{A}$ and $\mathscr{B}$ be categories. A **covariant functor** $T : \mathscr{A} \to \mathscr{B}$ is an assignment of an object $T(A) \in \mathscr{B}$ to each object $A \in \mathscr{A}$ and a morphism $T(\alpha) : T(A) \to T(A')$ to each morphism $\alpha : A \to A'$ in $\mathscr{A}$, subject to the following conditions:

(1) Preservation of composition. If $\alpha'\alpha$ is defined in $\mathscr{A}$, then

$$T(\alpha'\alpha) = T(\alpha')T(\alpha).$$

(2) Preservation of identities. For each $A \in \mathscr{A}$ we have $T(1_A) = 1_{T(A)}$.

It follows easily from (1) and (2) that if θ is a retraction in $\mathscr{A}$, then $T(\theta)$ is a retraction in $\mathscr{B}$. We shall call $\mathscr{A}$ the **domain** of T and $\mathscr{B}$ the **codomain,** and we shall say that T has values in $\mathscr{B}$.

An **additive** functor is one whose domain and codomain are additive categories, and which satisfies the condition $T(\alpha + \beta) = T(\alpha) + T(\beta)$ whenever $\alpha + \beta$ is defined in the domain. Hence $T : \mathscr{A} \to \mathscr{B}$ is additive if and only if the functions

$$[A, B]_{\mathscr{A}} \to [T(A), T(B)]_{\mathscr{B}}$$

induced by T are morphisms of abelian groups. If T is additive, then $T(0) = 0$ for any zero morphism.

Replacing the conditions $\alpha : A \to A' \Rightarrow T(\alpha) : T(A) \to T(A')$ and $T(\alpha'\alpha) = T(\alpha')T(\alpha)$ by the conditions $\alpha : A \to A' \Rightarrow T(\alpha) : T(A') \to T(A)$ and $T(\alpha'\alpha) = T(\alpha)T(\alpha')$ in the above, we obtain the definition of a **contravariant** functor from $\mathscr{A}$ to $\mathscr{B}$. The unqualified term "functor" will usually mean covariant functor.

We consider some examples of functors.

1. The covariant functor $1_{\mathscr{A}} : \mathscr{A} \to \mathscr{A}$ such that $1_{\mathscr{A}}(A) = A$ for all $A \in \mathscr{A}$ and $1_{\mathscr{A}}(\alpha) = \alpha$ for all morphisms α in $\mathscr{A}$ is called the **identity** functor on $\mathscr{A}$.

2. The contravariant functor $D : \mathscr{A} \to \mathscr{A}^*$ such that $D(A) = A^*$ for all $A \in \mathscr{A}$ and $D(\alpha) = \alpha$ for all morphisms α in $\mathscr{A}$ is called the **duality** functor on $\mathscr{A}$.

3. If $\mathscr{A}'$ is a subcategory of $\mathscr{A}$, then the covariant functor $I : \mathscr{A}' \to \mathscr{A}$ such that $I(A) = A$ for all $A \in \mathscr{A}'$ and $I(\alpha) = \alpha$ for all morphisms α in $\mathscr{A}'$ is called the **inclusion** functor of $\mathscr{A}'$ in $\mathscr{A}$.

4. If $\mathscr{A}''$ is a quotient category of $\mathscr{A}$, then the covariant functor $P : \mathscr{A} \to \mathscr{A}''$ such that $P(A) = A$ for all $A \in \mathscr{A}$ and $P(\alpha) = [\alpha]$ for all morphisms α in A is called the **projection** functor of $\mathscr{A}$ onto $\mathscr{A}''$.

5. The **forgetful** functor $F : \mathscr{G} \to \mathscr{S}$ from the category of abelian groups to the category of sets is the functor which forgets the abelian group structure on the objects of $\mathscr{G}$. That is, if G is an abelian group, then $F(G)$ is the underlying set $\bar{G}$ of G, and if α is a group morphism, then $F(\alpha) = \alpha$. Likewise we have a forgetful functor $F_0 : \mathscr{G} \to \mathscr{S}_0$ which assigns to the abelian group G the object $(\bar{G}, 0)$ where 0 is the zero element of G.

6. Let $T : \mathscr{A} \to \mathscr{B}$ and $S : \mathscr{B} \to \mathscr{C}$ be two functors. We define the **composition** $ST : \mathscr{A} \to \mathscr{C}$ by the rules $ST(A) = S(T(A))$ and $ST(\alpha) = S(T(\alpha))$. If T and S are both covariant or contravariant, then ST is covariant, whereas if one is covariant and the other is contravariant, then ST is contravariant. If S and T are additive functors, then ST is also additive.

7. If $T : \mathscr{A} \to \mathscr{B}$ is a covariant (contravariant) functor, then we obtain a contravariant (covariant)functor $T_* : \mathscr{A}^* \to \mathscr{B}$ by composing T with the duality functor on $\mathscr{A}$. Likewise we obtain a contravariant (covariant) functor $T^* : \mathscr{A} \to \mathscr{B}^*$ by composing T with the duality functor on $\mathscr{B}$. We write $T^*_* = (T^*)_* = (T_*)^*$.

8. Let $\mathscr{A}$ be any category and let $A \in \mathscr{A}$. We have a covariant functor $H^A : \mathscr{A} \to \mathscr{S}$ called the **covariant morphism functor** with respect to A. Explicitly, if $B \in \mathscr{B}$ then $H^A(B) = [A, B]$, and if $\alpha : B \to C$ then

$$H^A(\alpha) : [A, B] \to [A, C]$$

is given by the rule $H^A(\alpha)(x) = \alpha x$. If $\mathscr{A}$ is a category with zero, then H^A can be regarded as a functor with values in $\mathscr{S}_0$ by defining $H^A(B) = ([A, B], 0_{AB})$. If $\mathscr{A}$ is an additive category, then $H^A(B)$ is an abelian group, and $H^A(\alpha)$ is a group morphism. Furthermore, in this case we have

$$H^A(\alpha + \beta) = H^A(\alpha) + H^A(\beta).$$

Hence H^A may be considered as an additive functor with values in $\mathscr{G}$, or an additive **group valued** functor as we shall say. Composing this group valued functor with the forgetful functor $F : \mathscr{G} \to \mathscr{S}$ gives us the set valued morphism functor defined originally.

Likewise we have the **contravariant morphism functor** $H_A : \mathscr{A} \to \mathscr{S}$ defined by $H_A(B) = [B, A]$ and $H_A(\alpha)(x) = x\alpha$ for $\alpha : B \to C$ and $x \in [C, A]$. The remarks made for H^A in the case where $\mathscr{A}$ has a zero or is additive apply to H_A. Notice that $(H^A)_* = H_{A^*}$.

9. If $\varphi : \mathbf{R} \to \mathbf{S}$ is a covariant functor and $\mathbf{R}$ and $\mathbf{S}$ are semigroups (that is, categories with one object each) then we call φ a **semigroup morphism**, and if $\mathbf{R}$ and $\mathbf{S}$ are rings and φ is additive, then we call φ a **ring morphism**.

4. Preservation Properties of Functors

Let $T : \mathscr{A} \to \mathscr{B}$ be a covariant functor. We shall call T a **monofunctor** if $T(\alpha)$ is a monomorphism in $\mathscr{B}$ whenever α is a monomorphism in $\mathscr{A}$. Dually we call T an **epifunctor** if $T(\alpha)$ is an epimorphism whenever α is an epimorphism. Hence T is an epifunctor if and only if T_*^* is a monofunctor. If $\mathscr{A}$ and $\mathscr{B}$ are categories with zero objects, then T is called a **zero preserving** functor if $T(0)$ is a zero object in $\mathscr{B}$ for 0 a zero object in $\mathscr{A}$. In this case T necessarily takes zero morphisms into zero morphisms. Conversely, if T takes zero morphisms into zero morphisms, then using the fact that a zero object is characterized by its identity morphism being zero we see that T must be zero preserving. In particular an additive functor is zero preserving.

We call T **kernel preserving** if $T(u)$ is the kernel of $T(\alpha)$ when $u: K \to A$ is the kernel of $\alpha: A \to B$. Taking $K = A = B = 0$, we see that a kernel preserving functor is necessarily zero preserving. If $\mathscr{A}$ is normal and T is kernel preserving then T is a monofunctor.

If $\mathscr{A}$ and $\mathscr{B}$ are exact categories, then we say that T is an **exact** functor if $T(A) \to T(B) \to T(C)$ is exact for every exact sequence $A \to B \to C$.

Proposition 4.1. *Let $\mathscr{A}$ and $\mathscr{B}$ be exact categories, and let $T: \mathscr{A} \to \mathscr{B}$ be any covariant functor. Then*

1. *T is kernel preserving if and only if for every short exact sequence*

$$0 \to A \to B \to C \to 0 \tag{1}$$

in $\mathscr{A}$, the sequence $0 \to T(A) \to T(B) \to T(C)$ is exact in $\mathscr{B}$.

2. *T is cokernel preserving if and only if for every short exact sequence (1), the sequence $T(A) \to T(B) \to T(C) \to 0$ is exact.*

3. *T is exact if and only if for every short exact sequence (1), the sequence*

$$0 \to T(A) \to T(B) \to T(C) \to 0$$

is exact.

Proof. 1. If T is kernel preserving, then clearly $0 \to T(A) \to T(B) \to T(C)$ is exact. Conversely, suppose that T satisfies the given condition and let $\alpha: A_1 \to A_2$ be any morphism in $\mathscr{A}$. Then we can find two short exact sequences

$$0 \to K \to A_1 \to I \to 0$$
$$0 \to I \to A_2 \to K' \to 0$$

where $K \to A$ is the kernel of α, $A_2 \to K'$ is the cokernel of α, and $A_1 \to I \to A_2$ is α. The condition on T then says that $0 \to T(K) \to T(A_1) \to T(I)$ and $0 \to T(I) \to T(A_2) \to T(K')$ are exact. Hence $T(K) \to T(A_1)$ is the kernel of $T(A_1) \to T(I)$, and $T(I) \to T(A_2)$ is a monomorphism. Consequently $T(K) \to T(A_1)$ is the kernel of $T(A_1) \to T(I) \to T(A_2)$. But since T preserves compositions, the last composition is just $T(\alpha)$.

Part 2 follows from part 1 by duality, and part 3 is proved similarly to part 1. ▌

The functor T is called a **faithful** functor if for every pair of objects $A, B \in \mathscr{A}$ the function

$$[A, B] \to [T(A), T(B)] \tag{2}$$

induced by T is univalent. That is, T is faithful if it preserves distinctness of morphisms. If T is additive, then T is faithful if and only if it takes nonzero morphisms into nonzero morphisms. A faithful functor which takes distinct objects into distinct objects is called an **imbedding**.

If instead of being univalent, the functions (2) are all onto, then T is called **full**. We shall say that T is **representative** if for every $B \in \mathscr{B}$ there is an object $A \in \mathscr{A}$ such that $T(A)$ and B are isomorphic. A full representative, faithful functor is called an **equivalence**. An equivalence which actually produces a one to one correspondence between the objects of $\mathscr{A}$ and $\mathscr{B}$ is called an **isomorphism**. However, isomorphisms of categories are rare. As we shall see presently the thing to look for when we wish to show that two categories are essentially the same is an equivalence (§10).

Let D be a diagram in $\mathscr{A}$ over a scheme $\Sigma = (I, M, d)$. We define a diagram TD in $\mathscr{B}$ over Σ by taking $TD_i = T(D_i)$ and $TD(m) = T(D(m))$. If $\{\alpha_i : X \to D_i\}$ is a compatible system for D in $\mathscr{A}$, then $\{T(\alpha_i) : T(X) \to T(D_i)\}$ is a compatible system for TD in $\mathscr{B}$. However if $\{\alpha_i\}$ is the limit of D, it does not necessarily follow that $\{T(\alpha_i)\}$ is the limit of TD. In fact we shall call T a **limit preserving** functor if $\{T(\alpha_i)\}$ is the limit of TD whenever $\{\alpha_i\}$ is the limit of D. If T is limit preserving, then T must preserve pullbacks and products. Since a zero object is the product of the empty class of objects it follows that a limit preserving functor is zero preserving. Using the description of the kernel of a morphism f as $f^{-1}(0)$ we see then that a limit preserving functor is kernel preserving. However, a limit preserving functor need not be a monofunctor unless the domain is normal.

Dually T is called a **colimit preserving** functor if T^*_* is limit preserving. The forgetful functor $F : \mathscr{G} \to \mathscr{S}$ is mono, epi, and limit preserving. It is also faithful and representative, but it is neither full nor colimit preserving. The same remarks apply to $F_0 : \mathscr{G} \to \mathscr{S}_0$.

Let $\mathscr{A}$ be a category and $\mathscr{A}'$ a subcategory. Then the inclusion functor $I : \mathscr{A}' \to \mathscr{A}$ is an imbedding, but it need not be mono, epi, limit preserving, or colimit preserving. If $\mathscr{A}'$ is complete and I is limit preserving then we shall say that $\mathscr{A}'$ is a **complete subcategory** of $\mathscr{A}$. Equivalently, $\mathscr{A}'$ is a complete subcategory if every diagram in $\mathscr{A}'$ has a limit in $\mathscr{A}$ and this limit is in $\mathscr{A}'$. This says more than simply that $\mathscr{A}'$ is a cocomplete category which is a subcategory of $\mathscr{A}$. If $\mathscr{A}'$ and $\mathscr{A}$ are exact categories and I is an exact functor then we call $\mathscr{A}'$ an **exact subcategory** of $\mathscr{A}$, and if I is additive we call $\mathscr{A}'$ an **additive subcategory**. If I is an equivalence then $\mathscr{A}'$ is called an **equivalent subcategory** of $\mathscr{A}$. Thus $\mathscr{A}'$ is an equivalent subcategory if and only if it is a full subcategory such that every object in $\mathscr{A}$ has an isomorphic object in $\mathscr{A}'$.

The properties of functors defined in this section are called **preservation properties** of functors. If $T : \mathscr{A} \to \mathscr{B}$ and $S : \mathscr{B} \to \mathscr{C}$ are covariant functors both having a certain preservation property, then ST also has that property.

We shall say that a contravariant functor $T : \mathscr{A} \to \mathscr{B}$ has a preservation property if and only if the covariant functor $T_* : \mathscr{A}^* \to \mathscr{B}$ has that property.

5. Morphism Functors

Proposition 5.1. *A morphism $B \to C$ is a monomorphism in a category $\mathscr{A}$ if and only if the induced morphism $H^A(B) \to H^A(C)$ is a monomorphism in $\mathscr{S}$ for all $A \in \mathscr{A}$. Similarly a family of morphisms $\mathscr{F} = \{f_i : L \to D_i\}$ is a limit for a diagram D in $\mathscr{A}$ if and only if the family $H^A(\mathscr{F}) = \{H^A(f_i) : H^A(L) \to H^A(D_i)\}$ is a limit for $H^A D$ in $\mathscr{S}$ for all $A \in \mathscr{A}$.*

If $\mathscr{A}$ has a zero object (resp., is additive) then the category $\mathscr{S}$ may be replaced by the category $\mathscr{S}_0$(resp. $\mathscr{G}$) in the above.

Proof. By definition a morphism $B \to C$ is a monomorphism if and only if for each $A \in \mathscr{A}$ the induced morphism $[A, B] \to [A, C]$ is univalent. But a morphism in the category of sets is univalent if and only if it is a monomorphism, hence we have the first statement.

Now suppose that $\mathscr{F}$ is the limit of D, and consider a compatible family $\{\alpha_i : X \to H^A(D_i)\}$ for $H^A D$ in $\mathscr{S}$. Then for each $x \in X$ we have a compatible family $\{\alpha_i(x) : A \to D_i\}$ for D in $\mathscr{A}$, and so we get unique morphisms $\alpha(x) : A \to L$ into the limit such that $f_i \alpha(x) = \alpha_i(x)$ for all i. It follows that $\alpha : X \to H^A(L)$ is the unique morphism in $\mathscr{S}$ such that $H^A(f_i)\alpha = \alpha_i$ for all i. Therefore $H^A(\mathscr{F})$ is the limit of $H^A D$.

Conversely, suppose that $\mathscr{F}$ is not a limit for D. There are three possibilities.

1. $\mathscr{F}$ is not a compatible family. Then for some arrow m the diagram

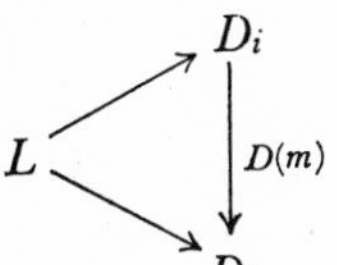

is not commutative. By examining what happens to $1_L \in H^L(L)$ we see that the diagram

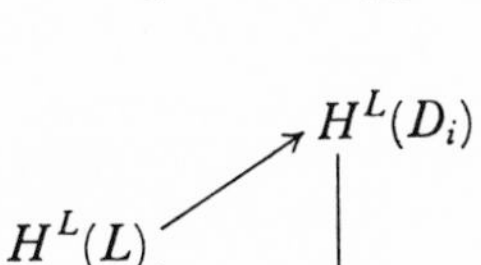

is not commutative. Hence $H^L(\mathscr{F})$ is not a limit for $H^L D$.

2. There exists a compatible family $\{\gamma_i : X \to D_i\}$ corresponding to which there are two distinct factorizations $\gamma, \gamma' : X \to L$. Then

$$H^X(\gamma)(1_X) = \gamma \neq \gamma' = H^X(\gamma')(1_X),$$

and consequently $H^X(\gamma)$ and $H^X(\gamma')$ are distinct factorizations for the family $\{H^X(\gamma_i)\}$. Therefore $H^X(\mathscr{F})$ is not the limit of H^XD.

3. For some compatible family $\{X \to D_i\}$ there is no factorization $X \to L$. Then there is no factorization $\mu : H^X(X) \to H^X(L)$ corresponding to the family $\{H^X(X) \to H^X(D_i)\}$. For if there were such a μ, then $\mu(1_X) : X \to L$ would yield a factorization for $\{X \to D_i\}$. Hence $H^X(\mathscr{F})$ is not the limit of H^XD.

If $\mathscr{S}$ is replaced by $\mathscr{S}_0$ the only difference in the proof comes at the point where we show that $H^A(\mathscr{F})$ is a limit for H^AD. Here it must be checked that the morphism α defined is actually a morphism of sets with base point. But this follows since the morphisms α_i are all necessarily morphisms of sets with base point. A similar remark applies to the case where $\mathscr{S}$ is replaced by $\mathscr{G}$. ▌

Using the relation $(H_A)_* = H^{A^*}$ we have:

Proposition 5.1*. *A morphism $C \to B$ is an epimorphism in a category $\mathscr{A}$ if and only if the induced morphism $H_A(B) \to H_A(C)$ is a monomorphism in $\mathscr{S}$ for all $A \in \mathscr{A}$. Similarly a family of morphisms $\{D_i \to L\}$ is a colimit for a diagram D in $\mathscr{A}$ if and only if the corresponding family $\{H_A(L) \to H_A(D_i)\}$ is a limit for H_AD in $\mathscr{S}$ for all $A \in \mathscr{A}$.* ▌

6. Limit Preserving Functors

We shall say that $T : \mathscr{A} \to \mathscr{B}$ is **finite intersection preserving** if whenever T preserves two monomorphisms for which the intersection is defined, then T preserves this intersection. Notice that this definition does not say that T is a monofunctor nor does it require that T take every pullback diagram describing an intersection into a pullback diagram.

Proposition 6.1. *If $\mathscr{A}$ has products and $\mathscr{B}$ is arbitrary, then $T : \mathscr{A} \to \mathscr{B}$ is limit preserving if and only if it preserves products and finite intersections.*

Proof. If T is limit preserving, then since products and intersections are special cases of limits it follows that T preserves products and finite intersections.

Conversely suppose that T preserves products and finite intersections. Let $\{L \to D_i\}$ be the limit of a diagram D in $\mathscr{A}$ and form the diagram

$$\begin{array}{ccc} L & \xrightarrow{\gamma} & P \\ {\scriptstyle\gamma}\downarrow & & \downarrow{\scriptstyle\Delta} \\ P & \xrightarrow{\mu} & P^M \end{array} \qquad (1)$$

of 2.4. As usual there is no loss in generality by assuming that in D no vertex is the extremity of all arrows, so that by 2.4, (1) is an intersection diagram. Now $T(\Delta) : T(P) \to T(P^M) = T(P)^M$ is again a diagonal morphism. Similarly the morphism $T(\mu)$ bears the same relation to the diagram TD that μ bears to D. In particular, this means that $T(\Delta)$ and $T(\mu)$ are monomorphisms, and consequently if we apply T to the diagram (1), by assumption on T we get an intersection diagram. A final application of 2.4 then shows that $\{T(L) \to T(D_i)\}$ is the limit for TD. ▮

Corollary 6.2. *Let $\mathscr{A}$ be a category with products and let $\mathscr{B}$ be any category. Then the functor $T : \mathscr{A} \to \mathscr{B}$ is limit preserving if and only if it preserves products and equalizers.*

Proof. It follows from I, 17.4, that if T preserves limits, then T preserves equalizers. Conversely if T preserves products and equalizers, then by I, 17.5, we see that T preserves pullbacks, and in particular finite intersections. Therefore, by 6.1, T is limit preserving. ▮

Corollary 6.3. *If $\mathscr{A}$ is a normal category with products, then $T : \mathscr{A} \to \mathscr{B}$ is limit preserving if and only if it preserves products and kernels.*

Proof. We have already seen that if T is limit preserving, then T preserves products and kernels. Conversely it follows from I, 13.2, that if T preserves kernels then T is finite intersection preserving. Hence if T also preserves products, then by 6.1 T is limit preserving. ▮

Proposition 6.4. *Let $\mathscr{A}$ be an additive category with finite products, and let $\mathscr{B}$ be an additive category. Then $T : \mathscr{A} \to \mathscr{B}$ preserves finite products if and only if it is additive.*

Proof. If T preserves finite products then it follows from I, 18.3, that T is additive. Conversely if T is additive, then T preserves finite products by I, 18.1. ▮

Corollary 6.5. *Let $\mathscr{A}$ be an additive category with finite products, and let $\mathscr{B}$ be an additive category. Then $T : \mathscr{A} \to \mathscr{B}$ preserves limits of finite diagrams if and only if T is kernel preserving and additive.*

Proof. If T is additive and kernel preserving, then T must preserve equalizers. Hence the conclusion follows from 6.4 and from 6.2 restricted to finite diagrams. ▮

Let $\mathscr{A}$ and $\mathscr{B}$ be exact categories. We shall call a functor $T : \mathscr{A} \to \mathscr{B}$ a **half-exact** functor if relative to every short exact sequence

$$0 \to A \to B \to C \to 0$$

in $\mathscr{A}$, the sequence $T(A) \to T(B) \to T(C)$ is exact in $\mathscr{B}$.

Proposition 6.6. *Consider a half exact functor $T : \mathscr{A} \to \mathscr{B}$ where $\mathscr{A}$ is abelian and $\mathscr{B}$ is exact and additive. Then T is additive.*

Proof. From I, 19.2, it follows that T preserves finite products, and so by 6.4, T is additive. ▮

Combining 6.5 and 6.6 we have

Corollary 6.7. *If $\mathscr{A}$ is abelian and $\mathscr{B}$ is exact and additive, then a functor $T : \mathscr{A} \to \mathscr{B}$ preserves limits of finite diagrams if and only if it is kernel preserving.* ▮

From 6.7 and 6.7* we see now that if $\mathscr{A}$ and $\mathscr{B}$ are abelian categories, then a functor $T : \mathscr{A} \to \mathscr{B}$ is exact if and only if it preserves limits and colimits of all finite diagrams. If T is the inclusion of one abelian category into a larger abelian category and if T is exact, then we shall call $\mathscr{A}$ an **abelian subcategory** of $\mathscr{B}$. Again this is to be distinguished from a subcategory of $\mathscr{B}$ which is an abelian category.

7. Faithful Functors

We say that a functor $T : \mathscr{A} \to \mathscr{B}$ **reflects** a property of a diagram D in $\mathscr{A}$ if the condition that TD has the property implies that D has the property. Thus for example T reflects limits if $\{\alpha_i : L \to D_i\}$ is a limit for the diagram D whenever $\{T(\alpha_i) : T(L) \to TD_i\}$ is a limit for TD for all diagrams D in $\mathscr{A}$.

Theorem 7.1 (Freyd). *Let $T : \mathscr{A} \to \mathscr{B}$ be a faithful functor where $\mathscr{A}$ and $\mathscr{B}$ are arbitrary categories. Then T reflects monomorphisms, epimorphisms, and commutative diagrams. If $\mathscr{A}$ and $\mathscr{B}$ are categories with zero, then T reflects zero objects. If $\mathscr{A}$ and $\mathscr{B}$ are exact categories then T reflects exact sequences. If $\mathscr{A}$ is an abelian category, $\mathscr{B}$ is an additive category, and T is additive, then T reflects limits and colimits of finite diagrams. Finally, if T is full, then without any conditions on $\mathscr{A}$ and $\mathscr{B}$, T reflects limits and colimits.*

Proof. Consider a morphism α in $\mathscr{A}$, and suppose that $\alpha f = \alpha g$. Then $T(\alpha)T(f) = T(\alpha)T(g)$, and so if $T(\alpha)$ is a monomorphism we must have $T(f) = T(g)$. Since T is faithful this implies $f = g$. In other words α is a monomorphism. Thus T reflects monomorphisms and by duality T reflects epimorphisms.

A noncommutative diagram is one in which two compositions with common origin and common extremity are not the same. Since T preserves compositions it is clear then that T carries noncommutative diagrams into noncommutative diagrams, or in other words that T reflects commutative diagrams.

Since a zero object is characterized by its identity morphism being equal to its zero endomorphism we see that T reflects zero objects.

Suppose that $\mathscr{A}$ and $\mathscr{B}$ are exact categories. There are two ways in which a sequence $A' \xrightarrow{\alpha} A \xrightarrow{\beta} A''$ in $\mathscr{A}$ can fail to be exact. First we may have $\beta\alpha \neq 0$. Then $T(\beta\alpha) = T(\beta)T(\alpha)$ cannot be zero since T is faithful, and so $T(A') \to T(A) \to T(A'')$ is not exact. Second, $\mathrm{Ker}(\beta)$ may not be a subobject of $\mathrm{Im}(\alpha)$. Letting $u : K \to A$ and $p : A \to F$ be the kernel of β and the cokernel of α, respectively, we then see that the composition pu is not zero. Applying T we have a commutative diagram

$$\begin{array}{ccccc} & & T(K) & & \\ & & \downarrow{\scriptstyle T(u)} & \searrow{\scriptstyle 0} & \\ T(A') & \xrightarrow{T(\alpha)} & T(A) & \xrightarrow[T(\beta)]{} & T(A'') \\ & \searrow{\scriptstyle 0} & \downarrow{\scriptstyle T(p)} & & \\ & & T(F) & & \end{array}$$

Consequently $T(u)$ factors through $\operatorname{Ker} T(\beta)$ and $T(p)$ factors through $\operatorname{Coker} T(\alpha)$. If the horizontal sequence were exact then the composition $\operatorname{Ker} T(\beta) \to T(A) \to \operatorname{Coker} T(\alpha)$ would be zero. Thus $T(pu) = T(p)T(u)$ would be zero, contradicting the faithfulness of T.

Finally, without making any assumptions on $\mathscr{A}$ and $\mathscr{B}$, there are three ways in which a family $\mathscr{F} = \{L \to D_i\}$ can fail to be a limit for D in $\mathscr{A}$. First, $\mathscr{F}$ is not compatible. Second, there exists a compatible family which factors through $\mathscr{F}$ but not uniquely. Third, $\mathscr{F}$ is compatible, and for every other compatible family there is at most one factorization through $\mathscr{F}$, but for some compatible family $\mathscr{F}' = \{L' \to D_i\}$ there is no factorization. In the first two cases it is immediate from the faithfulness of T that $T(\mathscr{F})$ is not a limit for TD. If, further, T is full then it is clear in the third case that $T(\mathscr{F}')$ cannot be factored through $T(\mathscr{F})$, and so again $T(\mathscr{F})$ is not a limit for TD. If T is not full, then assume that $\mathscr{A}$ is abelian, $\mathscr{B}$ and T are additive, and D is finite. Consider the finite product $\underset{i}{\times} D_i$ and the morphisms $L \to \times D_i$ and $L' \to \times D_i$ induced by $\mathscr{F}$ and $\mathscr{F}'$, respectively. The uniqueness of factorizations tells us that the first of these morphisms is a monomorphism. Consequently, if we let $\times D_i \to F$ be its cokernel, then the nonexistence of a factorization for $\mathscr{F}'$ shows that the composition $L' \to \times D_i \to F$ is not zero. Now T, being additive, preserves finite products. Hence if $T(\mathscr{F}')$ could be factored through $T(\mathscr{F})$ then we would have

$$T(L') \to T(\times D_i) \to T(F) \;=\; T(L') \to T(L) \to T(\times D_i) \to T(F) \;=\; 0.$$

Since T is faithful this is a contradiction. Therefore again $T(\mathscr{F})$ cannot be the limit of TD. That T reflects colimits now follows by duality. ▌

Proposition 7.2. *Let $\mathscr{A}$ be an abelian category and $\mathscr{B}$ an exact additive category. If $T : \mathscr{A} \to \mathscr{B}$ is an exact functor which reflects zero objects then T is faithful.*

Proof. By 6.6, T is additive and so it suffices to show that if $\alpha \neq 0$ then $T(\alpha) \neq 0$. Now if $\alpha \neq 0$ then $\operatorname{Im}(\alpha) \neq 0$, and so $T(\operatorname{Im}(\alpha)) \neq 0$ by hypothesis. But by exactness of T we have $T(\operatorname{Im}(\alpha)) = \operatorname{Im}(T(\alpha))$, and consequently $T(\alpha) \neq 0$. ▌

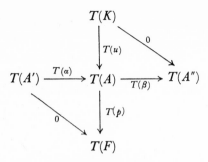

8. Functors of Several Variables

Consider $n+1$ categories $\mathscr{A}_1, \mathscr{A}_2, \ldots, \mathscr{A}_n, \mathscr{B}$, and let $I \cup J$ be a partition of the integers between 1 and n. A functor of n variables

$$T : \mathscr{A}_1 \times \mathscr{A}_2 \times \ldots \times \mathscr{A}_n \to \mathscr{B}$$

covariant in the ith variable for $i \in I$ and contravariant in the jth variable for $j \in J$ is defined as follows. To each n-tuple of objects $(A_1, A_2, \ldots, A_n)$ with $A_i \in \mathscr{A}_i$ for $1 \leqslant i \leqslant n$ there is assigned an object $T(A_1, A_2, \ldots, A_n)$ in $\mathscr{B}$. Furthermore, to each n-tuple of morphisms $(\alpha_1, \alpha_2, \ldots, \alpha_n)$ where $\alpha_i : A_i \to A_i'$ is in $\mathscr{A}_i$ for $i \in I$ and $\alpha_j : A_j' \to A_j$ is in $\mathscr{A}_j$ for $j \in J$, there is assigned a morphism

$$T(\alpha_1, \alpha_2, \ldots, \alpha_n) : T(A_1, \ldots, A_n) \to T(A_1', \ldots, A_n')$$

in $\mathscr{B}$. If $\gamma_i = \beta_i \alpha_i$ for $i \in I$ and $\gamma_j = \alpha_j \beta_j$ for $j \in J$, then we require that

$$T(\gamma_1, \ldots, \gamma_n) = T(\beta_1, \ldots, \beta_n) T(\alpha_1, \ldots, \alpha_n),$$

and if $\alpha_i = 1_{A_i}$ for $1 \leqslant i \leqslant n$, then we require that $T(\alpha_1, \ldots, \alpha_n)$ be the identity morphism on $T(A_1, \ldots, A_n)$. If $n = 2$ we call T a **bifunctor**, and if $n = 3$ we call T a **trifunctor**.

Let k be an integer between 1 and n, and let $A_i \in \mathscr{A}_i$ for $i \neq k$. Then we have the single variable functor

$$T(A_1, A_2, \ldots, A_{k-1}, \quad , A_{k+1}, \ldots, A_n) : \mathscr{A}_k \to \mathscr{B}$$

which gives the object $A \in \mathscr{A}_k$ the value $T(A_1, A_2, \ldots, A_{k-1}, A, A_{k+1}, \ldots, A_n)$ and the morphism α in $\mathscr{A}_k$ the value $T(A_1, \ldots, A_{k-1}, \alpha, A_{k+1}, \ldots, A_n)$, where we have written A_i in place of 1_{A_i} for $i \neq k$. Such a functor is called a **partial functor of one variable** for T. Likewise we could define various partial functors of several variables for T by fixing corresponding subsets of the variables. We will say that T is mono, kernel preserving, limit preserving, etc., if all of its partial functors of one variable have the corresponding property. Likewise, if all $n+1$ categories are additive, we call T additive if all its partial one variable functors are additive.

Let $\mathscr{A}_1$ and $\mathscr{A}_2$ be any two categories. We form the **product category** $\mathscr{A}_1 \times \mathscr{A}_2$ as follows. The class of objects in $\mathscr{A}_1 \times \mathscr{A}_2$ is the class of ordered pairs (A_1, A_2) with $A_1 \in \mathscr{A}_1$ and $A_2 \in \mathscr{A}_2$. The set of morphisms from (A_1, A_2) to (B_1, B_2) is the product of sets $[A_1, B_1]_{\mathscr{A}_1} \times [A_2, B_2]_{\mathscr{A}_2}$. Composition is defined by the rule $(\beta_1, \beta_2)(\alpha_1, \alpha_2) = (\beta_1 \alpha_1, \beta_2 \alpha_2)$. Then a covariant bifunctor $T : \mathscr{A}_1 \times \mathscr{A}_2 \to \mathscr{B}$ can be regarded as a functor of a single variable from the product category to $\mathscr{B}$. If T is contravariant in the first variable, then T can be considered as a covariant functor of a single variable from the product category $\mathscr{A}_1^* \times \mathscr{A}_2$. Similarly, we can define the product category for any number of categories, and then a functor of any number of variables and any variance can be regarded as a functor of one variable from a suitable product category.

However, it must be observed that the preservation properties of T as a functor of several variables in general differ from the preservation properties of T as a functor of a single variable. Always in speaking of a preservation property of T we shall be referring to the preservation property of T as a functor of several variables.

If $\mathscr{A}$ is any category, then the definition of category gives us a bifunctor

$$[\ ,\ ] : \mathscr{A} \times \mathscr{A} \to \mathscr{S}$$

whose value on the pair (A_1, A_2) is $[A_1, A_2]$. For a pair of morphisms $\alpha_1 : A_1' \to A_1$ and $\alpha_2 : A_2 \to A_2'$ we have

$$[\alpha_1, \alpha_2] : [A_1, A_2] \to [A_1', A_2']$$

defined by $[\alpha_1, \alpha_2](x) = \alpha_2 x \alpha_1$. Then it is immediately verified that $[\ ,\ ]$ satisfies the rules for a bifunctor, contravariant in the first variable and covariant in the second. If $\mathscr{A}$ has a zero (resp. is additive) then $[\ ,\ ]$ can be regarded as a bifunctor into $\mathscr{S}_0$ (resp. $\mathscr{G}$). The partial one variable functors of $[\ ,\ ]$ are the functors H^A and H_A described in §3. From 5.1 and 5.1* it follows that $[\ ,\ ]$ is a limit preserving monofunctor.

9. Natural Transformations

Let $S, T : \mathscr{A} \to \mathscr{B}$ be covariant functors. Suppose that for every object $A \in \mathscr{A}$ we have a morphism $\eta_A : S(A) \to T(A)$ in $\mathscr{B}$ such that for every morphism $\alpha : A \to A'$ in $\mathscr{A}$ the diagram

$$\begin{array}{ccc} S(A) & \xrightarrow{\eta_A} & T(A) \\ {\scriptstyle S(\alpha)}\downarrow & & \downarrow{\scriptstyle T(\alpha)} \\ S(A') & \xrightarrow{\eta_{A'}} & T(A') \end{array}$$

is commutative. Then we call η a **natural transformation** from S to T and we write $\eta : S \to T$. If η_A is an isomorphism for each $A \in \mathscr{A}$ then η is called a **natural equivalence**. In this case we have a natural equivalence $\eta^{-1} : T \to S$ defined by $(\eta^{-1})_A = (\eta_A)^{-1}$. If $\eta : S \to T$ and $\rho : T \to U$ then we have a composition $\rho\eta : S \to U$ defined by $(\rho\eta)_A = \rho_A \eta_A$. For any functor T we have the identity transformation $1_T : T \to T$ such that $(1_T)_A = 1_{T(A)}$ for all $A \in \mathscr{A}$. If $\eta : S \to T$ where $S, T : \mathscr{A} \to \mathscr{B}$ and $U : \mathscr{B} \to \mathscr{C}$ is any functor, then we have a natural transformation $U\eta : US \to UT$ defined by $(U\eta)_A = U(\eta_A)$ for all $A \in \mathscr{A}$. Similarly if $V : \mathscr{D} \to \mathscr{A}$ then $\eta V : SV \to TV$ is given by $(\eta V)_D = \eta_{V(D)}$ for all $D \in \mathscr{D}$.

More generally, if S and T are functors of several variables which have the same variables, the same variance for each of the variables, and the same codomain, then a natural transformation from S to T is simply a natural transformation of the single variable functors from the product category which were associated with S and T in §8.

Let $T: \mathscr{A}_1 \times \mathscr{A}_2 \times \ldots \times \mathscr{A}_n \to \mathscr{B}$ be an n-variable functor, where in order to simplify the notation we assume that all variables are covariant. For fixed objects $A_i \in \mathscr{A}_i$, $1 \leqslant i \leqslant k < n$, denote the corresponding partial functor of T by $T_{A_1A_2\ldots A_k}$. Then morphisms $\alpha_i : A_i \to A_i'$, $1 \leqslant i \leqslant k$, induce a natural transformation

$$\eta_{\alpha_1\alpha_2\ldots\alpha_k} : T_{A_1A_2\ldots A_k} \to T_{A_1'A_2'\ldots A_k'} \tag{1}$$

and if $\gamma_i = \beta_i\alpha_i$ then we have

$$\eta_{\gamma_1\gamma_2\ldots\gamma_k} = \eta_{\beta_1\beta_2\ldots\beta_k}\eta_{\alpha_1\alpha_2\ldots\alpha_k}. \tag{2}$$

Conversely, suppose that to each k-tuple of objects $(A_1, A_2, \ldots, A_k)$ with $A_i \in \mathscr{A}_i$ for $1 \leqslant i \leqslant k$ we have a covariant functor

$$T_{A_1A_2\ldots A_k} : \mathscr{A}_{k+1} \times \mathscr{A}_{k+2} \times \ldots \times \mathscr{A}_n \to \mathscr{B}$$

and to each k-tuple of morphisms $(\alpha_1, \alpha_2, \ldots, \alpha_k)$ with $\alpha_i : A_i \to A_i'$ we have a natural transformation (1) such that (2) is satisfied. Then defining

$$T(A_1, A_2, \ldots, A_n) = T_{A_1A_2\ldots A_k}(A_{k+1}, A_{k+2}, \ldots, A_n)$$

and

$$\begin{aligned} T(\alpha_1, \alpha_2, \ldots, \alpha_n) &= \eta_{\alpha_1\alpha_2\ldots\alpha_k} T_{A_1A_2\ldots A_k}(\alpha_{k+1}, \alpha_{k+2}, \ldots, \alpha_k) \\ &= T_{A_1'A_2'\ldots A_k'}(\alpha_{k+1}, \alpha_{k+2}, \ldots, \alpha_n)\eta_{\alpha_1\alpha_2\ldots\alpha_k} \end{aligned}$$

we obtain an n-variable functor T.

Consider a natural transformation $\eta : S \to T$, and suppose that for each $A \in \mathscr{A}$ the morphism $\eta_A : S(A) \to T(A)$ is a monomorphism. Then we call η a **pointwise** monomorphism. A dual definition applies to **pointwise epimorphisms**. If η is a pointwise monomorphism and if T is an additive functor, then it is easy to see that S is also additive. Dually if η is a pointwise epimorphism and S is additive, then T is additive.

Let $S, T : \mathscr{A} \to \mathscr{B}$ be covariant, and let $\theta : S \to T$ be a natural equivalence. If D is a diagram in $\mathscr{A}$, then SD and TD are isomorphic diagrams in B. Now suppose that S is limit preserving, and let $\{L \to D_i\}$ be a limit for D. Then $\{S(L) \to S(D_i)\}$ is a limit for SD. Hence by 2.2 $\{S(L) \to S(D_i) \to T(D_i)\}$ is a limit for TD. Therefore, letting $T(L) \to S(L)$ be θ_L^{-1} we see by 2.1 that $\{T(L) \to S(L) \to S(D_i) \to T(D_i)\}$ is a limit for TD. But by naturality of θ this last family is just $\{T(L) \to T(D_i)\}$. In other words, if T is naturally equivalent to S and S is limit preserving, then T is also limit preserving. In a similar way we can show that T has any of the preservation properties which S has. Since the preservation properties functors of several variables are defined in terms of the preservation properties of the partial one variable functors, it is clear that these remarks apply to functors of any number of variables and any variance.

10. Equivalence of Categories

Let $\mathscr{A}$ and $\mathscr{B}$ be any two categories. Write $\mathscr{A} \sim \mathscr{B}$ if there is an equivalence $T : \mathscr{A} \to \mathscr{B}$. Then $\sim$ is clearly a reflexive, transitive relation. The following proposition tells us that $\sim$ is also a symmetric relation.

Proposition 10.1. *A functor $T : \mathscr{A} \to \mathscr{B}$ is an equivalence if and only if there is a functor $S : \mathscr{B} \to \mathscr{A}$ together with natural equivalences*

$$\varphi : 1_{\mathscr{B}} \approx TS, \qquad \psi : ST \approx 1_{\mathscr{A}}.$$

If such is the case, then we can always choose ψ such that $T\psi = (\varphi T)^{-1}$ and $S\varphi = (\psi S)^{-1}$.

Proof. Suppose first that we are given φ and ψ. Then the relation $B \approx T(S(B))$ for all $B \in \mathscr{B}$ shows that T is representative. Relative to a morphism $A \to A'$ we have a commutative diagram

$$\begin{array}{ccc} ST(A) & \overset{\psi_A}{\approx} & A \\ \downarrow & & \downarrow \\ ST(A') & \overset{\psi_{A'}}{\approx} & A' \end{array} \tag{1}$$

from which it follows that T is faithful. Then by symmetry S is also faithful. A morphism $\beta : T(A) \to T(A')$ induces a morphism $\alpha : A \to A'$ via (1), and we have $S(\beta) = S(T(\alpha))$. Since S is faithful it follows that $\beta = T(\alpha)$. This shows that T is full, and consequently T is an equivalence.

Conversely, suppose that T is an equivalence. Then for $B \in \mathscr{B}$ we can find an object $S(B) \in \mathscr{A}$ and an isomorphism $\varphi_B : B \approx TS(B)$. A morphism $\beta : B \to B'$ in $\mathscr{B}$ induces the morphism

$$\varphi_{B'}\beta\varphi_B^{-1} : TS(B) \to TS(B').$$

Since T is full and faithful there is a unique morphism $S(\beta) : S(B) \to S(B')$ such that $\varphi_{B'}\beta\varphi_B^{-1} = T(S(\beta))$, or in other words such that the diagram

$$\begin{array}{ccc} B & \overset{\varphi_B}{\approx} & TS(B) \\ \beta\downarrow & & \downarrow TS(\beta) \\ B' & \overset{\varphi_B}{\approx} & TS(B') \end{array} \tag{2}$$

is commutative. Using the uniqueness of $S(\beta)$ and the functorial properties of T it is easily checked that S is a functor. From (2) we then see that φ is a natural equivalence. Now for $A \in \mathscr{A}$ we have an isomorphism

$$\varphi_{T(A)} : T(A) \to TST(A)$$

and so again since T is full and faithful, there is a unique isomorphism $\psi_A : ST(A) \to A$ such that

$$T(\psi_A) = \varphi_{T(A)}^{-1}. \tag{3}$$

To show that ψ is a natural equivalence we must show that relative to a morphism $A \to A'$ the diagram (1) is commutative. Applying T to (1) and using (3) we obtain a commutative diagram by naturality of φ. Since T is faithful it follows that (1) is commutative.

Finally, observe that the relation $T\psi = (\varphi T)^{-1}$ is just (3). It remains to be shown that $S(\varphi_B) = \psi_{S(B)}^{-1}$ for all $B \in \mathscr{B}$. Since T is faithful it suffices to show that $TS(\varphi_B) = T(\psi_{S(B)}^{-1})$. Using (3) we have $T(\psi_{S(B)}^{-1}) = \varphi_{TS(B)}$. The result then follows by replacing β by φ_B in (2). ▮

Proposition 10.2. *Let $T : \mathscr{A} \to \mathscr{B}$ be an equivalence. Then T is mono, epi, limit preserving, and colimit preserving. Furthermore, $\mathscr{A}$ is complete, cocomplete, normal, conormal, or exact if and only if $\mathscr{B}$ has the corresponding property. If either category is additive then there is a unique additive structure on the other making T additive.*

Proof. Let $S : \mathscr{B} \to \mathscr{A}$ be the equivalence of 10.1. To show that T is limit preserving, let $\{L \to D_i\}$ be the limit of a diagram D in $\mathscr{A}$. If $\{T(L) \to T(D_i)\}$ is not a limit for TD, then by 7.1 $\{ST(L) \to ST(D_i)\}$ is not a limit for STD. But then as we saw at the end of the previous section $\{L \to D_i\}$ is not a limit for D in view of the natural equivalence ψ. This contradiction shows that T is limit preserving. The other preservation properties of T follow similarly.

Suppose that $\mathscr{B}$ is complete. Then if D is a diagram in $\mathscr{A}$, we can find a limit $\{X \to T(D_i)\}$ for TD in $\mathscr{B}$. Since S is limit preserving this means that $\{S(X) \to ST(D_i)\}$ is a limit for STD. Therefore by 2.2 $\{S(X) \to ST(D_i) \xrightarrow{\psi} D_i\}$ is a limit for D. This shows that $\mathscr{A}$ is complete. The proofs of the other assertions are similar and are left to the reader. ▮

If we define the **image** of a functor $T : \mathscr{A} \to \mathscr{B}$ (or $\text{Im}(T)$) as the class $\{T(A) \mid A \in \mathscr{A}\}$ of objects together with the class $\{T(\alpha) \mid \alpha \text{ is a morphism in } \mathscr{A}\}$ of morphisms, it is not necessarily true that $\text{Im}(T)$ is a subcategory of $\mathscr{B}$. The difficulty arises from the fact that T may not be univalent on objects. If $\alpha_1 : A_1 \to A$ and $\alpha_2 : A' \to A_2$ where $T(A) = T(A')$ but $A \neq A'$, then $T(\alpha_1)$ and $T(\alpha_2)$ are in $\text{Im}(T)$, but $T(\alpha_2)\,T(\alpha_1)$ need not be in $\text{Im}(T)$. However, if T is univalent with respect to objects, then $\text{Im}(T)$ is a subcategory of $\mathscr{B}$. The following proposition says that in a sense we lose no generality by assuming always that T is univalent on objects.

Proposition 10.3. *Let $T : \mathscr{A} \to \mathscr{B}$ be any functor. Then there is a category $\mathscr{B}'$ which contains $\mathscr{B}$ as an equivalent subcategory, and a functor $T' : \mathscr{A} \to \mathscr{B}'$ such that T' is univalent on objects and is naturally equivalent to IT where $I : \mathscr{B} \to \mathscr{B}'$ is the inclusion functor.*

Proof. Define a category $\mathscr{B}_1$ as follows. The class of objects of $\mathscr{B}_1$ is $\mathscr{A} \times \mathscr{B}$. A morphism in $\mathscr{B}_1$ from (A, B) to (A', B') is a triple (A, A', β), where $\beta : B \to B'$ is a morphism in $\mathscr{B}$. Composition is defined by the rule

$$(A', A'', \beta')(A, A', \beta) = (A, A'', \beta'\beta).$$

Fix an object $A_0 \in \mathscr{A}$ and define $I_1 : \mathscr{B} \to \mathscr{B}_1$ by $I_1(B) = (A_0, B)$ for objects and $I_1(\beta) = (A_0, A_0, \beta)$ for morphisms. Then I_1 is a full imbedding. Furthermore, I_1 is an equivalence since for any $(A, B) \in \mathscr{B}_1$ we have an isomorphism $(A, A_0, 1_B) : (A, B) \to (A_0, B) = I_1(B)$. We define a functor $T_1 : \mathscr{A} \to B_1$ by $T_1(A) = (A, T(A))$ for objects A and $T_1(\alpha) = (A, A', T(\alpha))$ for a morphism $\alpha : A \to A'$. Then for each $A \in \mathscr{A}$ we have an isomorphism $\theta_A : T_1(A) \to I_1 T(A)$ in $\mathscr{B}_1$, given by $\theta_A = (A, A_0, 1_{T(A)})$. The naturality of θ is readily verified. Since I_1 is univalent on objects and morphisms we obtain a category $\mathscr{B}'$ from $\mathscr{B}_1$ by replacing $\mathrm{Im}(I_1)$ by $\mathscr{B}$. Then composing T_1 with the "replacement" functor $\mathscr{B}_1 \to \mathscr{B}'$ we obtain T' as required. ▮

The following proposition shows that if we replace $\mathscr{B}$ by $\mathscr{G}$ in 10.2, then we can always take $\mathscr{B}' = \mathscr{G}$. The reason is essentially that $\mathscr{G}$ has an "inexhaustable" supply of objects which are isomorphic to any given one.

Proposition 10.4. *If $T : \mathscr{A} \to \mathscr{G}$ is any group valued functor, then T is naturally equivalent to a functor $T' : \mathscr{A} \to \mathscr{G}$ which is univalent with respect to objects.*

Proof. For $A \in \mathscr{A}$, define $T'(A)$ to be the group whose elements are ordered pairs (A, x), where x runs through all elements of the group $T(A)$. Addition in $T'(A)$ is defined by $(A, x) + (A, y) = (A, x + y)$. For a morphism $\alpha : A \to A'$ in $\mathscr{A}$ we define $T'(\alpha)(A, x) = (A', T(\alpha)(x))$. The natural equivalence $\theta : T \to T'$, given by $\theta_A(x) = (A, x)$, then gives us the result. ▮

11. Functor Categories

For any two categories $\mathscr{A}$ and $\mathscr{B}$ let $[\mathscr{A}, \mathscr{B}]$ denote the class of all covariant functors from $\mathscr{A}$ to $\mathscr{B}$. For $S, T \in [\mathscr{A}, \mathscr{B}]$ let $[S, T]$ denote the class of natural transformations from S to T. With the law of composition of natural transformations of functors given in §9, $[\mathscr{A}, \mathscr{B}]$ comes very close to being a category. The only requirement that is missing is that $[S, T]$ may not be a set. However if we assume that $\mathscr{A}$ is small, then the natural transformations from S to T may be regarded as a subclass of the cartesian product $\bigtimes_{A \in \mathscr{A}} [S(A), T(A)]$, and since the latter is a set so is $[S, T]$. In speaking of the functor category $[\mathscr{A}, \mathscr{B}]$ we shall always assume that $\mathscr{A}$ is small.

Corresponding to $T \in [\mathscr{A}, \mathscr{B}]$ we have the covariant functor $T^*_* \in [\mathscr{A}^*, \mathscr{B}^*]$, and corresponding to a natural transformation $\eta : S \to T$ we get a natural transformation $\eta^*_* : T^*_* \to S^*_*$, defined by the rule $\eta^*_{*A^*} = \eta_A$ where η_A is regarded as a morphism in $\mathscr{B}^*$. Clearly this gives us a contravariant isomorphism from $[\mathscr{A}, \mathscr{B}]$ to $[\mathscr{A}^*, \mathscr{B}^*]$. In other words $[\mathscr{A}^*, \mathscr{B}^*]$ is isomorphic to the dual category of $[\mathscr{A}, \mathscr{B}]$.

In general, $[\mathscr{A}, \mathscr{B}]$ inherits the properties of $\mathscr{B}$, and a morphism $\eta : S \to T$ in $[\mathscr{A}, \mathscr{B}]$ has the properties which are common to all the morphisms $\eta_A : S(A) \to T(A)$ in $\mathscr{B}$. Thus η is an isomorphism if and only if it is pointwise an isomorphism; in other words, if and only if θ_A is an isomorphism in $\mathscr{B}$ for every $A \in \mathscr{A}$. If η is a pointwise monomorphism, then η is a monomorphism in $[\mathscr{A}, \mathscr{B}]$. For otherwise we would have $\eta\varphi = \eta\psi$ for some $\varphi \neq \psi$. Now $\varphi \neq \psi$ means that for some $A \in \mathscr{A}$, $\varphi_A \neq \psi_A$. But then since $\eta_A\varphi_A = \eta_A\psi_A$ this contradicts the fact that η_A is a monomorphism in $\mathscr{B}$. The converse need not be true, although it will be true if $\mathscr{B}$ is an exact category. That is, if η is a monomorphism in $[\mathscr{A}, \mathscr{B}]$, it need not be a pointwise monomorphism.

If $\mathscr{B}$ has a zero object 0, then the functor $T : \mathscr{A} \to \mathscr{B}$ such that $T(A) = 0$ for all $A \in \mathscr{A}$ is a zero object for $[\mathscr{A}, \mathscr{B}]$. In this case T also will be denoted by 0. If $\mathscr{B}$ is additive and $\varphi, \psi : S \to T$ are two natural transformations, then we can define $\varphi + \psi : S \to T$ by the relation $(\varphi + \psi)_A = \varphi_A + \psi_A$, and in this way $[\mathscr{A}, \mathscr{B}]$ becomes an additive category.

Suppose that D is a diagram in $[\mathscr{A}, \mathscr{B}]$ over a scheme $\Sigma = (I, M, d)$. Let $D(A)$ be the diagram in $\mathscr{B}$ over Σ defined for each $A \in \mathscr{A}$ as follows. We take $D(A)_i = D_i(A)$ for $i \in I$ and $D(A)(m) = D(m)_A$ for $m \in M$. Suppose that $\{L(A) \to D_i(A)\}_{i \in I}$ is a limit for $D(A)$ for every $A \in \mathscr{A}$. We make L into a functor, that is, an object in $[\mathscr{A}, \mathscr{B}]$, as follows. If $\alpha : A \to A'$ and $m \in M$ is such that $d(m) = (i, j)$, then we have

$$\begin{aligned} L(A) \to D_i(A) \to D_i(A') \to D_j(A') &= L(A) \to D_i(A) \to D_j(A) \to D_j(A') \\ &= L(A) \to D_j(A) \to D_j(A'). \end{aligned}$$

The first equality comes from the fact that $D(m)$ is a natural transformation, and the second from the fact that $\{L(A) \to D_i(A)\}_{i \in I}$ is a compatible family. Hence $\{L(A) \to D_i(A) \to D_i(A')\}$ is a compatible family for $D(A')$, and so since $L(A')$ is the limit of $D(A')$ we have a unique morphism $L(\alpha) : L(A) \to L(A')$ such that

$$L(A) \to L(A') \to D_i(A') = L(A) \to D_i(A) \to D_i(A') \tag{1}$$

for all $i \in I$. The functorial properties of L now follow from the uniqueness of the morphism $L(\alpha)$, and Eq. (1) shows that for each vertex i the family $\{L(A) \to D_i(A)\}_{A \in \mathscr{A}}$ is a natural transformation from L to D_i. Then $\{L \to D_i\}_{i \in I}$ is a compatible family for D since it is so pointwise. One can then check using arguments similar to the above that $\{L \to D_i\}_{i \in I}$ is actually the limit of D in the category $[\mathscr{A}, \mathscr{B}]$.

It follows that if $\mathscr{B}$ is Σ-complete then the same is true of $[\mathscr{A}, \mathscr{B}]$. In particular, if $\mathscr{B}$ has products, then the product $\times\, T_i$ of a family in $[\mathscr{A}, \mathscr{B}]$ is such that $(\times\, T_i)\,(A) = \times\, T_i\,(A)$, and the kth projection (natural transformation) $\times\, T_i \to T_k$ is given pointwise by the projection $\times\, T_i(A) \to T_k(A)$ from the product in $\mathscr{B}$. If $\alpha : A \to A'$ then $(\times\, T_i)(\alpha) = \times\, T_i(\alpha)$. If $\mathscr{B}$ has kernels, then the kernel $K \to S$ of a transformation $S \to T$ is such that $K(A) \to S(A)$ is the kernel of $S(A) \to T(A)$ for all $A \in \mathscr{A}$.

Suppose now that $\mathscr{B}$ is an exact category. Let $\varphi : T' \to T$ be a monomorphism in $[\mathscr{A}, \mathscr{B}]$. Then φ has kernel 0. Hence φ_A has kernel 0 in $\mathscr{B}$ for every $A \in \mathscr{A}$, and so since $\mathscr{B}$ is exact this implies that φ_A is a monomorphism. Let $T \to T''$ be the cokernel of φ in $[\mathscr{A}, \mathscr{B}]$, so that by the above $T(A) \to T''(A)$ is the cokernel of φ_A for all A. Then by normality for $\mathscr{B}$, φ_A is the kernel of $T(A) \to T''(A)$, and so φ is the kernel of $T \to T''$. Therefore $[\mathscr{A}, \mathscr{B}]$ is normal and by duality it is conormal. If $S \to T$ is any natural transformation, we let $I \to T$ be the kernel of its cokernel. Then $I(A) \to T(A)$ is the image of $S(A) \to T(A)$, and so we get an epimorphism $S(A) \to I(A)$ for all $A \in \mathscr{A}$. That this gives us a natural transformation $S \to I$ is easily verified from the fact that $I \to T$ is a pointwise monomorphism. Therefore we have shown that every morphism in $[\mathscr{A}, \mathscr{B}]$ can be written as an epimorphism followed by a monomorphism, and so $[\mathscr{A}, \mathscr{B}]$ is an exact category. Hence by the preceding paragraph we see that if $\mathscr{B}$ is abelian then so is $[\mathscr{A}, \mathscr{B}]$.

Suppose that $\mathscr{B}$ is exact and locally small. Given an object $T \in [\mathscr{A}, \mathscr{B}]$, for each $A \in \mathscr{A}$ let $\mathscr{C}_A$ be a representative set of subobjects of $T(A)$. Then a representative set of subobjects for T can be found as a subset of the cartesian product $\underset{A \in \mathscr{A}}{\times} \mathscr{C}_A$. Consequently we see that $[\mathscr{A}, \mathscr{B}]$ is also locally small.

Let $\mathscr{A}$ and $\mathscr{B}$ be any categories with $\mathscr{A}$ small. We have a bifunctor $E : [\mathscr{A}, \mathscr{B}] \times \mathscr{A} \to \mathscr{B}$ defined by $E(T, A) = T(A)$ and

$$E(\eta, \psi) = \eta_{A'} S(\alpha) = T(\alpha)\eta_A$$

for $\eta : S \to T$ and $\alpha : A \to A'$. For fixed T the partial one variable functor associated with E is just T. For fixed A the partial one variable functor is called the **evaluation functor at** A and is denoted by E_A. Hence $E_A(T) = T(A)$, and $E_A(\eta) = \eta_A$. If $\mathscr{B}$ is an exact category, then E is an exact functor. If $\mathscr{B}$ is an additive category, then we have

$$E_A(\varphi + \psi) = (\varphi + \psi)_A = \varphi_A + \psi_A = E_A(\varphi) + E_A(\psi)$$

and so E_A is an additive functor. Finally, if $\mathscr{B}$ is Σ-complete (cocomplete) then E_A preserves limits (colimits) of diagrams over Σ. Hence if $\mathscr{B}$ is complete (cocomplete) then E_A is limit (colimit) preserving.

12. Diagrams as Functors

In §1 it was pointed out that the diagrams over a scheme Σ in a category $\mathscr{A}$ themselves form a category. More generally, if Σ_0 is the scheme obtained from Σ by adding identity arrows at each vertex and $\sim$ is a commutativity relation, then the diagrams in $\mathscr{A}$ over Σ which are compatible with $\sim$ form a category $[\Sigma/\sim, \mathscr{A}]$. We define a category $\Sigma/\sim$ as follows. The objects in

$\Sigma/\sim$ are the vertices of Σ. The morphisms from i to j are the equivalence classes modulo $\sim$ of composite arrows in Σ_0 from i to j. If b and c are composite arrows such that the origin of c is the extremity of b, then we define the composition of the two morphisms $[b]$ and $[c]$ by $[c][b] = [cb]$. Then rule (ii) for commutativity relations insures that composition is independent of representatives, and rule (iii) shows that $[1_i]$ behaves as an identity for the object i. It is then clear that the functors from $\Sigma/\sim$ to a category $\mathscr{A}$ are in one to one correspondence with the diagrams in $\mathscr{A}$ over Σ satisfying $\sim$, and the natural transformations between two functors from $\Sigma/\sim$ to $\mathscr{A}$ are in one to one correspondence between the morphisms of the corresponding diagrams. In other words the category of diagrams $[\Sigma/\sim, \mathscr{A}]$ is isomorphic to the category of covariant functors from $\Sigma/\sim$ to $\mathscr{A}$.

Conversely, if $\mathscr{A}$ is any small category, then $\mathscr{A}$ is isomorphic to a category of the type $\Sigma/\sim$ for some diagram scheme Σ and some commutativity relation $\sim$ (exercise 13). Hence the study of functor categories is entirely equivalent to the study of categories of diagrams.

If $\sim$ is the largest commutativity relation for Σ, then $\Sigma/\sim$ has the property that from any object to any other object there is at most one morphism. In other words a commutative diagram can be interpreted as a functor from an ordered set.

It follows from §11 that if $\mathscr{B}$ is Λ-complete for some scheme Λ, then $[\Sigma/\sim, \mathscr{B}]$ is Λ-complete. The limit of a diagram in $[\Sigma/\sim, \mathscr{B}]$ over Λ is obtained by taking pointwise the limits in $\mathscr{B}$ for each vertex in Σ, and then using induced morphisms to turn this into a diagram over Σ. Since this process has nothing to do with $\sim$, we see that if $\sim$ is a subrelation of a commutativity relation $\approx$, then $[\Sigma/\approx, \mathscr{B}]$ is a Λ-complete subcategory of $[\Sigma/\sim, \mathscr{B}]$. In terms of functor categories this principle is as follows: If $\mathscr{A}''$ is a quotient category of $\mathscr{A}$ and if $\mathscr{B}$ is Λ-complete, then $[\mathscr{A}'', \mathscr{B}]$ is a Λ-complete subcategory of $[\mathscr{A}, \mathscr{B}]$.

Suppose that $\mathscr{B}$ is Σ-complete. If D is a diagram in $\mathscr{B}$ over Σ, denote the limit of D by $L(D)$. Then a morphism $f: D \to D'$ of diagrams induces a unique morphism $L(f): L(D) \to L(D')$ of the limits, and in this way L becomes a functor from the category $[\Sigma, \mathscr{B}]$ to the category $\mathscr{B}$. We define a functor $I: \mathscr{B} \to [\Sigma, \mathscr{B}]$ by taking $I(B)$ as the diagram which has B at every vertex with identity morphisms throughout. If $\beta: B \to B'$ then $I(\beta)$ is taken to be β at every vertex. It is clear from the definition of limit that we have a one to one correspondence

$$\eta_{B,D}: [I(B), D]_{[\Sigma,B]} \to [B, L(D)]_{\mathscr{B}} \tag{1}$$

for every $B \in \mathscr{B}$ and $D \in [\Sigma, \mathscr{B}]$. Furthermore, it is easy to check that η is natural in B and D. More generally suppose that we have covariant functors $T: \mathscr{A} \to \mathscr{B}$ and $S: \mathscr{B} \to \mathscr{A}$ where $\mathscr{A}$ and $\mathscr{B}$ are arbitrary categories, and

$$\eta_{B,A}: [S(B), A] \to [B, T(A)] \tag{2}$$

is a natural equivalence of set-valued bifunctors. Then we say that T is an **adjoint** for S, or that S is a **coadjoint** for T.

Proposition 12.1. *If $T : \mathscr{A} \to \mathscr{B}$ has a coadjoint $S : \mathscr{B} \to \mathscr{A}$, then T is a limit preserving monofunctor.*

Proof. Let $\mathscr{F} = \{X \to D_i\}$ be a limit for a diagram D in $\mathscr{A}$. Then by 5.1, $H^{S(B)}(\mathscr{F})$ is a limit for $H^{S(B)}D$ in $\mathscr{S}$ for all $B \in \mathscr{B}$. In view of the natural equivalence (2) this says that for each $B \in \mathscr{B}$ the family $H^B(T(\mathscr{F}))$ is a limit for the diagram $H^B TD$ in $\mathscr{S}$. Hence, again by 5.1 this shows that $T(\mathscr{F})$ is a limit for TD in $\mathscr{B}$, and so T is limit preserving. In the same way it can be shown that T is a monofunctor. ∎

Corollary 12.2. *If $\mathscr{B}$ is Σ-complete and $L : [\Sigma, \mathscr{B}] \to \mathscr{B}$ is the functor which assigns to a diagram its limit then L is a limit preserving monofunctor.* ∎

Corollary 12.3. *If $\{u_i\}$ is a family of monomorphisms in a category with products, then $\times_i u_i$ is a monomorphism. If u_i is the kernel of f_i for each i, then $\times_i u_i$ is the kernel of $\times_i f_i$.* ∎

Corollary 12.4. *Let $\mathscr{A}$ be a small category and let $\mathscr{B}$ be a complete category. For some class $\mathscr{D}$ of diagrams in $\mathscr{A}$ and some class $\mathscr{M}$ of monomorphisms in $\mathscr{A}$, let $\mathscr{L}$ denote the full subcategory of $[\mathscr{A}, \mathscr{B}]$ whose objects are those functors T which preserve limits of diagrams in $\mathscr{D}$ and which preserve monomorphisms in $\mathscr{M}$. Then $\mathscr{L}$ is a complete subcategory of $[\mathscr{A}, \mathscr{B}]$.* ∎

13. Categories of Additive Functors; Modules

If $\mathscr{A}$ and $\mathscr{B}$ are additive categories with $\mathscr{A}$ small we let $(\mathscr{A}, \mathscr{B})$ denote the full subcategory of $[\mathscr{A}, \mathscr{B}]$ consisting of all additive functors from $\mathscr{A}$ to $\mathscr{B}$. If $\mathscr{B}$ is Σ-complete (Σ-cocomplete) then it is easily seen that the limit (colimit) of a diagram D in $[\mathscr{A}, \mathscr{B}]$ over Σ is also in $(\mathscr{A}, \mathscr{B})$. That is, $(\mathscr{A}, \mathscr{B})$ is a Σ-complete (Σ-cocomplete) subcategory of $[\mathscr{A}, \mathscr{B}]$. Furthermore if $\mathscr{B}$ is exact, then $(\mathscr{A}, \mathscr{B})$ is an exact subcategory of $[\mathscr{A}, \mathscr{B}]$. The discussion of the preservation properties of the evaluation functors E_A given in §11 applies also to the restriction of E_A to $(\mathscr{A}, \mathscr{B})$ (which we denote also by E_A).

Let $\mathscr{A}$ be any small category and let $T : \mathscr{B} \to \mathscr{C}$ be a covariant functor. Then we have an induced functor $T_0 : [\mathscr{A}, \mathscr{B}] \to [\mathscr{A}, \mathscr{C}]$ defined by $T_0(S) = TS$ for $S \in [\mathscr{A}, \mathscr{B}]$ and $T_0(\eta) = T\eta$ for a morphism η in $[\mathscr{A}, \mathscr{B}]$. If $\mathscr{B}$ and $\mathscr{C}$ are additive and T is an additive functor, then T_0 is additive. If, furthermore, $\mathscr{A}$ is additive and S is additive, then $T_0(S)$ is additive. In other words the restriction of T_0 to $(\mathscr{A}, \mathscr{B})$ gives us a functor from $(\mathscr{A}, \mathscr{B})$ to $(\mathscr{A}, \mathscr{C})$ (also denoted by T_0). A contravariant functor $T : \mathscr{B} \to \mathscr{C}$ induces a covariant functor $T_0 : [\mathscr{A}, \mathscr{B}] \to [\mathscr{A}^*, \mathscr{C}]$ defined by $T_0(S) = TS_*$.

On the other hand a covariant functor $T : \mathscr{A} \to \mathscr{A}'$ of small categories induces a covariant functor $T^0 : [\mathscr{A}', \mathscr{B}] \to [\mathscr{A}, \mathscr{B}]$ for any category $\mathscr{B}$, defined by $T^0(S) = ST$ and $T^0(\eta) = \eta T$. If $\mathscr{B}$ is additive then T^0 is additive, and if furthermore $\mathscr{A}$ and $\mathscr{A}'$ are additive and T is an additive functor, then T^0 induces a functor from $(\mathscr{A}', \mathscr{B})$ to $(\mathscr{A}, \mathscr{B})$.

Let $\mathbf{R}$ be a ring; that is, an additive category with a single object X. If $\mathscr{B}$ is any additive category, we shall call $(\mathbf{R}, \mathscr{B})$ the **category of left R-objects in** $\mathscr{B}$. A left $\mathbf{R}$-object in $\mathscr{B}$ is therefore an object $B \in \mathscr{B}$ together with a morphism of rings $\rho : \mathbf{R} \to [B, B]$. Formally this is the functor $S : \mathbf{R} \to \mathscr{B}$ such that $S(X) = B$ and $S(r) = \rho(r)$ for r a morphism in $\mathbf{R}$. Informally we shall say that B has a left $\mathbf{R}$-object structure, or simply that B is a left $\mathbf{R}$-object, but in doing so we will always have a particular ring morphism ρ in mind. The category $(\mathbf{R}^*, \mathscr{B})$ is called the **category of right R-objects in** $\mathscr{B}$. We shall frequently denote the categories $(\mathbf{R}, \mathscr{B})$ and $(\mathbf{R}^*, \mathscr{B})$ by ${}^{\mathbf{R}}\mathscr{B}$ and $\mathscr{B}^{\mathbf{R}}$, respectively. A morphism of left $\mathbf{R}$-objects $(B, \rho) \to (B', \rho')$ is a morphism $\beta : B \to B'$ in $\mathscr{B}$ such that for every $r \in \mathbf{R}$ the diagram

$$\begin{array}{ccc} B & \longrightarrow & B' \\ {\scriptstyle \rho(r)}\downarrow & & \downarrow{\scriptstyle \rho'(r)} \\ B & \longrightarrow & B' \end{array}$$

is commutative. The group of left $\mathbf{R}$-object morphisms from B to B' will be denoted by ${}^{\mathbf{R}}[B, B']$. If B and B' are right $\mathbf{R}$-objects then the right $\mathbf{R}$-object morphisms from B to B' are denoted by $[B, B']^{\mathbf{R}}$.

If $\mathbf{Z}$ is the ring of integers, then ${}^{\mathbf{Z}}\mathscr{B}$ is isomorphic to $\mathscr{B}$. This is a result of the fact that for $B \in \mathscr{B}$ there is one and only one morphism of rings $\mathbf{Z} \to [B, B]$.

An additive covariant functor $T : \mathscr{B} \to \mathscr{C}$ induces the additive functor $T_0 : {}^{\mathbf{R}}\mathscr{B} \to {}^{\mathbf{R}}\mathscr{C}$ discussed above. Hence if B is an $\mathbf{R}$-object in B, then $T(B)$ becomes an $\mathbf{R}$-object in $\mathscr{C}$. If T is contravariant, then $T_0 : {}^{\mathbf{R}}\mathscr{B} \to \mathscr{C}^{\mathbf{R}}$. Similarly a morphism of rings $\varphi : \mathbf{R} \to \mathbf{S}$ induces the "change of rings" functor $\varphi^0 : {}^{\mathbf{S}}\mathscr{B} \to {}^{\mathbf{R}}\mathscr{B}$.

Let $\mathbf{R}$ and $\mathbf{S}$ be rings, and let $\mathscr{B}$ be any additive category. The category ${}^{\mathbf{S}}({}^{\mathbf{R}}\mathscr{B})$ is called the category of left $\mathbf{S}$, left $\mathbf{R}$-biobjects in $\mathscr{B}$. From the isomorphism of categories $(\mathbf{S}, (\mathbf{R}, \mathscr{B})) \approx (\mathbf{R}, (\mathbf{S}, \mathscr{B}))$ (exercise 4) we see that a left $\mathbf{S}$, left $\mathbf{R}$-biobject may be regarded also as a left $\mathbf{R}$, left $\mathbf{S}$-biobject. A right $\mathbf{S}$, left $\mathbf{R}$-biobject is an object in the category $({}^{\mathbf{R}}\mathscr{B})^{\mathbf{S}} \approx {}^{\mathbf{R}}(\mathscr{B}^{\mathbf{S}})$, with a similar definition of right $\mathbf{S}$, right $\mathbf{R}$-biobjects. The reader may formulate a more general definition for multiobjects over any number of rings.

If $T : \mathscr{A} \times \mathscr{B} \to \mathscr{C}$ is an additive covariant bifunctor and (A, ρ) is a left $\mathbf{R}$-object in $\mathscr{A}$, then $T(A, B)$ takes on a left $\mathbf{R}$-object structure for any $B \in \mathscr{B}$. Furthermore, if $\alpha : A \to A'$ is morphism of $\mathbf{R}$-objects and $\beta : B \to B'$ is any morphism in $\mathscr{B}$, then for $r \in \mathbf{R}$ we have

$$\begin{aligned} T(\rho'(r), B')\,T(\alpha, \beta) &= T(\rho'(r)\alpha, \beta) \\ &= T(\alpha\rho(r), \beta) \\ &= T(\alpha, \beta)\,T(\rho(r), B). \end{aligned}$$

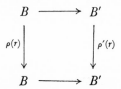

In other words $T(\alpha, \beta)$ is a morphism of **R**-objects and consequently T induces a covariant functor from ${}^{\mathbf{R}}\mathscr{A} \times \mathscr{B}$ to ${}^{\mathbf{R}}\mathscr{C}$. Likewise if A is a left **R**-object and B is a left **S**-object, then $T(A, B)$ is a left **R**, left **S**-biobject, and so T induces a bifunctor from ${}^{\mathbf{R}}\mathscr{A} \times {}^{\mathbf{S}}\mathscr{B}$ to ${}^{\mathbf{RS}}\mathscr{C}$. If T is contravariant in $\mathscr{A}$ and covariant in $\mathscr{B}$, then the induced bifunctor goes from ${}^{\mathbf{R}}\mathscr{A} \times {}^{\mathbf{S}}\mathscr{B}$ to ${}^{\mathbf{S}}\mathscr{C}^{\mathbf{R}}$. Again these are just a few examples of a general principle.

The category ${}^{\mathbf{R}}\mathscr{G}$ (resp. $\mathscr{G}^{\mathbf{R}}$) is called the **category of left** (resp. right) **R-modules**. Hence a left **R**-module is an ordered pair (G, ρ) where G is an abelian group and $\rho : \mathbf{R} \to [G, G]$ is a morphism of rings. If we write $\rho(r)(x) = rx$ for $r \in \mathbf{R}$ and $x \in G$, then we see that a left **R**-module satisfies the following rules:

(1) $1x = x$ for all $x \in G$.
(2) $r(x_1 + x_2) = rx_1 + rx_2$.
(3) $(r_1 + r_2)x = r_1x + r_2x$.
(4) $r_1(r_2x) = (r_1r_2)x$.

Conversely, given an abelian group G and an operation $\mathbf{R} \times G \to G$ satisfying the rules (1) to (4), then this defines a left **R**-module. For a right **R**-module the first three rules are the same, but the fourth rule must be replaced by $r_1(r_2x) = (r_2r_1)x$. For this reason we write xr instead of rx for right **R**-modules, in which case rule (4) becomes $(xr_2)r_1 = x(r_2r_1)$. Notice that a morphism of left **R**-modules is a morphism $\alpha : A \to B$ of abelian groups such that $\alpha(rx) = r\alpha(x)$ for all $r \in \mathbf{R}$ and $x \in A$. If **S** is another ring, then the objects of the category ${}^{\mathbf{SR}}\mathscr{G}$ are called **left S, left R-bimodules**. An abelian group A is a bimodule if it is at once an **R**-module and an **S**-module, and if the operations of **R** and **S** on A commute; that is, if $r(sx) = s(rx)$ for all $r \in \mathbf{R}$, $s \in \mathbf{S}$, and $x \in G$.

Since $\mathscr{G}$ is a complete and cocomplete abelian category, the same is true of the functor category ${}^{\mathbf{R}}\mathscr{G}$. Furthermore, from general properties of functor categories we know that a sequence in ${}^{\mathbf{R}}\mathscr{G}$ is exact, or that a family of morphisms is a limit for a diagram in ${}^{\mathbf{R}}\mathscr{G}$, if and only if the corresponding statement is true after we apply the evaluation functor (forgetful functor) from ${}^{\mathbf{R}}\mathscr{G}$ to $\mathscr{G}$.

14. Projectives, Injectives

An object P in a category $\mathscr{A}$ is **projective** if the functor $H^P : \mathscr{A} \to \mathscr{S}$ is an epifunctor. Equivalently, P is projective if and only if for every diagram

$$\begin{array}{ccc} & & P \\ & & \downarrow \\ A & \longrightarrow & A'' \end{array}$$

with $A \to A''$ an epimorphism there is a morphism $P \to A$ making the diagram commutative. If $\mathscr{A}$ is an exact additive category we know by 5.1 that the group valued functor H^P is kernel preserving for every object P. Hence in this case P is projective if and only if H^P is an exact functor.

Proposition 14.1. *If P is a retract of P' and P' is projective, then P is projective*

Proof. Let $P \to P' \to P = 1_P$. If $A \to A''$ is an epimorphism and $P \to A''$ is any morphism, then using projectivity of P' we have

$$P \to A'' = P \to P' \to P \to A'' = P \to P' \to A \to A''$$

for some morphism $P' \to A$. This establishes projectivity of P. ▌

We say that a category $\mathscr{A}$ **has projectives** if for each $A \in \mathscr{A}$ there is an epimorphism $P \to A$ with P projective.

Proposition. 14.2. *If P is projective in $\mathscr{A}$, then every epimorphism $A \to P$ is a retraction. Conversely if P has the property that every epimorphism $A \to P$ is a retraction, and if $\mathscr{A}$ either has projectives or is abelian, then P is projective.*

Proof. If P is projective, then given an epimorphism $A \to P$ there is a morphism $P \to A$ such that $P \to A \to P$ is 1_P. In other words $P \to A$ is a retraction.

Conversely, suppose that every epimorphism $A \to P$ is a retraction. If $\mathscr{A}$ has projectives then we may take A projective and then it follows from 14.1 that P is projective. On the other hand, if $\mathscr{A}$ is abelian, then, given an epimorphism $f: A \to A''$ and a morphism $u : P \to A''$, we can form the pullback diagram

$$\begin{array}{ccc} X & \xrightarrow{g} & P \\ {\scriptstyle v}\downarrow & & \downarrow{\scriptstyle u} \\ A & \xrightarrow{f} & A'' \end{array}$$

where we know by I, 20.2, that g is an epimorphism. Then by assumption we can find $h : P \to X$ such that $gh = 1_P$. Then we have

$$fvh = ugh = u.$$

This proves that P is projective. ▌

Proposition 14.3. *If $P = \bigoplus_i P_i$ and if each P_i is projective, then P is projective. Conversely, in a category with zero, if P is projective then each P_i is projective.*

Proof. Suppose that P_i is projective for each i and let $A \to A''$ be an epimorphism. A morphism $P \to A''$ is determined by a family of morphisms $P_i \to A''$ for each of which we can write $P_i \to A'' = P_i \to A \to A''$. Then the morphisms $P_i \to A$ give us a morphism $P \to A$ with the right property.

The converse follows from 14.1 since in a category with zero, injections into coproducts are coretractions. ▌

An object is called **injective** if it is projective in the dual category. Hence Q is injective if and only if for every diagram

$$\begin{array}{ccc} A' & \longrightarrow & A \\ \big\downarrow & & \\ Q & & \end{array}$$

with $A' \rightarrow A$ a monomorphism there is a morphism $A \rightarrow Q$ making the diagram commutative. If every object $A \in \mathscr{A}$ admits a monomorphism $A \rightarrow Q$ then we say that $\mathscr{A}$ **has injectives**. Retracts and products of injectives are injective, and if a product is injective in a category with zero, then each component is injective.

In an exact category $\mathscr{A}$ we say that an infinite sequence

$$\ldots P_{i+1} \rightarrow P_i \rightarrow P_{i-1} \rightarrow \ldots \rightarrow P_1 \rightarrow P_0 \rightarrow A \rightarrow 0 \tag{1}$$

is a **projective resolution** for A if it is exact and if P is projective for each $i \geqslant 0$.

Proposition 14.4. *The exact category $\mathscr{A}$ has projective resolutions for each of its objects if and only if it has projectives.*

Proof. If $A \in \mathscr{A}$ has a projective resolution (1), then in particular $P_0 \rightarrow A$ must be an epimorphism. Hence if $\mathscr{A}$ has projective resolutions, then $\mathscr{A}$ has projectives.

Conversely, suppose that $\mathscr{A}$ has projectives. Given A we can find an epimorphism $P_0 \rightarrow A$ with P_0 projective. Let $K_1 \rightarrow P_0$ be the kernel. Define inductively $P_i \rightarrow K_i$ as an epimorphism with P_i projective, and $K_{i+1} \rightarrow P_i$ as its kernel. Then letting $P_i \rightarrow P_{i-1}$ be the composition $P_i \rightarrow K_i \rightarrow P_{i-1}$ we get an exact sequence (1). ▮

The sequence (1) becomes an **injective resolution** for A^* in the dual category. An exact category has injective resolutions if and only if it has injectives.

15. Generators

A family of objects $\{U_i\}_{i \in I}$ is called a **family of generators** for a category $\mathscr{A}$ if for every pair of distinct morphisms $\alpha, \beta : A \rightarrow B$ there is a morphism $u : U_i \rightarrow A$ for some i such that $\alpha u \neq \beta u$. In an additive category the above is a family of generators if and only if for each nonzero morphism α in $\mathscr{A}$ there is a morphism $u : U_i \rightarrow A$ such that $\alpha u \neq 0$.

Proposition 15.1. *A balanced category with finite intersections and a family of generators is locally small.*

Proof. We show that a subobject of A is completely characterized by the morphisms $U_i \to A$ which factor through it. That is, if A_1 and A_2 are nonisomorphic subobjects of A then there is a morphism $U_i \to A$ for some i which factors through one of A_1 or A_2 but not the other. Our result will then follow from the fact that $[U_i, A]$ is a set for all i.

Suppose that A_1 and A_2 are nonisomorphic subobjects of A. Now $A_1 \cap A_2$ is a subobject of both of them. If $A_1 \cap A_2 \to A_2$ is an epimorphism, then since $\mathscr{A}$ is balanced, $A_1 \cap A_2$ and A_2 are isomorphic subobjects. Hence $A_1 \cap A_2 \to A_1$ cannot also be an epimorphism, and so there are distinct morphisms $\alpha, \beta : A_1 \to B$ such that

$$A_1 \cap A_2 \to A_1 \xrightarrow{\alpha} B = A_1 \cap A_2 \to A_1 \xrightarrow{\beta} B.$$

Let $u : U_i \to A_1$ be such that $\alpha u \neq \beta u$. Then u cannot be factored through $A_1 \cap A_2$, and so $U_i \xrightarrow{u} A_1 \to A$ cannot be factored through A_2. ∎

An object U in $\mathscr{A}$ is called a **generator** for $\mathscr{A}$ if $\{U\}$ is a family of generators for $\mathscr{A}$. Equivalently U is a generator for $\mathscr{A}$ if and only if the set valued functor H^U is an imbedding functor. If $U = \bigoplus_{i \in I} U_i$ and if $[U_i, A]$ is not empty for all $i \in I$ and $A \in \mathscr{A}$, then U is a generator for $\mathscr{A}$ if and only if $\{U_i\}_{i \in I}$ is a family of generators for $\mathscr{A}$. An object C is called a **cogenerator** for $\mathscr{A}$ if and only if it is a generator for $\mathscr{A}^*$.

Proposition 15.2. *If $\mathscr{A}$ has coproducts, then U is a generator for $\mathscr{A}$ if and only if for each $A \in \mathscr{A}$ there is an epimorphism $\gamma : {}^I U \to A$ for some set I. Furthermore, in this case we can take $I = [U, A]$ with γ the morphism whose uth coordinate is u for all $u \in [U, A]$.*

Proof. Suppose that U is a generator. Taking $I = [U, A]$ and γ as described above, it is immediate that γ is an epimorphism. Conversely, suppose that ${}^I U \to A$ is an epimorphism and let $\alpha, \beta : A \to B$ be distinct morphisms. Then for some injection into the coproduct we must have

$$U \to {}^I U \to A \xrightarrow{\alpha} B \neq U \to {}^I U \to A \xrightarrow{\beta} B.$$

This shows that U is a generator. ∎

We shall call an object **finitely generated** with respect to a family of generators $\{U_i\}_{i \in I}$ if it is a quotient object of a finite coproduct of the form $\bigoplus_{k=1}^{n} U_{i_k}$ where $i_k \in I$ for $1 \leqslant k \leqslant n$. We shall call an object **free** with respect to the above family if it is of the form $\bigoplus_{k \in K} U_{i_k}$ where $i_k \in I$ for all $k \in K$ (K not necessarily finite).

Of particular interest are generators which are also projective. If in category with projectives we can find a generator, then we can also find a projective generator. For if $P \to U$ is an epimorphism and U is a generator, then clearly

P is also a generator. On the other hand if $\mathscr{A}$ is a category with coproducts and a projective generator, then we see from 14.3 and 15.2 that $\mathscr{A}$ has projectives.

Proposition 15.3. *If $\mathscr{A}$ is an abelian category and U is a projective object such that $[U, A] \neq 0$ for all $A \in \mathscr{A}$ with $A \neq 0$, then U is a generator for $\mathscr{A}$.*

Proof. Since U is projective, H^U is an exact, group-valued functor. By hypothesis H^U preserves nonzero objects, hence by 7.2 H^U is an imbedding. Therefore U is a generator. ▮

Let **R** be any ring. Using ring multiplication, **R** can be considered as a left **R**-module over itself. (Actually **R** is a left **R**, right **R**-bimodule.) If A is a left **R**-module, then the left **R**-module morphisms from **R** to A are in one to one correspondence with the elements of A. Corresponding to $a \in A$ we have the morphism $\varphi_a : \mathbf{R} \to A$ defined by $\varphi_a(r) = ra$ for $r \in \mathbf{R}$ (exercise 11). Hence, given a diagram of **R**-module morphisms

$$\begin{array}{ccc} & & \mathbf{R} \\ & & \downarrow{\scriptstyle \varphi_b} \\ A & \xrightarrow{\alpha} & A'' \end{array}$$

where α is an epimorphism, let $a \in A$ be such that $\alpha(a) = b$. Then $\varphi_a : \mathbf{R} \to A$ is such that $\alpha\varphi_a = \varphi_b$. This shows that **R** is a projective object in ${}^{\mathbf{R}}\mathscr{G}$. Furthermore, if A is a nonzero **R**-module, say $0 \neq a \in A$, then $0 \neq \varphi_a \in {}^{\mathbf{R}}[\mathbf{R}, A]$. Therefore by 15.3, **R** is a projective generator for ${}^{\mathbf{R}}\mathscr{G}$. In particular ${}^{\mathbf{R}}\mathscr{G}$ has projective resolutions.

It is a more difficult job to show that ${}^{\mathbf{R}}\mathscr{G}$ has an injective cogenerator. We begin by showing that $\mathscr{G}$ has an injective cogenerator (that is, that the statement is true when $\mathbf{R} = \mathbf{Z}$). An abelian group D is called **divisible** if for any $d \in D$ and any nonzero integer n there is an element $x \in D$ such that $nx = d$.

Lemma 15.4. *A divisible abelian group is an injective object in $\mathscr{G}$.*

Proof. Let D be a divisible group and consider a diagram of abelian groups

$$\begin{array}{ccc} A' & \xrightarrow{u} & A \\ {\scriptstyle f}\downarrow & & \\ D & & \end{array}$$

where u is a monomorphism. We may assume that u is the inclusion of a subset of A. We wish to extend f to A. Consider the set of pairs (B, g) such that B is a subgroup of A, $A' \subset B$, and $g : B \to D$ extends f. Define $(B_1, g_1) \leqslant (B_2, g_2)$ if $B_1 \subset B_2$ and g_2 extends g_1. Then this set is clearly inductive, hence by Zorn's

Lemma it has a maximal element (B_0, g_0). Suppose $B_0 \neq A$, and let $a \in A - B_0$. Then the subgroup

$$B' = \{b + na | b \in B_0, n \in \mathbf{Z}\}$$

properly contains B_0. If $na \notin B_0$ for all nonzero integers n, then g_0 can be extended to $g' : B' \to D$ by defining $g'(b + na) = g_0(b)$. Otherwise let m be the least positive integer such that $ma \in B_0$, and let $d = g_0(ma)$. Define $g' : B' \to D$ by the rule $g'(b + na) = g_0(b) + nx$ where $x \in D$ is such that $mx = d$. Then again g' extends g_0. Hence in any case the maximality of (B_0, g_0) is contradicted, and so $B_0 = A$. This shows that D is injective. ▌

The converse of 15.4 is also true (exercise 17).

The additive group $\mathbf{Q}$ of rational numbers is clearly divisible, and since any quotient group of a divisible group is again divisible, it follows that $\mathbf{Q}/\mathbf{Z}$ is divisible, hence injective. Also for any nonzero group A we have $[A, \mathbf{Q}/\mathbf{Z}]_{\mathscr{G}} \neq 0$. To see this, let a be a nonzero element in A, and let $A' = \{na | n \in \mathbf{Z}\}$. We show that we can find a nonzero morphism $f: A' \to \mathbf{Q}/\mathbf{Z}$. This is trivial if a is not a torsion element (that is, if $na \neq 0$ for all $n \in \mathbf{Z}$). Otherwise we let m be the first positive integer such that $ma = 0$ and we define $f(na)$ as the class of n/m in $\mathbf{Q}/\mathbf{Z}$. Then we can extend f to A by injectivity of $\mathbf{Q}/\mathbf{Z}$. Hence by 15.3*, $\mathbf{Q}/\mathbf{Z}$ is an injective cogenerator for $\mathscr{G}$.

It is now easy to show that ${}^{\mathbf{R}}\mathscr{G}$ has an injective cogenerator for any ring $\mathbf{R}$. One establishes first the natural equivalence of group valued functors of the left $\mathbf{R}$-module A,

$$\varphi_A : {}^{\mathbf{R}}[A, [\mathbf{R}, G]_{\mathscr{G}}] \to [F(A), G]_{\mathscr{G}}. \tag{1}$$

Here G is any fixed abelian group, F is the forgetful functor from left $\mathbf{R}$-modules to groups, and $[\mathbf{R}, G]_{\mathscr{G}}$ is considered as a left $\mathbf{R}$-module by means of the operation of $\mathbf{R}$ on the right of itself. Explicitly we define $\varphi_A(\alpha)(a) = \alpha(a)(1)$ where $\alpha : A \to [\mathbf{R}, G]_{\mathscr{G}}$ is a left $\mathbf{R}$-module morphism and $a \in A$. The inverse ψ of φ is given by $\psi_A(\beta)(a)(r) = \beta(ra)$ where $\beta : F(A) \to G$, $a \in A$, and $r \in \mathbf{R}$. In particular, if we take $G = \mathbf{Q}/\mathbf{Z}$, then the right-hand side of (1) is an exact functor of A which takes nonzero objects into nonzero objects. Therefore the same is true of the left-hand side. This shows that $[\mathbf{R}, \mathbf{Q}/\mathbf{Z}]_{\mathscr{G}}$ is an injective cogenerator for ${}^{\mathbf{R}}\mathscr{G}$. Similarly, if we regard $[\mathbf{R}, \mathbf{Q}/\mathbf{Z}]_{\mathscr{G}}$ as a right $\mathbf{R}$-module by means of left operations of $\mathbf{R}$ on itself, we obtain an injective cogenerator for $\mathscr{G}^{\mathbf{R}}$. In the following chapter we shall extend this result to certain classes of cocomplete abelian categories which have a generator. A proof that ${}^{\mathbf{R}}\mathscr{G}$ has injectives was first given by Baer [1].

16. Small Objects

We shall call an object $A \in \mathscr{A}$ a **small** object if whenever we have a morphism $A \to \bigoplus_{i \in I} A_i$ from A into a coproduct, there is a factorization

$$A \longrightarrow \bigoplus_{i \in J} A_i \xrightarrow{u_{JI}} \bigoplus_{i \in I} A_i$$

for some finite set $J \subset I$. In the category $\mathscr{G}^{\mathbf{R}}$ the right $\mathbf{R}$-module $\mathbf{R}$ is easily seen to be small.

Lemma 16.1. *In an additive category a morphism* $\alpha : A \to \bigoplus_{i \in I} A_i$ *factors through a finite coproduct of the form* $\bigoplus_{i \in J} A_i \xrightarrow{u_{JI}} \bigoplus_{i \in I} A_i$ *if and only if* $\alpha = \sum_{i \in J} u_i p_i \alpha$, *where* u_i *and* p_i *are the ith injection and projection, respectively, for the coproduct* $\bigoplus_{i \in I} A_i$.

Proof. Denote by $\bar{u}_i$ and $\bar{p}_i$, respectively, the ith injection and projection for the finite coproduct $\bigoplus_{i \in J} A_i$. Then the morphism u_{JI} is $\sum_{i \in I} u_i \bar{p}_i$. Now if α factors through the finite coproduct we have

$$\alpha = \sum_{i \in J} u_i \bar{p}_i \bar{\alpha}. \tag{1}$$

Composing both sides of (1) with p_k for any $k \in J$ we see $p_k \alpha = \bar{p}_k \bar{\alpha}$. Hence (1) can be rewritten $\alpha = \sum_{i \in J} u_i p_i \alpha$. Conversely if this last equation holds, then we can define $\bar{\alpha} = \sum_{i \in J} \bar{u}_i p_i \alpha$ and we have

$$u_{JI} \bar{\alpha} = \sum_{k \in J} u_k \bar{p}_k \sum_{i \in J} \bar{u}_i p_i \alpha = \sum_{i \in J} u_i p_i \alpha = \alpha. \quad \blacksquare$$

Proposition 16.2. *Let* $\mathscr{A}$ *be an additive category with coproducts. Then an object* $A \in \mathscr{A}$ *is small if and only if the group valued functor* H^A *is coproduct preserving.*

Proof. Consider a coproduct $\bigoplus_{i \in I} A_i$ in $\mathscr{A}$ with injections u_i and projections p_i. The family of morphisms $\{H^A(u_i)\}_{i \in I}$ gives rise to a morphism of groups

$$\bigoplus_{i \in I} H^A(A_i) \to H^A(\bigoplus_{i \in I} A_i). \tag{2}$$

To say that H^A is coproduct preserving is equivalent to saying that (2) is an isomorphism for every coproduct in $\mathscr{A}$. Now a member of the left side of (2) can be considered as a family $\alpha_i : A \to A_i$ such that $\alpha_i = 0$ for all but a finite number of $i \in I$. Under (2) the element α is carried into $\sum_{i \in I} u_i \alpha_i$. If $\alpha \neq 0$, then $\alpha_k \neq 0$ for some k, and so we have

$$p_k \sum_{i \in I} u_i \alpha_i = \alpha_k \neq 0.$$

Therefore $\sum_{i \in I} u_i \alpha_i \neq 0$, and so this shows that under any circumstances (2) is a monomorphism. Now suppose that (2) is an epimorphism, and consider a morphism $\alpha : A \to \bigoplus_{i \in I} A_i$. Then we can write $\alpha = \sum_{i \in I} u_i \alpha_i$ for some family α_i, and composing both sides with p_k we have $p_k \alpha = \alpha_k$ for all $k \in I$. Hence $\alpha = \sum_{i \in I} u_i p_i \alpha$ and so by 16.1, α factors through a finite coproduct. Hence A is small. Conversely, suppose that A is small and consider a morphism α in the right side of (2). Then writing $\alpha_i = p_i \alpha$, we have $\alpha = \sum_{i \in I} u_i \alpha_i$ by 16.1. This shows that (2) is an epimorphism, hence an isomorphism. $\blacksquare$

Exercises

1. Examine the preservation properties of the various forgetful functors that exist among the categories $\mathscr{S}, \mathscr{T}, \mathscr{S}_0, \mathscr{T}_0$, and show that they are all representative.

2. The forgetful (evaluation) functor from ${}^{\mathbf{R}}\mathscr{G}$ to $\mathscr{G}$ is representative if and only if there exists a morphism of rings $\varphi : \mathbf{R} \to \mathbf{Z}$.

3. If $T : \mathscr{B} \to \mathscr{C}$ is an equivalence, then for any small category $\mathscr{A}$ the functor $T_0 : [\mathscr{A}, \mathscr{B}] \to [\mathscr{A} \to \mathscr{C}]$ is also an equivalence. Likewise if $T : \mathscr{A} \to \mathscr{A}'$ is an equivalence of small categories, then for any category $\mathscr{B}$ the functor $T^0 : [\mathscr{A}', \mathscr{B}] \to [\mathscr{A}, \mathscr{B}]$ is an equivalence.

4. If $\mathscr{A}$ and $\mathscr{B}$ are small categories and $\mathscr{C}$ is arbitrary, then we have isomorphisms of categories

$$[\mathscr{A}, [\mathscr{B}, \mathscr{C}]] \approx [\mathscr{A} \times \mathscr{B}, \mathscr{C}] \approx [\mathscr{B}, [\mathscr{A}, \mathscr{C}]].$$

If $\mathscr{A}$, $\mathscr{B}$, and $\mathscr{C}$ are additive, then $(\mathscr{A}, (\mathscr{B}, \mathscr{C}))$ and $(\mathscr{B}, (\mathscr{A}, \mathscr{C}))$ are isomorphic to the category of covariant additive bifunctors from $\mathscr{A} \times \mathscr{B}$ to $\mathscr{C}$.

5. Let $\mathscr{A}'$ be a full subcategory of $\mathscr{A}$ and suppose that $0 \in \mathscr{A}'$ where 0 is a zero object for $\mathscr{A}$. Let $\alpha : A \to B$ be a morphism in $\mathscr{A}'$ and let $u : K \to A$ be the kernel of α in $\mathscr{A}$. If $K \in \mathscr{A}'$ then u is also the kernel of α in $\mathscr{A}'$. Hence, if $\mathscr{A}$ is an exact category and if $\mathscr{A}'$ contains representatives for kernels and cokernels in $\mathscr{A}$ of all its morphisms, then $\mathscr{A}'$ is an exact subcategory of $\mathscr{A}$. If, further, $\mathscr{A}$ is an abelian category and $\mathscr{A}'$ contains representatives for all finite products in $\mathscr{A}$ of its objects, then $\mathscr{A}'$ is an abelian subcategory of $\mathscr{A}$.

6. Consider $T : \mathscr{A} \to \mathscr{G}$, and for each $A \in \mathscr{A}$ let S_A be a subset (possibly empty) of $T(A)$. **The subfunctor of *T* generated by *S*** is defined as the smallest subfunctor M of T such that $S_A \subset M(A)$ for all $A \in \mathscr{A}$ (that is, the intersection of all such subfunctors). Show that $M(A)$ is the subgroup of $T(A)$ consisting of all finite sums of the form $\sum_i T(\alpha_i)(x_i)$ where $\alpha_i : A_i \to A$ and $x_i \in S_{A_i}$.

If T is an additive functor, then the subfunctor of T generated by a single element $x_0 \in T(A_0)$ is given by

$$M(A) = \{T(\alpha)(x_0) \,|\, \alpha : A_0 \to A\}.$$

If S is a subset of a left $\mathbf{R}$-module A, then (S) is defined as the smallest submodule of A containing each member of S. Show that (S) is the set of all finite sums of the form $\sum_i r_i s_i$ where $r_i \in \mathbf{R}$, $s_i \in S$. Interpret this as a special case of the above.

Show that $1_A \in H^A(A)$ generates all of H^A.

7. Let $T : \mathscr{A} \times \mathscr{B} \to \mathscr{C}$ be a limit preserving bifunctor, covariant in both variables. Let D be a diagram in $\mathscr{A}$ over a scheme Σ with limit $\{\alpha_i : L \to D_i\}_{i \in I}$

and let E be a diagram in $\mathscr{B}$ over a scheme Λ with limit $\{\beta_j : M \to E_j\}_{j\in J}$. Show that

$$\{T(\alpha_i,\beta_j) : T(L, M) \to T(D_i,E_j)\}_{(i,j)\in I\times J}$$

is the limit of the diagram $T(D, E)$ over $\Sigma \times \Lambda$. In particular, if $\bigtimes_{i\in I} A_i$ is a product in $\mathscr{A}$ with projections p_i and $\bigtimes_{j\in J} B_j$ is a product in $\mathscr{B}$ with projections q_j, then $T(\bigtimes_{i\in I} A_i, \bigtimes_{j\in J} B_j)$ is a product in $\mathscr{C}$ with projections $T(p_i, q_j)$.

Generalize this result to n-variable functors of arbitrary variance.

8. If $\mathscr{A}$ is an additive category with products and $\mathscr{B}$ is any category with zero, then $T : \mathscr{A} \to \mathscr{B}$ is limit preserving if and only if it preserves kernels and products. (Cf. 6.3. Normality for $\mathscr{A}$ was assumed in 6.3 to assure that $\Delta : P \to P^M$ is the kernel of some morphism. However, if $\mathscr{A}$ is additive, then one can construct a morphism $P^M \to P^M$ whose kernel is Δ.)

9. If T is an additive functor between exact additive categories such that T reflects either limits or exact sequences, then T is faithful.

10. Let $T : \mathscr{A} \times \mathscr{B} \to \mathscr{C}$ be an additive covariant bifunctor where $\mathscr{A}$, $\mathscr{B}$, and $\mathscr{C}$ are abelian categories. Then T is kernel preserving as a bifunctor if and only if for every pair of exact sequences

$$0 \longrightarrow A' \xrightarrow{\alpha_1} A \xrightarrow{\alpha_2} A''$$

$$0 \longrightarrow B' \xrightarrow{\beta_1} B \xrightarrow{\beta_2} B'',$$

the sequence

$$0 \to T(A', B') \to T(A, B) \to T(A'', B) \times T(A, B'')$$

is exact, where the first morphism is $T(\alpha_1, \beta_1)$ and the second morphism has coordinates $T(\alpha_2, B)$ and $T(A, \beta_2)$.

11. Poincaré duality for discrete and compact abelian groups says that the dual of $\mathscr{G}$ is equivalent to the category of compact (Hausdorff) abelian groups with continuous group morphisms as morphisms. Show that the dual of ${}^{\mathbf{R}}\mathscr{G}$ is equivalent to the category of compact abelian groups on which $\mathbf{R}$ acts continuously on the right, with continuous right $\mathbf{R}$-module morphisms as morphisms.

12. Let $\mathbf{R}$ be any ring. Then the ring of endomorphisms of the right (left) $\mathbf{R}$-module $\mathbf{R}$ is ring isomorphic to $\mathbf{R}$ ($\mathbf{R}^*$).

If A is any left $\mathbf{R}$-module, then considering $\mathbf{R}$ as a left $\mathbf{R}$, right $\mathbf{R}$-bimodule, the group ${}^{\mathbf{R}}[\mathbf{R}, A]$ has a left $\mathbf{R}$-module structure. Show that $\varphi_A : A \to {}^{\mathbf{R}}[\mathbf{R}, A]$ defined by $\varphi_A(a)(r) = ra$ gives us a natural equivalence of functors of the left $\mathbf{R}$-module A.

13. Let $\mathscr{A}$ be an additive category and let A be a fixed object in $\mathscr{A}$. Suppose that for each $B \in \mathscr{A}$ the group $[A, B]$ has a left $\mathbf{R}$-object structure, and that for each morphism $B \to B'$ in $\mathscr{A}$ the induced morphism $[A, B] \to [A, B']$ is a morphism of **R**-modules. Show that there is a unique right **R**-object structure on A which induces the given left **R**-object structure on $[A, B]$ for all $B \in \mathscr{A}$.

14. If $\mathscr{A}$ is any small category, find a diagram scheme Σ and a commutativity relation $\sim$ for Σ such that $\mathscr{A}$ is isomorphic to $\Sigma/\sim$.

15. Let $\mathscr{A}$ be any category and let Add$(\mathscr{A})$ be as in I, exercise 11. If $\mathscr{B}$ is any additive category establish an isomorphism of categories

$$[\mathscr{A}, \mathscr{B}] \approx (\mathrm{Add}(\mathscr{A}), \mathscr{B}).$$

16. Generalize the notion of commutativity for diagrams in an additive category as follows. Let Σ be a diagram scheme, and let S be a set of formal linear combinations of the form $\sum_{i \in I} n_i c_i$ where I is finite, the n_i's are integers, and the c_i's are composite arrows in Σ_0 with the same origin and the same extremity for all $i \in I$. Let $\mathscr{B}$ be an additive category and let $(\Sigma/S, \mathscr{B})$ be the full subcategory of $[\Sigma, \mathscr{B}]$ consisting of all diagrams D satisfying $\sum_{i \in I} n_i D(c_i) = 0$ for $\sum_{i \in I} n_i c_i \in S$, where $D(1_i)$ is understood to be 1_{D_i}. Define an additive category Σ/S so that the above diagram category $(\Sigma/S, \mathscr{B}))$ is actually the category of additive functors from Σ/S to $\mathscr{B}$ (use exercise 15).

What are the objects and morphisms in Σ/S corresponding to the category of anticommutative diagrams in $\mathscr{B}$; that is, diagrams of the form

$$\begin{array}{ccc} A & \xrightarrow{\alpha} & B \\ {\scriptstyle\gamma}\downarrow & & \downarrow{\scriptstyle\beta} \\ C & \xrightarrow{\delta} & D \end{array}$$

such that $\beta\alpha + \delta\gamma = 0$?

If $\mathscr{A}$ is any small additive category, interpret $(\mathscr{A}, \mathscr{B})$ as a category of diagrams satisfying a generalized commutativity relation.

17. If **R** is a left Noetherian ring, then the full subcategory of ${}^{\mathbf{R}}\mathscr{G}$ consisting of all finitely generated **R**-modules is an abelian subcategory of ${}^{\mathbf{R}}\mathscr{G}$. In particular this is true if $\mathbf{R} = \mathbf{Z}$. Hence if we let $\overline{\mathscr{G}}$ be a full subcategory of $\mathscr{G}$ consisting of one group from every class of isomorphic finitely generated groups, then $\overline{\mathscr{G}}$ is a small abelian subcategory of $\mathscr{G}$. Furthermore, $\overline{\mathscr{G}}$ has projective resolutions (but not injective resolutions).

18. Let **R** be an integral domain. An **R**-module A is called **divisible** if for every nonzero element $r \in \mathbf{R}$ and every $a \in A$ there is an element $x \in A$ such that $rx = a$. Then an injective **R**-module is divisible. Hence an abelian group is injective if and only if it is divisible, and consequently a quotient of an injective group is injective.

19. If U is a small generator in an exact category and if A is finitely generated, then A is small. In particular, any finitely generated **R**-module is small.

If P is a small projective in a category with a generator, then P is finitely generated. Hence a projective **R**-module is small if and only if it is finitely generated.

20. In the category of sets, $\mathcal{S}$, every set is projective and every nonempty set is injective. Any one element set is a generator and any two-element set is a cogenerator. A set is small if and only if it has only a finite number of elements.

In the category of topological spaces $\mathcal{T}$ a space is projective if and only if it has the discrete topology and is injective if and only if it is nonempty and has the indiscrete topology. Any one-point space is a generator and any two-point space with the indiscrete topology is a cogenerator. A space is small if and only if it is finite.

Examine also the categories with base point $\mathcal{S}_0$ and $\mathcal{T}_0$.

21. Let **R** be a commutative ring, and let $\mathcal{A}_{\mathbf{R}}$ be the category of algebras over **R** (so that in particular $\mathcal{A}_{\mathbf{Z}}$ is the category of rings). The polynomial algebra in one variable $\mathbf{R}[X]$ is a generator for $\mathcal{A}_{\mathbf{R}}$. A morphism in $\mathcal{A}_{\mathbf{R}}$ is a monomorphism if and only if it is univalent as a function. $\mathcal{A}_{\mathbf{R}}$ has products and coproducts. (For the coproduct of a family of algebras A_i, consider an appropriate quotient algebra of the polynomial algebra over **R** with variables the disjoint union of sets $\bigcup_i A_i$ where the variables do not commute). Also $\mathcal{A}_{\mathbf{R}}$ has pullbacks and pushouts, and hence is complete and cocomplete. The trivial algebra consisting of one element is a null object for $\mathcal{A}_{\mathbf{R}}$, whereas **R** considered as an algebra over itself is a conull object. Hence $\mathcal{A}_{\mathbf{R}}$ does not have a zero object. Furthermore, a morphism in $\mathcal{A}_{\mathbf{R}}$ may be an epimorphism without being onto as a function. (Let $\mathbf{R} = \mathbf{Z}$, and consider the inclusion $\mathbf{Z} \subset \mathbf{Q}$ where **Q** is the rationals.)

CHAPTER III

Complete Categories

Introduction

We now study categories satisfying the Grothendieck axiom A. B. 5 [20] (herein called a C_3 category). In §1 we establish a few equivalent formulations of this axiom. A number of the results here were first stated in [20]. In §2 we generalize the Eckmann-Schopf theory of injective envelopes [8] to abelian categories satisfying the axiom C_3. Section 3 is devoted to showing the existence of injective resolutions for C_3 categories having a generator. This was first proved in [20] using a transfinite induction method. The proof given here utilizes the fact that the result is already known for **R**-modules (II, §15).

1. C_i Categories

A category $\mathscr{A}$ with coproducts is called a **C_1 category** if for every family of monomorphisms $\{u_i : A_i \to B_i\}$ the morphism $\bigoplus_i u_i : \bigoplus_i A_i \to \bigoplus_i B_i$ is a monomorphism. $\mathscr{A}$ is called a **C_2 category** if it has products, coproducts, and a zero, and if the morphism $\delta : \bigoplus A_i \to \mathsf{X}\, A_i$ is a monomorphism for any family of objects $\{A_i\}$ in $\mathscr{A}$.

Proposition 1.1. *A C_2 category is C_1.*

Proof. Relative to a family of monomorphisms $\{u_i : A_i \to B_i\}$ we have a commutative diagram

$$\begin{array}{ccc} \bigoplus A_i & \longrightarrow & \bigoplus B_i \\ {\scriptstyle\delta}\downarrow & & \downarrow \\ \mathsf{X}\, A_i & \longrightarrow & \mathsf{X}\, B_i \end{array}$$

where the top morphism is $\bigoplus u_i$ and the bottom morphism is $\mathsf{X}\, u_i$. Now δ is a monomorphism by assumption, and $\mathsf{X}\, u_i$ is a monomorphism by II, 12.3. Hence it follows that $\bigoplus u_i$ is a monomorphism. ▌

Observe that a C_2 category has the following property: If $\bigoplus_{i \in I} A_i$ is a coproduct with projections p_i and if $f, g : A \to \bigoplus_{i \in I} A_i$ are such that $p_i f = p_i g$ for all $i \in I$, then $f = g$.

The familiar distributivity relation for sets

$$(\bigcup A_i) \cap B = \bigcup (A_i \cap B) \tag{1}$$

does not hold in general in the category $\mathcal{G}$. However, if we assume that $\{A_i\}$ is a direct family of subgroups of an abelian group A and B is another subgroup of A, then it can be seen that (1) holds (exercise 1). We shall call a category $\mathscr{A}$ a **C_3 category** if $\mathscr{A}$ is a cocomplete abelian category such that (1) holds for any direct family $\{A_i\}$ and any subobject B.

Proposition 1.2. *Let $\mathscr{A}$ be a cocomplete abelian category. Then $\mathscr{A}$ is C_3 if and only if the direct limit of every direct family of subobjects $\{A_i\}$ of an object A is $\bigcup A_i$.*

Proof. Suppose that $\mathscr{A}$ is C_3 and let $\{A_i\}$ be a direct family of subobjects of A. Let $\{\pi_i : A_i \to L\}$ be the direct limit. Then we have the induced morphism $u : L \to A$ whose image is $\bigcup A_i$ by II, 2.8. We wish to show that u is a monomorphism. Let K be the kernel of u, and let A'_i be the image of π_i. Then again by II, 2.8, we know $L = \bigcup A'_i$, and by C_3 we have $K = \bigcup (A'_i \cap K)$. If $K \neq 0$, then $A'_i \cap K \neq 0$ for some i, and so by I, 16.4, we have $\pi_i^{-1}(K) \neq 0$. It follows that $A_i \to A$ has a nonzero kernel, contradicting the fact that A_i is a subobject of A. Therefore $K = 0$ and so u is a monomorphism.

Conversely, suppose that direct limits of direct families of subobjects are subobjects. Let $\{A_i\}$ be a family of subobjects of A and let B be another subobject. By assumption the direct limit of the family $\{A_i \cup B\}$ is

$$\bigcup (A_i \cup B) = (\bigcup A_i) \cup B.$$

By II, 12.2*, the family of exact sequences

$$B \to A_i \cup B \to (A_i \cup B)/B \to 0$$

gives rise to an exact direct limit sequence

$$B \to (\bigcup A_i) \cup B \to \varinjlim (A_i \cup B)/B \to 0$$

which shows that the direct limit of the family $\{A_i \cup B/B\}$ is $(\bigcup A_i) \cup B/B$. Then the family of exact sequences

$$0 \to A_i \cap B \to A_i \to A_i \cup B/B \to 0$$

(see I, 16.7) gives an exact direct limit sequence

$$0 \to \bigcup (A_i \cap B) \to \bigcup A_i \to (\bigcup A_i) \cup B/B \to 0. \tag{2}$$

But by I, 13.2, (2) is just another way of expressing (1). ∎

Corollary 1.3. *A complete C_3 category $\mathscr{A}$ is C_2.*

Proof. Given a family of objects $\{A_i\}_{i \in I}$, the objects of the form $\bigoplus_{i \in F} A_i$ for F a finite subset of I, form a direct family of subobjects of the product $\bigtimes_{i \in I} A_i$. The direct limit is $\bigoplus_{i \in I} A_i$, and by 1.2 the limit morphism $\delta : \bigoplus_{i \in I} A_i \to \bigtimes_{i \in I} A_i$ is a monomorphism. Therefore $\mathscr{A}$ is C_2. ▮

Corollary 1.4. *Let A be an object in a C_3 category $\mathscr{A}$ with a family of generators. Then the finitely generated subobjects of A form a direct family of subobjects whose direct limit is A.*

Proof. By II, 15.1, $\mathscr{A}$ is locally small, and so the class of all finitely generated subobjects of A form a set (or better, have a representative subclass which is a set). Furthermore, from I, 17.2, we see that the union of two finitely generated subobjects is also finitely generated, so that we have a direct system. By 1.2 the direct limit L is a subobject of A. If L is not equal to A, then there is a morphism from one of the generators to A which does not factor through L. But the image of such a morphism is finitely generated, hence is contained in L. This contradiction proves that $L = A$. ▮

Lemma 1.5. *Let $\{A_i\}_{i \in I}$ be a direct family of subobjects of A in a cocomplete abelian category. Then the direct limit of the corresponding family of quotient objects $\{A/A_i\}$ is $A/\bigcup A_i$.*

Proof. The family of exact sequences

$$0 \to A_i \to A \to A/A_i \to 0$$

gives us an exact limit sequence

$$\varinjlim A_i \xrightarrow{u} A \to \varinjlim A/A_i \to 0$$

by II, 12.2*. But by II, 2.8, the image of u is $\bigcup A_i$. In other words $\varinjlim A/A_i = A/\bigcup A_i$. ▮

Proposition 1.6. *Let $\mathscr{A}$ be a cocomplete abelian category. Then $\mathscr{A}$ is C_3 if and only if for every direct family of subobjects $\{A_i\}$ of an object A and every morphism $f: B \to A$ we have*

$$f^{-1}(\bigcup A_i) = \bigcup f^{-1}(A_i). \tag{3}$$

Proof. If $\mathscr{A}$ satisfies condition (3), then taking for f the inclusion of a subobject $B \subset A$ we obtain Eq. (1). Conversely, suppose that $\mathscr{A}$ is C_3 and let I be the image of f. Then by I, 16.4, we have the exact sequence

$$0 \to f^{-1}(A_i) \to B \to I/A_i \cap I \to 0.$$

Passing to direct limits and using 1.2 and 1.5 we obtain an exact sequence

$$0 \to \bigcup f^{-1}(A_i) \to B \to I/\bigcup (A_i \cap I) \to 0. \tag{4}$$

But by C_3 we have $\bigcup (A_i \cap I) = (\bigcup A_i) \cap I$, so that by I, 16.4, we see that (4) is simply another way of expressing (3). ▮

Proposition 1.7. *Let $\{A_i, \pi\}$ be a direct system in a C_3 category. Denote by K_{kp} the kernel of π_{kp} for $k \leqslant p$, and let K_k be the kernel of π_k. Then*

$$K_k = \bigcup_{k \leqslant p} K_{kp}.$$

Proof. First it is clear that $\bigcup_{k \leqslant p} K_{kp} \subset K_k$, so that we need only prove the reverse inclusion. Let R be the subset of $I \times I$ consisting of all ordered pairs (i, j) such that $i \leqslant j$. Let $A = \bigoplus_{i \in I} A_i$ with injections u_i. If S is any subset of R, let

$$\bigcup_{(i,j) \in S} \operatorname{Im}(u_i - u_j \pi_{ij}) = A_S \subset A.$$

Then by II, 2.10, we have $\varinjlim_{i \in I} A_i = A/A_R$. Now $A_R = \bigcup_F A_F$ where F runs through all finite subsets of R. Hence by 1.6 we have

$$K_k = u_k^{-1}(A_R) = \bigcup_F u_k^{-1}(A_F),$$

and so it suffices to show that for each finite subset F of R we have $u_k^{-1}(A_F) \subset K_k$ for some $p \geqslant k$. Given F, let p be any index which follows k and all indices which appear either in the first position or the second position in a member of F. Now $u_k^{-1}(A_F)$ is the kernel of the composition

$$A_k \xrightarrow{u_k} A \longrightarrow A/A_F.$$

Define a morphism $f: A \to A_p$ by taking $fu_i = \pi_{ip}$ for $i \leqslant p$, and $fu_i = 0$ otherwise. Then for $(i, j) \in F$ we have

$$f(u_i - u_j \pi_{ij}) = \pi_{ip} - \pi_{jp} \pi_{ij} = \pi_{ip} - \pi_{ip} = 0.$$

Consequently, f factors through $A \to A/A_F$, and so using I, 10.3, we have

$$0 = f(u_k(u_k^{-1}(A_F))) = \pi_{kp}(u_k^{-1}(A_F)).$$

This shows that $u_k^{-1}(A_F) \subset K_{kp}$ as required. ▮

Corollary 1.8. *Consider a direct system $\{A_i, \pi\}_{i \in I}$ in a C_3 category, and let $f: B \to A_k$ for some $k \in I$. Then*

$$\operatorname{Ker}(\pi_k f) = \bigcup_{p \geqslant k} \operatorname{Ker}(\pi_{kp} f).$$

Proof. We form a new directed set I_0 by adding one new vertex i_0 to I and defining $i_0 < i$ if and only if $k \leqslant i$. A direct system over I_0 is obtained by taking the original direct system, adding B at the vertex i_0, and using the morphisms $\pi_{kp}f$ for $p \geqslant k$. Now I is a cofinal subset of I_0. Consequently the conclusion follows from 1.5 and II, 2.11. ▌

Theorem 1.9. *A cocomplete abelian category $\mathscr{A}$ is C_3 if and only if, relative to every directed set I, the functor which assigns to each direct system over I its direct limit is an exact functor.*

Proof. Direct limit functors are cokernel preserving by II, 12.2*. Hence it suffices to show that $\mathscr{A}$ is C_3 if and only if the morphism induced on the direct limits by a family of monomorphisms is again a monomorphism. Suppose that $\mathscr{A}$ has the latter property, and let $\{A_i\}$ be a direct family of subobjects of A. Then the limit morphism of the family $A_i \to A$, which can be regarded as a morphism from the direct system $\{A_i\}$ to the constant direct system which has A at every vertex, is a monomorphism. Therefore, by 1.2, $\mathscr{A}$ is C_3.

Conversely, suppose that $\mathscr{A}$ is C_3 and let $\{u_i : A_i \to B_i\}_{i\in I}$ be a family of monomorphisms defining a morphism from the direct system $(A_i, \pi\}_{i\in I}$ to the direct system $\{B_i, \mu\}_{i\in I}$. Consider the commutative diagram

$$\begin{array}{ccccccc} & & & & A_i & \xrightarrow{u_i} & B_i \\ & & & & \downarrow{\scriptstyle \pi_i} & & \downarrow{\scriptstyle \mu_i} \\ 0 & \longrightarrow & K & \longrightarrow & A & \xrightarrow{u} & B \end{array}$$

where K is the kernel of u. Let $A'_i = \operatorname{Im}(\pi_i)$, so that by II, 2.8, we have $A = \bigcup_{i\in I} A'_i$. By C_3 we can then write $K = \bigcup_{i\in I} (A'_i \cap K)$, and so if $K \neq 0$, then $A'_k \cap K \neq 0$ for some $k \in I$. Denoting $M = \pi_k^{-1}(A'_k \cap K)$ we see from I, 16.4, that $\pi_k(M) \neq 0$. On the other hand using I, 10.3, we have

$$\begin{aligned} \mu_k(u_k(M)) &= u(\pi_k(M) = u(\pi_k(\pi_k^{-1}(A'_k \cap K))) \\ &\subset u(A'_k \cap K) \subset u(K) = 0. \end{aligned}$$

Therefore by 1.7, $u_k(M)$ is a subobject of $\bigcup_{k\leqslant p} L_{kp}$ where $L_{kp} = \operatorname{Ker}(\mu_{kp})$. Again using C_3 we then have

$$u_k(M) = \bigcup_{k\leqslant p} L_{kp} \cap u_k(M).$$

Hence

$$M = u_k^{-1}(u_k(M)) = u_k^{-1}\left(\bigcup_{k\leqslant p} L_{kp} \cap u_k(M)\right) = \bigcup_{k\leqslant p} u_k^{-1}(L_{kp} \cap u_k(M)), \qquad (5)$$

the first equality being true because u_k is a monomorphism, and the third equality being true by 1.6. It follows from the fact that u_p is a monomorphism that $\pi_{kp}(u_k^{-1}(L_{kp} \cap u_k(M))) = 0$ for $p \geqslant k$, and so $\pi_k(u_k^{-1}(L_{kp} \cap u_k(M))) = 0$ for all $p \geqslant k$. But then using (5) and I, 11.2, we see $\pi_k(M) = 0$. This contradiction proves that $K = 0$, and so u is a monomorphism. ▮

We shall say that $\mathscr{A}$ is a $\mathbf{C}_i^*$ **category** ($i = 1, 2$, or 3) if $\mathscr{A}^*$ is a C_i category. It follows from pointwise considerations that a functor category $[\mathscr{A}, \mathscr{B}]$ or $(\mathscr{A}, \mathscr{B})$ has any of the properties C_i or C_i^* that $\mathscr{B}$ has. In particular, since $\mathscr{G}$ has properties C_3 and C_1^*, the same is true for ${}^{\mathbf{R}}\mathscr{G}$ for any ring $\mathbf{R}$.

Proposition 1.10. *A complete C_3 category $\mathscr{A}$, which is also C_2^*, consists only of zero objects.*

Proof. By 1.3, $\mathscr{A}$ is C_2, and so since it is also C_2^* we have $\bigoplus_{i\in I} A_i = \mathsf{X}_{i\in I} A_i$ for every set $\{A_i\}_{i\in I}$ of objects in $\mathscr{A}$. In particular, given $A \in \mathscr{A}$, let I be the set of positive integers and take $A_i = A$ for all $i \in I$. Let $A^n = \bigoplus_{i=1}^{n} A_i$ for n a positive integer and let $A^\infty = \bigoplus_{i=1}^{\infty} A_i$. Then we have the diagonal morphism $\Delta : A \longrightarrow A^\infty$ which is such that $p_i\Delta = 1_A$ for all projections p_i from the coproduct. Also it is clear that $A^\infty = \bigcup_{n=1}^{\infty} A^n$ and so from 1.6 we have $A = \bigcup_{n=1}^{\infty} \Delta^{-1}(A^n)$. We show that $\Delta^{-1}(A^n) = 0$ for all n. Let $\bar{\Delta}$ be the composition $A \xrightarrow{\Delta} A^\infty \rightarrow A^\infty/A^n$. Then the exact sequence

$$0 \rightarrow \Delta^{-1}(A^n) \rightarrow A \xrightarrow{\bar{\Delta}} A^\infty/A^n$$

defines $\Delta^{-1}(A^n)$. Also $p_{n+1}|A^n = 0$, so that we have a morphism $\bar{p}_{n+1} : A/A^n \rightarrow A_{n+1}$ which when composed with $A^\infty \rightarrow A^\infty/A^n$ gives us p_{n+1}. Then the composition

$$A \xrightarrow{\bar{\Delta}} A^\infty/A^n \xrightarrow{\bar{p}_{n+1}} A_{n+1}$$

is 1_A, and so $\bar{\Delta}$ must be a monomorphism. Therefore

$$\Delta^{-1}(A^n) = \operatorname{Ker}(\bar{\Delta}) = 0. \qquad ▮$$

2. Injective Envelopes

Throughout this section all categories will be abelian.

We define an **essential extension** of an object A' to be a monomorphism $u : A' \rightarrow A$ such that for any nonzero subobject A_1 of A we have $A' \cap A_1 \neq 0$. Equivalently, by I, 19.3, $A' \rightarrow A$ is an essential extension if and only if A' is a retract of no other subobject of A. We call u a **proper** extension if u is not an isomorphism. An inclusion $A' \subset A$ is an essential extension in ${}^{\mathbf{R}}\mathscr{G}$ if and only if for each $a \in A$ with $a \neq 0$ there is an $r \in \mathbf{R}$ such that $ra \in A'$ and $ra \neq 0$.

Lemma 2.1. *A monomorphism $u : A' \rightarrow A$ is an essential extension if and only if every morphism $f : A \rightarrow B$ such that fu is a monomorphism is itself a monomorphism.*

Proof. If f is not a monomorphism, the $K = \text{Ker}(f)$ is not zero, hence $K \cap A' \neq 0$. But $K \cap A'$ is the kernel of fu, so that fu is not a monomorphism.

If u is not an essential extension, then there is a subobject $A_1 \neq 0$ such that $A_1 \cap A' = 0$. Then the composition $A' \to A \to A/A_1$ is a monomorphism, but $A \to A/A_1$ is not a monomorphism. ▮

Lemma 2.2. *Let Q be an object in a locally small C_3 category. Then Q is injective if and only if Q admits no proper essential extensions.*

Proof. Let Q be injective and suppose that $u : Q \to A$ is an essential extension. By II, 14.2*, we know u is a coretraction and so by I, 19.1, we can write $A = Q \oplus Q'$ for some subobject Q'. But then $Q \cap Q' = 0$ and so $Q' = 0$ since u is essential. Hence u is an isomorphism.

Conversely, suppose that Q admits no proper essential extensions. To show that Q is injective it suffices to show that Q is a retract of every containing object (II, 14.2*). Suppose that Q is a subobject of A but not a retract. Let $\mathscr{C}$ be the set of subobjects of A which intersect Q trivially. Under the natural ordering of subobjects, if $\{A_i\}$ is a linearly ordered subset of $\mathscr{C}$ then by C_3

$$\left(\bigcup A_i\right) \cap Q = \bigcup (A_i \cap Q) = 0.$$

Hence $\mathscr{C}$ is inductive, and so by Zorn's lemma we can find a maximal member A_0 for $\mathscr{C}$. Since $Q \cap A_0 = 0$ the composition $Q \to A \to A/A_0$ is a monomorphism. Furthermore, it cannot be an epimorphism for then it would be an isomorphism, and so Q would be a retract of A. Therefore, by assumption we can find a nonzero subobject $\bar{B}$ of A/A_0 such that $Q \cap \bar{B} = 0$. Consider the commutative diagram

$$\begin{array}{ccccc}
Q \cap B & \longrightarrow & B & \longrightarrow & \bar{B} \\
\downarrow & & \downarrow & & \downarrow \\
Q & \longrightarrow & A & \longrightarrow & A/A_0
\end{array}$$

where each of the squares is a pullback. Then by I, 7.2, the rectangle is a pullback; that is, $Q \cap B = Q \cap \bar{B} = 0$. Now by I, 16.3, the morphism $B \to \bar{B}$ is an epimorphism, and so it follows that $B \to A \to A/A_0$ is not zero. Consequently B properly contains A_0 as a subobject of A, contradicting maximality of A_0. Therefore Q is a retract of A. ▮

Lemma 2.3. *In a C_3 category suppose that each member of a direct family of subobjects $\{A_i\}$ of an object A is an essential extension of another subobject A' of A. Then $\bigcup A_i$ is also an essential extension of A'.*

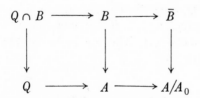

Proof. Let $\bar{A}$ be a nonzero subobject of $\bigcup A_i$. Then by C_3 we can write $\bar{A} = \bigcup (A_i \cap \bar{A})$, and so for some i we have $A_i \cap \bar{A} \neq 0$. Therefore since A_i is an essential extension of A' we have

$$0 \neq (A_i \cap \bar{A}) \cap A' \subset \bar{A} \cap A'.$$

This shows that $\bigcup A_i$ is an essential extension of A'. ▮

The proof of the following lemma is left to the reader.

Lemma 2.4. *If $u : A \to B$ and $v : B \to C$ are monomorphisms, then vu is an essential extension if and only if both u and v are essential extensions.* ▮

An **injective envelope** for an object A is an essential extension $A \to Q$ with Q injective.

Proposition 2.5. *Let $u : A \to Q$ and $u' : A \to Q'$ be injective envelopes for A. Then there is an isomorphism $\theta : Q \approx Q'$ (not necessarily unique) such that $\theta u = u'$.*

Proof. Let $\theta : Q \to Q'$ be such that $u' = \theta u$ (injectivity of Q'). Then θ is a monomorphism (essentiality of u) and so by 2.4 θ is an essential extension (essentiality of u'). Therefore θ is an isomorphism (injectivity of Q). ▮

Proposition 2.6. *Let A be an object in a locally small C_3 category, and suppose that A is a subobject of an injective object Q. Then A has an injective envelope.*

Proof. Let $\mathscr{C}$ be the set of all subobjects of Q which contain A and which are essential extensions of A. Then $A \in \mathscr{C}$ so that $\mathscr{C}$ is not empty, and by 2.3 we see that $\mathscr{C}$ is inductive. Hence let Q_1 be a maximal element. We show that Q_1 is injective. If Q_1 is not injective, then by 2.2 there is a proper essential extension $u : Q_1 \to B$. Since Q is injective there is a morphism $v : B \to Q$ such that vu is the inclusion of Q_1 in Q. Since u is essential it follows from 2.1 that v is a monomorphism. But then by 2.4, B is an essential extension of A in Q, contradicting the maximality of Q_1. Therefore Q_1 is injective, and so $A \to Q_1$ is an injective envelope. ▮

3. Existence of Injectives

Let U be any object in an additive category $\mathscr{A}$, and let $\mathbf{R}$ denote the ring of endomorphisms of U. Then we have a functor $T : \mathscr{A} \to \mathscr{G}^{\mathbf{R}}$ defined by $T(A) = [U, A]_{\mathscr{A}}$, where $[U, A]$ is considered as a right $\mathbf{R}$-module by defining the product of a ring element $r \in [U, U]$ and a group element $f \in [U, A]$ as the composition $fr \in [U, A]$. Then T is kernel preserving, and if U is a generator then T is an imbedding.

Lemma 3.1. *Let U be a generator in an abelian category $\mathscr{A}$ and let T be as above. If $u : A \to B$ is an essential extension, then $T(u)$ is an essential extension.*

Proof. Since T is kernel preserving, $T(u)$ is a monomorphism. Suppose that $f \in [U, B] = T(B)$ and $f \neq 0$. We must find $r \in \mathbf{R} = [U, U]$ such that $0 \neq fr$ and $fr \in [U, A]$ (or, more correctly, $\mathrm{Im}(fr) \subset \mathrm{Im}(u)$). Consider the diagram

$$\begin{array}{ccccc} V & \xrightarrow{g} & A \cap I & \xrightarrow{w} & A \\ \downarrow{\scriptstyle h} & & \downarrow & & \downarrow{\scriptstyle u} \\ U & \xrightarrow{q} & I & \xrightarrow{v} & B \end{array}$$

where the bottom row is the factorization of f through its image and each square is a pullback. Since $f \neq 0$ we know $I \neq 0$, and so since u is essential we have $A \cap I \neq 0$. Since q is an epimorphism, so is g, and consequently $g \neq 0$. Therefore there is a morphism $k : U \rightarrow V$ such that $gk \neq 0$, and so since u and w are monomorphisms, $uwgk \neq 0$. Therefore $vqhk = fhk \neq 0$ and we can take $r = hk$. ▌

Theorem 3.2. *A C_3 category $\mathscr{A}$ with a generator U has injective envelopes for each of its objects.*

Proof. By 2.6 it would suffice to show that $\mathscr{A}$ has injectives. However we shall construct the injective envelope directly, without use of 2.6.

Let $\mathbf{R}$ and T be as above, and let A be any object in $\mathscr{A}$. Then by II, §15, we can find a monomorphism $T(A) \rightarrow M$ in the category $\mathscr{G}^{\mathbf{R}}$ with M injective. Let $\mathscr{C}$ be the class of all triples (B, u, f) such that $u : A \rightarrow B$ is an essential extension and $f : T(B) \rightarrow M$ is a morphism of right $\mathbf{R}$-modules making the diagram

$$\begin{array}{ccc} T(A) & \xrightarrow{T(u)} & T(B) \\ & \searrow \quad \swarrow{\scriptstyle f} & \\ & M & \end{array}$$

commutative. By 3.1, $T(u)$ is an essential extension, and so f must be a monomorphism. We write $(B, u, f) \leqslant (B', u', f')$ if there is a morphism $v : B \rightarrow B'$ such that the diagrams

$$\begin{array}{ccc} & A & \\ {\scriptstyle u}\swarrow & & \searrow{\scriptstyle u'} \\ B & \xrightarrow{v} & B' \end{array} \qquad \begin{array}{ccc} T(B) & \xrightarrow{T(v)} & T(B') \\ {\scriptstyle f}\searrow & & \swarrow{\scriptstyle f'} \\ & M & \end{array}$$

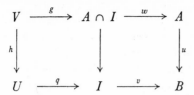

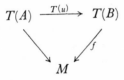

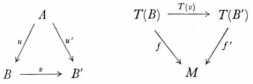

are commutative. This defines an ordering on $\mathscr{C}$. Notice that v must be a monomorphism since u is an essential extension. Also v is unique, for if v_1 were another morphism having the properties of v, then $f' T(v) = f' T(v_1)$ and so $T(v) = T(v_1)$ since f' is a monomorphism. Therefore $v = v_1$ since T is an imbedding. It follows that if also $(B', u', f') \leqslant (B, u, f)$, then v is an isomorphism. In this case we say that (B, u, f) and (B', u', f') are equivalent. Now since $f: T(B) \to M$ is a monomorphism, the cardinal number of $T(B) = [U, B]$ is less than or equal to the cardinal number of M. Hence by II, 15.2 B is a quotient object of ${}^M U$. But $\mathscr{A}$ is locally small by II, 15.1, and so there are no more than a set of such quotient objects. Consequently the class $\mathscr{C}_0$ of equivalence classes in $\mathscr{C}$ is a set. Let $\{(B_i, u_i, f_i)\}$ represent a linearly ordered subset of $\mathscr{C}_0$. Again making use of the uniqueness of v we see that A, together with the B_i's, form a direct system in which all the morphisms are monomorphisms. Let $\bar{B}$ be the direct limit, and let $\bar{u}$ be the limit morphism from A to $\bar{B}$. From 1.7 it follows that $\bar{u}$ and all the other limit morphisms $B_i \to \bar{B}$ are monomorphisms. Then by 2.3 we see that $\bar{u}$ is an essential extension of A. Now $T(A)$, together with the $T(B_i)$'s, form a direct system of submodules of $T(\bar{B})$. Let L be the direct limit (or union, since $\mathscr{G}^{\mathbf{R}}$ is C_3). The morphisms $f_i : T(B_i) \to M$ define a morphism $f : L \to M$ which can be extended to a morphism $\bar{f}: T(\bar{B}) \to M$ by injectivity of M. Therefore $(\bar{B}, \bar{u}, \bar{f})$ follows every (B_i, u_i, f_i). Thus $\mathscr{C}_0$ is inductive, and so let (Q, w, h) be a maximal element. If Q is not injective, then there is a proper essential extension $Q \to Q_1$ by 2.2, and so $A \to Q \to Q_1$ is an essential extension of A by 2.4. Also by injectivity of M the morphism h can be extended to a morphism $h_1 : T(Q_1) \to M$. But this contradicts the maximality of (Q, w, h). Therefore Q is injective, and so $A \to Q$ is an injective envelope for A. ▌

Proposition 3.3. *A complete (cocomplete) abelian category $\mathscr{A}$ with a generator U and injectives has an injective cogenerator.*

Proof. Let C be the product (coproduct) of all quotient objects U/V where V runs through the set (II, 15.1) of subobjects of U. By assumption there is an injective Q containing C. We show that Q is a cogenerator. By II, 15.3* it suffices to show that for each nonzero $A \in \mathscr{A}$ there is a nonzero morphism $A \to Q$. We know there is a nonzero morphism $U \to A$ since U is a generator. The image of such a morphism is isomorphic to U/V for some subobject $V \neq U$. The injection $U/V \to C$ composed with $C \to Q$ is not zero since each of the morphisms is a monomorphism. Then, by injectivity of Q, this composition can be extended to a morphism $A \to Q$ as required. ▌

Combining 3.2 and 3.3 we have

Corollary 3.4. *A C_3 category with a generator has an injective cogenerator.* ▌

Exercises

1. Find three subgroups A_1, A_2, and B of $\mathbf{Z} \oplus \mathbf{Z}$ such that

$$(A_1 \cup A_2) \cap B \neq (A_1 \cap B) \cup (A_2 \cap B).$$

Show that $\mathscr{G}$ is C_3 and C_1^*.

2. A category with projectives and products is C_1^*.

3. If $\mathscr{A}$ is a category with products, coproducts, and a zero, and if $\mathscr{B}$ is a C_2 category, then for any functor $T : \mathscr{A} \to \mathscr{B}$ and any coproduct $\bigoplus A_i$ in $\mathscr{A}$ the morphism

$$\bigoplus_i T(A_i) \to T(\bigoplus_i A_i)$$

is a monomorphism.

4. An abelian group A is called a **torsion group** if for each $a \in A$ there is a nonzero integer n such that $na = 0$. Let $\mathscr{G}_0$ be the full subcategory of $\mathscr{G}$ consisting of all torsion groups. Then $\mathscr{G}_0$ is an abelian subcategory of $\mathscr{G}$, and coproducts in $\mathscr{G}_0$ are the same as in $\mathscr{G}$. However the product in $\mathscr{G}_0$ of a family $\{G_i\}$ of torsion groups is given by the subgroup of the product in $\mathscr{G}$ consisting of all elements of the form (x_i) such that the $x_i \in G_i$ have uniform order; that is, there is a nonzero integer n such that $nx_i = 0$ for all i. For each positive integer m, let $f_m : \mathbf{Z}_{2^m} \to \mathbf{Z}_2$ be the morphism which takes the coset of r modulo 2^m into the coset of r modulo 2. Then each f_m is an epimorphism, but $\underset{m>0}{\times} f_m$ is not an epimorphism. Thus a complete and cocomplete abelian category need not be C_1.

5. Let P be a small projective in a cocomplete abelian category. Then P has the following property: If $\{P_i\}$ is a direct family of proper subobjects of P, then $\bigcup P_i$ is a proper subobject of P.

Conversely, if A is any object in a C_3 category and if A has the above property with respect to subobjects, then A is small.

6. Generalize 1.7 to the case where I is an ordered set with the property that if $i \leqslant j$ and $i \leqslant k$ then there is a vertex p such that $j \leqslant p$ and $k \leqslant p$. (If i and j are vertices of a scheme, write $i \sim j$ if there is a composite arrow from i to j or from j to i. Then $\sim$ is an equivalence relation, and in this way the scheme can be broken up into components. The colimit of a diagram over the scheme is the coproduct of the colimits of the components. Show that for an ordered set I with the given property, the components are all directed sets.)

7. The additive group $\mathbf{Q}$ of rational numbers is an injective envelope for $\mathbf{Z}$.

Let p be any positive integer. The group $\mathbf{Z}_p$ can be regarded as the collection of cosets of rational numbers of the form n/p in $\mathbf{Q}/\mathbf{Z}$. Let $\mathbf{Z}_{p^\infty}$ be the set of cosets in $\mathbf{Q}/\mathbf{Z}$ represented by rational numbers whose denominator is a power of p. Show that $\mathbf{Z}_{p^\infty}$ is divisible, and therefore injective. Hence show that $\mathbf{Z}_{p^\infty}$ is the injective envelope of $\mathbf{Z}_p$. (To prove $\mathbf{Z}_{p^\infty}$ divisible, we must show that given $x = 1/p^m$ and n an integer > 0, there is a number y of the form s/p^{m+k} such that $ny - x$ is an integer. Equivalently, we must find positive integers s, k, and t such that $ns = p^k(1 + tp^m)$. Let n_1 be the product of all prime factors of n which divide p, and take k large enough so that n_1 divides p^k. Then use the fact that n/n_1 and p^m are relatively prime to find s and t.)

8. Prove the converse of 3.1; namely, if $T(u)$ is an essential extension, then so is u.

CHAPTER IV

Group Valued Functors

Introduction

The central result in this chapter is the group valued imbedding theorem: Every small abelian category admits an exact imbedding into the category of abelian groups (2.6). Proofs of this theorem have been given by Heron, Lubkin [27], and Freyd [14]. The one given here is by Freyd. The metatheoretic consequences of such a theorem are also examined. In general, any statement involving exactness, commutativity, and limits for a finite diagram which is true in the category of abelian groups is true in any abelian category. Furthermore, certain statements involving the existence of morphisms which are true in $\mathcal{G}$ are also true in the general abelian category. The connecting morphism provides a well-known example. In Chapter VI we shall prove that every small abelian category admits a full exact imbedding into a category of modules. This will enable us to improve on the metatheory developed in this chapter. In §3 it is proved that certain classes of abelian categories (not necessarily small) also admit exact, group valued imbeddings.

Let U be a projective generator in an abelian category $\mathcal{A}$, and let $\mathbf{R}$ be the ring of endomorphisms of U. Then the functor $T: \mathcal{A} \to \mathcal{G}^{\mathbf{R}}$ defined by $T(A) = [U, A]$ is an exact imbedding. A more careful analysis of this functor enables us to draw a characterization of module categories in 4.1. The result is generalized in §5 to functor categories.

The material in §1–§3 has been taken almost exclusively from the work of Peter Freyd.

1. Metatheorems

Let U be an object in an abelian category $\mathcal{A}$. We know that the functor $H^U : \mathcal{A} \to \mathcal{G}$ is kernel preserving. If U is projective then H^U is exact, and if U is a generator then H^U is an imbedding. Hence if $\mathcal{A}$ has a projective generator, then $\mathcal{A}$ admits an exact, covariant, group valued imbedding. The same is true if $\mathcal{A}$ has an injective cogenerator (exercise 1). We are going to examine the implications of an abelian category $\mathscr{A}$ admitting an exact group valued imbedding $T: \mathscr{A} \to \mathscr{G}$.

In the first place T, as do all functors, preserves commutative diagrams. By II, 6.7, T preserves limits and colimits for finite diagrams. Furthermore, by II, 7.1, T reflects commutative diagrams, limits and colimits for finite diagrams, and exact sequences. Let us say that a statement about a diagram in an abelian category is **categorical** if it states that certain parts of the diagram are or are not commutative, that certain sequences in the diagram are or are not exact, and that certain parts of the diagram are or are not limits or colimits for certain other finite parts of the diagram. Then in view of the above remarks we have the following metatheorem.

Metatheorem 1.1. *If a theorem is of the form "p implies q" where p and q are categorical statements about a diagram in an abelian category $\mathscr{A}$ admitting an exact group valued imbedding, and if the theorem is true in the category of abelian groups, then the theorem is true in $\mathscr{A}$.* ▮

Let us see how 1.1 works in a particular case. Consider the 5 lemma which was proved for $\mathscr{G}$ in I, 21.1. Suppose that the diagram of that lemma is a diagram in an abelian category $\mathscr{A}$ admitting an exact group valued imbedding T. Let us prove part (i) of the lemma. Suppose that under the given conditions

$$
\begin{array}{ccccccccc}
 & & 0 & & 0 & & 0 & & \\
 & & \downarrow & & \downarrow & & \downarrow & & \\
 & & K' & \longrightarrow & K & \longrightarrow & K'' & & \\
 & & \downarrow & & \downarrow & & \downarrow & & \\
 & & A' & \longrightarrow & A & \longrightarrow & A'' & \longrightarrow & 0 \\
 & & \downarrow & & \downarrow & & \downarrow & & \\
0 & \longrightarrow & B' & \longrightarrow & B & \longrightarrow & B'' & & \\
 & & \downarrow & & \downarrow & & \downarrow & & \\
 & & F' & \longrightarrow & F & \longrightarrow & F'' & & \\
 & & \downarrow & & \downarrow & & \downarrow & & \\
 & & 0 & & 0 & & 0 & &
\end{array}
\qquad (1)
$$

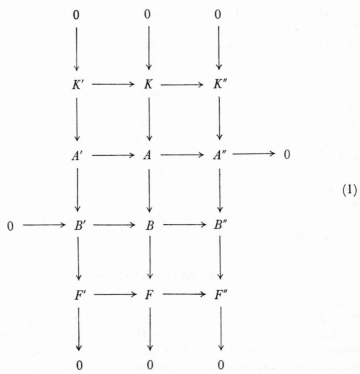

γ_3 is not a monomorphism. Applying T to the diagram we obtain a diagram in $\mathscr{G}$ satisfying the same conditions. But since γ_3 is not a monomorphism, $T(\gamma_3)$ is not a monomorphism, contradicting the fact that the lemma is true in $\mathscr{G}$.

Metatheorem 1.1 does not handle a case where we are required to show the existence of morphism having certain properties with regard to a diagram. We consider a familiar example. Suppose that we have the commutative diagram (1) in an abelian category $\mathscr{A}$, where the middle two rows and all columns are exact. If $\mathscr{A}$ is $\mathscr{G}$, then we can show without much difficulty that there is a morphism $K'' \to F'$ (called the **connecting morphism** for the diagram) such that the sequence

$$K' \to K \to K'' \to F' \to F \to F'' \tag{2}$$

is exact (I, exercise 20). The morphism $K'' \to F'$ is defined as a composition of relations; namely, the function $K'' \to A''$, followed by the inverse of $A \to A''$ (which is not a function, in general), followed by $A \to B$, followed by the inverse of $B' \to B$, followed by $B' \to F'$. One checks that this composition of relations is actually a function whose domain is all of K'', that this function is a morphism of groups, and finally that the sequence (2) is exact. Now if we were to try to prove the assertion in an abelian category $\mathscr{A}$ admitting an exact group valued imbedding T, we would apply T to (1), and we would obtain a morphism $\Delta : T(K'') \to T(F')$ as above. The difficulty now lies in the fact that we do not know if Δ is of the form $T(\delta)$ for some $\delta : K'' \to F'$, since in general T will not be full. However, we can prove in this particular case that there is such a morphism δ.

First of all there is no loss in generality in supposing that $\mathscr{A}$ is an abelian subcategory of $\mathscr{G}$. Let us define an **antimorphism** to be a relation which is the inverse of a morphism of abelian groups. If $\mathscr{A}$ is any subcategory of $\mathscr{G}$, then we define an **$\mathscr{A}$-relation** from group A to group B as a composition $\alpha_n \dots \alpha_2 \alpha_1$, where for each i, $1 \leqslant i \leqslant n$, α_i is a morphism in $\mathscr{A}$ from A_i to A_{i+1} (that is, an **$\mathscr{A}$-morphism**) or the inverse of a morphism in $\mathscr{A}$ from A_i to A_{i+1} (that is, an **$\mathscr{A}$-antimorphism**), and $A_1 = A$, $A_{n+1} = B$. An $\mathscr{A}$-relation from A to B which is a function with domain A is called an **$\mathscr{A}$-function** from A to B.

Proposition 1.2. *If $\mathscr{A}$ is an abelian subcategory of $\mathscr{G}$, then all $\mathscr{A}$-functions are $\mathscr{A}$-morphisms.*

Proof. First we define a **simple $\mathscr{A}$-relation** as an $\mathscr{A}$-relation which can be written as the composition of an $\mathscr{A}$-antimorphism followed by an $\mathscr{A}$-morphism. Then we have:

Lemma 1.3. *All $\mathscr{A}$-relations are simple $\mathscr{A}$-relations.*

Proof. It is clear that all $\mathscr{A}$-relations are compositions of simple $\mathscr{A}$-relations. Hence we need only prove that the composition of two simple $\mathscr{A}$-relations is simple. We have the following situation:

$$\begin{array}{ccc} & & C & \longrightarrow & A \\ & & \big\downarrow & & \\ E & \longrightarrow & D & & \\ \big\downarrow & & & & \\ B & & & & \end{array} \tag{3}$$

that is, a simple $\mathscr{A}$-relation from A to D followed by a simple $\mathscr{A}$-relation from D to B. Consider the pullback diagram in $\mathscr{A}$ (and hence in $\mathscr{G}$)

$$\begin{array}{ccc} P & \longrightarrow & C \\ \big\downarrow & & \big\downarrow \\ E & \longrightarrow & D \end{array}$$

Then the simple $\mathscr{A}$-relation given by

$$\begin{array}{ccccc} P & \longrightarrow & C & \longrightarrow & A \\ \big\downarrow & & & & \\ E & & & & \\ \big\downarrow & & & & \\ B & & & & \end{array}$$

is the same as that given by (3). Indeed it is readily verified that the two relations from C to D given by

$$\begin{array}{ccc} P & \longrightarrow & C \\ \big\downarrow & & \\ E & & \end{array} \qquad\qquad \begin{array}{ccc} & & C \\ & & \big\downarrow \\ E & \longrightarrow & D \end{array}$$

are the same. One uses the expression $P = \{(x, y) \in C \times E | \alpha(x) = \beta(y)\}$ for the pullback of abelian groups (I, 17.5). ▮

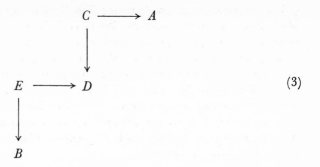

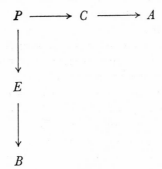

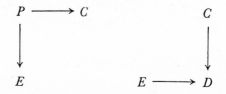

Lemma 1.4. *If a simple $\mathscr{A}$-relation is an $\mathscr{A}$-function, then it is an $\mathscr{A}$-morphism.*

Proof. Let an $\mathscr{A}$-function be given by the diagram

$$\begin{array}{ccc} C & \longrightarrow & A \\ \downarrow & & \\ B & & \end{array} \tag{4}$$

Its being defined on all of A is equivalent to $C \to A$ being an epimorphism. Let $K \to C$ be the kernel of $C \to A$ in $\mathscr{A}$ and hence in $\mathscr{G}$. Then the relation being well defined is equivalent to the composition $K \to C \to B$ being zero. Since $C \to A$ is the cokernel of $K \to C$, this means that there is a morphism $A \to B$ in $\mathscr{A}$ such that $C \to A \to B = C \to B$. Then $A \to B$ is the given $\mathscr{A}$-function. ∎

Proposition 1.2 now follows from 1.3 and 1.4. ∎

If we define **construction by diagram chasing** as the process of defining a morphism in $\mathscr{G}$ by composing morphisms and antimorphisms in a diagram, we can now state the following improvement on 1.1.

Metatheorem 1.5. *Let $\mathscr{A}$ be an abelian category admitting an exact group valued imbedding. If a theorem is of the form "p implies q", where p is a categorical statement concerning a diagram in $\mathscr{A}$, and q states that additional morphisms exist between certain objects in the diagram and that some categorical statement is true of the extended diagram, and if the theorem can be proved in $\mathscr{G}$ by constructing the additional morphisms through diagram chasing, then the theorem is true in $\mathscr{A}$.* ∎

We remark that a morphism $A \to B$ constructed by diagram chasing in an abelian category $\mathscr{A}$ must be such as to make a diagram (4) in $\mathscr{A}$ commutative. Since (4) is independent of any particular imbedding $\mathscr{A} \to \mathscr{G}$ and since $C \to A$ is an epimorphism, it follows that any morphism in $\mathscr{A}$ constructed by diagram chasing is independent of the particular imbedding used to define it. In particular, the connecting morphism of the diagram (1) is well defined.

2. The Group Valued Imbedding Theorem

We shall show in this section that every small abelian category admits an exact (covariant) group valued imbedding. Our approach is to study the functor category $(\mathscr{A}, \mathscr{G})$. The required imbedding will fall out as a special object in this category.

The following lemma is crucial.

Lemma 2.1. *Let $\mathscr{A}$ be any category, and consider a covariant set valued functor $T : \mathscr{A} \to \mathscr{S}$. Then for any object $A \in \mathscr{A}$ we have a one to one correspondence*

$$\theta = \theta_{A,T} : [H^A, T] \to T(A)$$

where $[H^A, T]$ is the class of natural transformations from the set valued functor H^A to the set valued functor T. Furthermore, θ is natural in both T and A.

If $\mathscr{A}$ is additive and $T : \mathscr{A} \to \mathscr{G}$ is an additive functor, then the same conclusion is valid relative to the group valued functor H^A. In this case θ is an isomorphism of groups.

Proof. For $\eta \in [H^A, T]$ we define $\theta(\eta) = \eta_A(1_A)$. Also we define a function $\theta' : T(A) \to [H^A, T]$ by the rule

$$\theta'(x)_B(f) = T(f)(x) \tag{1}$$

where $x \in T(A)$ and $f \in H^A(B) = [A, B]$. That $\theta'(x)$ is a natural transformation is an easy consequence of the functorial property $T(gf) = T(g)T(f)$. We show that $\theta'\theta$ is the identity function on $[H^A, T]$. For $\eta \in [H^A, T]$ we must prove that $\theta'(\theta(\eta)) = \eta$; that is, for each $B \in \mathscr{A}$ we must show that $\theta'(\theta(\eta))_B(f) = \eta_B(f)$ where $f \in [A, B]$. By naturality of η the diagram

$$\begin{array}{ccc} [A, A] & \xrightarrow{\eta_A} & T(A) \\ \downarrow{\scriptstyle [A,f]} & & \downarrow{\scriptstyle T(f)} \\ [A, B] & \xrightarrow{\eta_B} & T(B) \end{array} \tag{2}$$

is commutative. Chasing the element 1_A clockwise gives us

$$T(f)(\theta(\eta)) = \theta'(\theta(\eta))_B(f).$$

Chasing the same element counterclockwise gives us $\eta_B(f)$ as required. To show that $\theta\theta'$ is the identity, we have for $x \in T(A)$,

$$\theta(\theta'(x)) = \theta'(x)_A(1_A) = T(1_A)(x) = x.$$

Finally, we show that θ is natural. For a morphism $f : A \to B$ we must prove that the diagram

$$\begin{array}{ccc} [H^A, T] & \xrightarrow{\theta_{A,T}} & T(A) \\ \downarrow & & \downarrow \\ [H^B, T] & \xrightarrow[\theta_{B,T}]{} & T(B) \end{array}$$

is commutative. Starting with η in $[H^A, T]$ and going clockwise we obtain $T(f)(\eta_A(1_A))$. Going counterclockwise we obtain $\eta_B(f)$. Hence the result follows from the commutativity of the diagram (2). On the other hand, given a natural transformation $\rho : T \to S$ we must prove that the diagram

$$\begin{array}{ccc} [H^A, T] & \xrightarrow{\theta_{A,T}} & T(A) \\ \downarrow & & \downarrow \rho_A \\ [H^A, S] & \xrightarrow{\theta_{A,S}} & S(A) \end{array}$$

is commutative. Starting with $\eta \in [H^A, T]$ we obtain clockwise $\rho_A(\eta_A(1_A))$ and counterclockwise $(\rho\eta)_A(1_A)$. That these are equal follows from the definition of the composition of natural transformations.

In the case where $\mathscr{A}$ and T are additive, it is seen immediately from the definition of θ that it is additive. The only further detail that must be checked in this case is that $\theta'(x)_B$ is actually a morphism of groups. But this we see from (1) using the fact that T is additive. ▌

Corollary 2.2. *The function $\theta : [H^A, H^C] \to [C, A]$ defined by $\theta(\eta) = \eta_A(1_A)$ is a one to one correspondence, natural in both A and C. The inverse θ' of θ is given by $\theta'(x)_B(f) = fx$ where $x \in [C, A]$ and $f \in H^A(B) = [A, B]$. In the case of an additive category θ is an isomorphism of groups.* ▌

A functor $T : \mathscr{A} \to \mathscr{S}$ ($T : \mathscr{A} \to \mathscr{G}$ in the case where $\mathscr{A}$ is additive) is called a **representable** functor if it is naturally equivalent to a morphism functor H^A for some $A \in \mathscr{A}$. It follows from 2.2 that if T is representable, then the object $A \in \mathscr{A}$ which represents it is unique up to isomorphism.

Proposition 2.3. *If $\mathscr{A}$ is a small additive category and $A \in \mathscr{A}$, then H^A is a small projective in $(\mathscr{A}, \mathscr{G})$. Furthermore, the functor $G = \bigoplus_{A \in \mathscr{A}} H^A$ is an imbedding, and is a projective generator for $(\mathscr{A}, \mathscr{G})$.*

Proof. We first show that H^A is projective. Since a coproduct of projectives is projective, it will follow that G is projective. Let $T \to T''$ be an epimorphism in $(\mathscr{A}, \mathscr{G})$. Then from 2.1 (using naturality of θ with respect to T) we see that $[H^A, T] \to [H^A, T'']$ is an epimorphism. Therefore H^A is projective.

To prove H^A small, we must show that $[H^A, \ ]$ is a coproduct preserving functor (II, 16.2). But this follows again from 2.1 since we have

$$[H^A, \bigoplus T_i] = (\bigoplus T_i)(A) = \bigoplus T_i(A) = \bigoplus [H^A, T_i].$$

Since G is projective we will know it is a generator if $[G, T] \neq 0$ for any nonzero functor T (II, 15.3). We have

$$[G, T] = [\bigoplus_{A \in \mathscr{A}} H^A, T] = \mathop{\mathsf{X}}_{A \in \mathscr{A}} [H^A, T] = \mathop{\mathsf{X}}_{A \in \mathscr{A}} T(A)$$

where the middle equality comes from II, 5.1.* But $\mathop{\mathsf{X}}_{A \in \mathscr{A}} T(A) = 0$ if and only if $T(A) = 0$ for all $A \in \mathscr{A}$; that is, if and only if $T = 0$. Hence G is a generator.

It is trivial that G is an imbedding, for if $B \to B'$ is a nonzero morphism in $\mathscr{A}'$, then $H^B(B) \to H^B(B')$ is not zero, and consequently $\bigoplus_{A \in \mathscr{A}} H^A(B) \to \bigoplus_{A \in \mathscr{A}} H^A(B')$ cannot be zero. ▌

Proposition 2.4. *Suppose that $\mathscr{A}$ is a small, exact, additive category. If T is an injective object in $(\mathscr{A}, \mathscr{G})$, then T is a cokernel preserving functor.*

Proof. Suppose that $A' \to A \to A'' \to 0$ is exact in $\mathscr{A}$. Then $0 \to H^{A''} \to H^A \to H^A$ is exact in $(\mathscr{A}, \mathscr{G})$. Since T is injective, this means that the sequence

$$[H^{A'}, T] \to [H^A, T] \to [H^{A''}, T] \to 0$$

is exact in $\mathscr{G}$, or applying 2.1 and using naturality of θ in A,

$$T(A') \to T(A) \to T(A'') \to 0$$

is exact. In other words T is cokernel preserving. ▌

Remarks. (1) A cokernel preserving functor is not necessarily injective. Furthermore, an injective functor need not have injective values, nor is it true that an injective valued functor is an injective.

(2) It is true that a projective group valued functor is kernel preserving, although it does not follow from 2.4 by duality (exercise 3).

(3) Proposition 2.4 need not be true if $\mathscr{G}$ is replaced by a general abelian category (exercise 6).

Lemma 2.5. *Consider a pointwise monomorphism $M \to Q$ where M, $Q : \mathscr{A} \to \mathscr{G}$ are additive functors and $\mathscr{A}$ is any abelian category. If M is a monofunctor, and if for any other pointwise monomorphism $N \to Q$ with $N \neq 0$ there is an object A such that $0 \neq M(A) \cap N(A) \subset Q(A)$, then Q is a monofunctor.*

Remark. If $\mathscr{A}$ is a small abelian category, then 2.5 states simply that an essential extension in $(\mathscr{A}, \mathscr{G})$ of a monofunctor is again a monofunctor.

Proof. Suppose that Q is not a monofunctor. Then there is a monomorphism $\alpha : A' \to A$ in $\mathscr{A}$ such that $Q(\alpha)$ is not a monomorphism. Let $x \in Q(A')$ be such that $Q(\alpha)(x) = 0$, $x \neq 0$. Define $\bar{Q}$ as the subfunctor of Q generated by x; that is, $\bar{Q}(B) = \{Q(\beta)(x) \mid \beta \in [A', B]\}$ (II, exercise 6). Then $\bar{Q} \neq 0$, and so by assumption we can find $B \in \mathscr{A}$ such that $\bar{Q}(B) \cap M(B) \neq 0$. In other words there is a morphism $\beta : A' \to B$ such that $Q(\beta)(x) \neq 0$ and $Q(\beta)(x) \in M(B)$. Consider the pushout diagram

$$\begin{array}{ccc} A' & \xrightarrow{\alpha} & A \\ \Big\downarrow{\scriptstyle \beta} & & \Big\downarrow{\scriptstyle \bar{\beta}} \\ B & \xrightarrow{\bar{\alpha}} & P \end{array}$$

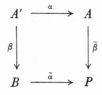

where $\bar{\alpha}$ is a monomorphism by I, 20.2*. Applying Q we obtain

$$0 = Q(\bar{\beta})Q(\alpha)(x) = Q(\bar{\alpha})Q(\beta)(x) = M(\bar{\alpha})Q(\beta)(x).$$

But this gives a contradiction since $Q(\beta)(x) \neq 0$ and $M(\bar{\alpha})$ is a monomorphism. Therefore Q is a monofunctor. ▮

Theorem 2.6 (The Group Valued Imbedding Theorem). *Any small abelian category $\mathscr{A}$ admits an exact covariant imbedding into the category of abelian groups.*

Proof. The category $(\mathscr{A}, \mathscr{G})$ is a C_3 category possessing a generator $G = \bigoplus_{A \in \mathscr{A}} H^A$ (2.3). Therefore by III, 3.2, $(\mathscr{A}, \mathscr{G})$ has injective envelopes for each of its objects. In particular, let $G \to Q$ be an injective envelope for G. Then Q is cokernel preserving by 2.4. Also since G is a monofunctor the same must be true of Q by 2.5. Therefore Q is an exact functor. Since G preserves nonzero objects the same is true of Q, and so by II, 7.2, Q is faithful. The conclusion now follows from II, 10.3. ▮

We see now that Metatheorem 1.5 applies to any small abelian category. We would like to show that the smallness condition can be removed. We accomplish this by proving the following lemma.

Lemma 2.7. *Let $\mathscr{A}_0$ be a small subcategory of an abelian category $\mathscr{A}$. Then there is a small, full, abelian subcategory $\mathscr{A}'$ of $\mathscr{A}$ such that $\mathscr{A}_0$ is a subcategory of $\mathscr{A}'$.*

Proof. We define inductively a sequence $\{\mathscr{A}_n\}_{n \geqslant 0}$ of subcategories of $\mathscr{A}$ as follows. The subcategory $\mathscr{A}_{n+1}$ is the full subcategory of $\mathscr{A}$ consisting of the objects in $\mathscr{A}_n$ together with single representatives for kernels and cokernels in $\mathscr{A}$ of every morphism in $\mathscr{A}_n$ and single representatives for all finite products in $\mathscr{A}$ of objects in $\mathscr{A}_n$. If $\mathscr{A}_n$ is small, then so is $\mathscr{A}_{n+1}$. It follows that since $\mathscr{A}_0$ is small, so is $\mathscr{A}_n$ for all $n \geqslant 0$. Consequently, $\mathscr{A}' = \bigcup_{n=0}^{\infty} \mathscr{A}_n$ is small, and it is easily shown that $\mathscr{A}'$ is a full abelian subcategory of $\mathscr{A}$ (II, exercise 5). ▮

Combining 1.5, 2.6, and 2.7 we now have:

Metatheorem 2.8. *Let $\mathscr{A}$ be any abelian category. If a theorem is of the form "p implies q," where p is a categorical statement concerning a diagram in $\mathscr{A}$, and q states that additional morphisms exist between certain objects in the diagram and that some categorical statement is true of the extended diagram, and if the theorem can be proved in $\mathscr{G}$ by constructing the additional morphisms through diagram chasing, then the theorem is true in $\mathscr{A}$.* ▮

3. An Imbedding for Big Categories

Given an object A in an additive category $\mathscr{A}$ and an abelian group E, we define a covariant additive functor $J_{A,E} : \mathscr{A} \to \mathscr{G}$ by the relation

$$J_{A,E}(B) = [[B, A]_{\mathscr{A}}, E]_{\mathscr{G}}.$$

Lemma 3.1. *Let $T : \mathscr{A} \to \mathscr{G}$ be any covariant additive functor. Then we have an isomorphism of groups*

$$\theta : [T, J_{A,E}] \to [T(A), E].$$

Furthermore, θ is natural in T, A, and E.

Proof. For $\eta \in [T, J_{A,E}]$ and $x \in T(A)$ we define $\theta(\eta)(x) = \eta_A(x)(1_A)$. Then it is clear that θ is a morphism of groups. To show that it is an isomorphism we define $\theta' : [T(A), E] \to [T, J_{A,E}]$ by the rule $\theta'(f)_B(y)(g) = f(T(g)(y))$ where $f \in [T(A), E]$, $y \in T(B)$, and $g \in [B, A]$. Additivity of T is used in showing that $\theta'(f)_B(y)$ is a morphism of groups. Now for $f \in [T(A), E]$ and $x \in T(A)$ we have

$$\theta(\theta'(f))(x) = \theta'(f)_A(x)(1_A) = f(T(1_A)(x)) = f(x).$$

Thus $\theta\theta'$ is the identity. On the other hand we have

$$\theta'(\theta(\eta))_B(y)(g) = \theta(\eta)(T(g)(y)) = \eta_A(T(g)(y))(1_A) = \eta_B(y)(g).$$

The last equality comes from the diagram

$$\begin{array}{ccc} T(B) & \xrightarrow{T(g)} & T(A) \\ \downarrow{\scriptstyle \eta_B} & & \downarrow{\scriptstyle \eta_A} \\ [[B, A], E] & \longrightarrow & [[A, A], E] \end{array}$$

which is commutative by naturality of η. Hence $\theta'\theta$ is the identity, and so θ is an isomorphism.

The proof of the naturality of θ in all three variables is left to the reader. ▌

Lemmas 2.1 and 3.1 suggest that $J_{A,E}$ plays some sort of dual role to H^A. In Chapter VI both of these functors will be generalized, and at that time we shall see more clearly the duality that exists between them.

Suppose for the moment that $\mathscr{A}$ is small. If E is an injective object in $\mathscr{G}$ (that is, a divisible group) then using the naturality of θ in T we see that $J_{A,E}$ is an injective object in $(\mathscr{A}, \mathscr{G})$ for all A. If E is an injective cogenerator in $\mathscr{G}$ (for example $\mathbf{Q}/\mathbf{Z}$) then we have for $T \neq 0$,

$$\left[T, \mathop{\times}_{A \in \mathscr{A}} J_{A,E}\right] = \mathop{\times}_{A \in \mathscr{A}} [T, J_{A,E}] = \mathop{\times}_{A \in \mathscr{A}} [T(A), E] \neq 0.$$

Therefore $\mathop{\times}_{A \in \mathscr{A}} J_{A,E}$ is an injective cogenerator for $(\mathscr{A}, \mathscr{G})$. In this way we see independently of III, 3.2, that $(\mathscr{A}, \mathscr{G})$ has injectives.

Returning to the case where $\mathscr{A}$ is not necessarily small, let A be a left $\mathbf{R}$-object in $\mathscr{A}$ and let $E \in {}^{\mathbf{R}}\mathscr{G}$ where $\mathbf{R}$ is any ring. Then we have the functor

$J_{A,\mathbf{R},E} : \mathscr{A} \to \mathscr{G}$ defined by $J_{A,\mathbf{R},E}(B) = {}^{\mathbf{R}}[[B, A], E]$ for $B \in \mathscr{A}$. In this case we obtain a natural equivalence

$$\theta : [T, J_{A,\mathbf{R},E}] \longrightarrow {}^{\mathbf{R}}[T(A), E].$$

In particular, take $\mathbf{R} = [A, A]$. Let $u : \mathbf{R} \to E$ be an injective envelope for $\mathbf{R}$ in ${}^{\mathbf{R}}\mathscr{G}$. Corresponding to $u : H^A(A) \to E$ we have the natural transformation $\eta = \theta'(u) : H^A \to J_{A,\mathbf{R},E}$ where $\eta_B(y)(g) = u(H^A(g)(y)) = u(gy)$ for $y \in [A, B]$ and $g \in [B, A]$.

Lemma 3.2. *If in the above A is cogenerator, then η is a pointwise monomorphism. Furthermore, if $\lambda : T \to J_{A,\mathbf{R},E}$ is another pointwise monomorphism and $T \neq 0$, then*

$$0 \neq \eta_A(H^A(A)) \cap \lambda_A(T(A)) \subset J_{A,\mathbf{R},E}(A).$$

Remark. In the case where $\mathscr{A}$ is small this will show that η is an injective envelope for H^A in $(\mathscr{A}, \mathscr{G})$.

Proof. Suppose that $0 \neq y \in H^A(B)$. Since A is a cogenerator we can find $g : B \to A$ such that $gy \neq 0$; hence $u(gy) \neq 0$ since u is a monomorphism. This shows that $\eta_B(y) \neq 0$ and so $\eta_B : H^A(B) \to {}^{\mathbf{R}}[[B, A], E]$ is a monomorphism. In other words η is a pointwise monomorphism.

Suppose now that $T \neq 0$, so that $T(B) \neq 0$ for some $B \in \mathscr{A}$. Let $0 \neq x \in T(B)$. Then $0 \neq \lambda_B(x) \in {}^{\mathbf{R}}[[B, A], E]$ since λ_B is a monomorphism, and so $\lambda_B(x)(g) \neq 0$ for some $g : B \to A$. Using naturality of λ we have $\lambda_A(T(g)(x))(1_A) = \lambda_B(x)(g) \neq 0$, and so $\lambda_A(T(g)(x)) \neq 0$. Therefore

$$0 \neq T(g)(x) \in T(A).$$

Denote $z = T(g)(x)$. Then $\lambda_A(z) = \bar{z} \in {}^{\mathbf{R}}[[A, A], E]$, and so if $e = \bar{z}(1_A)$, then $\bar{z}(r) = re$ for all $r \in \mathbf{R}$. Furthermore, since $\bar{z} \neq 0$ we must have $e \neq 0$. Since u is an essential extension of the left $\mathbf{R}$-module $\mathbf{R}$, there is some $s \in \mathbf{R}$ such that $0 \neq se = u(t)$ for some $t \in \mathbf{R}$. Now we have $s\bar{z} \in {}^{\mathbf{R}}[[A, A], E]$ defined by $(s\bar{z})(r) = \bar{z}(rs) = (rs)e = ru(t)$. Then $\eta_A(t)(r) = u(rt) = ru(t)$, the last equality being true since u is a morphism of $\mathbf{R}$-modules. Therefore $\eta_A(t) = s\bar{z}$. But again by naturality of λ we have $s\bar{z} = \lambda_A(T(s)(z))$. Consequently, since $t \neq 0$ and η_A is a monomorphism, we have

$$0 \neq \eta_A(t) = s\bar{z} \in \eta_A(H^A(A)) \cap \lambda_A(T(A)). \qquad \blacksquare$$

Theorem 3.3. *Let $\mathscr{A}$ be an abelian category with a cogenerator A and an object U such that $[U, B] \neq 0$ for all nonzero objects $B \in \mathscr{A}$. Then there is an exact covariant imbedding from $\mathscr{A}$ to $\mathscr{G}$.*

Proof. The product of U and A will be an object with the properties of both of them, hence we may assume $U = A$. Letting $\mathbf{R} \to E$ be an injective envelope in ${}^{\mathbf{R}}\mathscr{G}$ as above, we have the functor $J_{A,\mathbf{R},E}$ which is seen to be cokernel preserving from its definition. Since H^A is a monofunctor, it follows from 3.2 and 2.5 that $J_{A,\mathbf{R},E}$ is a monofunctor, hence is exact. Also since it contains H^A it must carry nonzero objects into nonzero objects. Therefore $J_{A,\mathbf{R},E}$ is an exact imbedding. ▌

4. Characterization of Categories of Modules

Let **R** be any ring. The category $\mathcal{G}^{\mathbf{R}}$ has a small projective generator, namely, **R** considered as a right **R**-module. Hence the same is true of any category which is equivalent to $\mathcal{G}^{\mathbf{R}}$. The following theorem shows that among other things the converse is true. That is, if $\mathscr{A}$ is a cocomplete abelian category possessing a small projective generator, then $\mathscr{A}$ is equivalent to $\mathcal{G}^{\mathbf{R}}$ for some ring **R**.

Theorem 4.1. *Let $\mathscr{A}$ be a cocomplete abelian category with a projective generator U, and let* **R** *denote the ring of endomorphisms of U. Then the functor $T : \mathscr{A} \to \mathcal{G}^{\mathbf{R}}$ defined by $T(A) = [U, A]$ is an exact imbedding such that the function $[A, B] \to [T(A), T(B)]$ induced by T is an isomorphism whenever A is finitely generated. If either U is small or $\mathscr{A}$ is C_3, then T is full. T is an equivalence if and only if U is small.*

Proof. Since U is a projective generator, T is an exact imbedding. Suppose that $A \in \mathscr{A}$ is finitely generated. Then we must show that every **R**-module morphism $\Phi : [U, A] \to [U, B]$ can be written as $T(\varphi)$ for some $\varphi \in [A, B]$. In other words we must find φ such that $\Phi(f) = \varphi f$ for all $f \in [U, A]$. First consider the case where $U = A$. Then $\Phi(f) = \Phi(1_U f) = \Phi(1_U)f$, since Φ is a morphism of **R**-modules. Therefore in this case we can take $\varphi = \Phi(1_U)$. Now, in general, if A is finitely generated, we can write an exact sequence

$$0 \to M \xrightarrow{\lambda} {}^I U \xrightarrow{\pi} A \to 0$$

where I is finite. For $i \in I$ we denote by u_i and p_i respectively the ith injection and projection of the coproduct. Let us denote by Φ_i the composition

$$[U, U] \xrightarrow{T(u_i)} [U, {}^I U] \xrightarrow{T(\pi)} [U, A] \xrightarrow{\Phi} [U, B].$$

Then Φ_i is a morphism of **R**-modules, and so by the case we have already treated we have for each i a morphism $\varphi_i : U \to B$ such that $\Phi_i(f) = \varphi_i f$ for all $f \in [U, U]$. The φ_i's then define a morphism $\bar{\varphi} = \sum_{i \in I} \varphi_i p_i : {}^I U \to B$. If we denote the composition $\Phi T(\pi)$ by $\bar{\Phi}$, then for $f \in [U, {}^I U]$ we have using I, 18.1,

$$\begin{aligned} \bar{\Phi}(f) &= \Phi(\pi f) = \Phi\left[\pi\left(\sum_{i \in I} u_i p_i\right) f\right] = \sum_{i \in I} \Phi(\pi u_i p_i f) \\ &= \sum_{i \in I} \Phi_i(p_i f) = \sum_{i \in I} \varphi_i p_i f = \bar{\varphi} f. \end{aligned} \tag{1}$$

We show that $\bar{\varphi}\lambda = 0$. If $\bar{\varphi}\lambda \neq 0$, then since U is a generator we can find $\alpha : U \to M$ such that $\bar{\varphi}\lambda\alpha \neq 0$. But we have

$$\bar{\varphi}\lambda\alpha = \bar{\Phi}(\lambda\alpha) = \Phi(\pi\lambda\alpha) = \Phi(0) = 0.$$

Therefore $\bar{\varphi}\lambda = 0$, and so there is a morphism $\varphi : A \to B$ such that $\bar{\varphi} = \varphi\pi$. Let $f : U \to A$. Since U is projective we can write $f = \pi g$ for some $g : U \to {}^I U$. Then

$$\Phi(f) = \Phi(\pi g) = \bar{\Phi}(g) = \bar{\varphi} g = \varphi\pi g = \varphi f.$$

In other words φ is the required morphism.

If U is small, then the above goes through even when A is not finitely generated, or in other words, when I is not necessarily finite. For if we have $f \in [U, {}^I U]$, then since U is small we may write $f = \sum_{i \in J} u_i p_i f$ in (1) where J is some finite subset of I (II, 16.1). The rest of the proof is the same.

Suppose now that $\mathscr{A}$ is C_3, but U is not necessarily small. Given any $A \in \mathscr{A}$ we can write $A = \varinjlim A_i$ where $\{A_i, \pi\}$ is the system of finitely generated subobjects of A (III, 1.4). Let $\Phi : [U, A] \to [U, B]$ be a morphism of **R**-modules, and define Φ_i as the composition

$$[U, A_i] \to [U, A] \xrightarrow{\Phi} [U, B].$$

By what we have already proved we have for each Φ_i a morphism $\varphi_i : A_i \to B$ such that $\Phi_i(f) = \varphi_i f$ for all $f \in [U, A_i]$. Furthermore, since T is an imbedding the φ_i's are unique. From this it follows that if $i \leqslant j$ then $\varphi_i = \varphi_j \pi_{ij}$; in other words $\{\varphi_i\}$ is a cocompatible family. Consequently, we get an induced morphism from the direct limit, say $\varphi : A \to B$. If $f \in [U, A]$, then the image of f is A_i for some i, and so we can write $f = \pi_i g$ for some $g : U \to A_i$. We then have

$$\Phi(f) = \Phi(\pi_i g) = \Phi_i(g) = \varphi_i g = \varphi\pi_i g = \varphi f.$$

This proves that T is full.

Finally, if T is an equivalence, then it is a coproduct preserving functor; hence by II, 16.1, U is small. Conversely, suppose that U is small, so that T preserves coproducts. Let M be any right **R**-module, and write an exact sequence of **R**-modules

$${}^I\mathbf{R} \xrightarrow{F} {}^J\mathbf{R} \to M \to 0.$$

Since T preserves coproducts we have $T({}^I U) = {}^I\mathbf{R}$ and $T({}^J U) = {}^J\mathbf{R}$. Also, since T is full we have $F = T(f)$ for some $f : {}^I U \to {}^J U$. Then by exactness of T it follows that M is isomorphic to $T(C)$ where C is the cokernel of f. This proves that T is representative, and so T is an equivalence. ∎

Theorem 4.1 will serve two important purposes in the sequel. In Chapter VI we shall use it to prove that any small abelian category admits a full exact imbedding into a category of modules, and in Chapter IX we shall see how it leads to the computation of global dimension for certain rings of matrices.

5. Characterization of Functor Categories

Lemma 5.1. *Consider the following diagram in an exact additive category $\mathscr{A}$:*

$$\begin{array}{ccccccc} P_1 & \xrightarrow{d} & P_0 & \xrightarrow{\epsilon} & A & & \\ & & & & \downarrow{\scriptstyle\alpha} & & \\ P_1' & \xrightarrow{d'} & P_0' & \xrightarrow{\epsilon'} & A' & \longrightarrow & 0 \end{array} \tag{1}$$

Suppose that P_1 and P_0 are projective, the bottom row is exact, and the top row is of order two. Then there exist morphisms $f_0 : P_0 \to P_0'$ and $f_1 : P_1 \to P_1'$ such that (1) *is commutative. Furthermore, let $T : \mathscr{A}' \to \mathscr{B}$ be a covariant additive functor into an exact additive category, where $\mathscr{A}'$ is a full subcategory of $\mathscr{A}$ containing P_0, P_1, P_0', and P_1'. Then the induced morphism* $\text{Coker}(T(d) \to \text{Coker}(T(d'))$ *is independent of the choice of f_0 and f_1.*

Proof. Using projectivity of P_0 we can find $f_0 : P_0 \to P_0'$ such that $\alpha\epsilon = \epsilon' f_0$. Now $\epsilon' f_0 d = \alpha\epsilon d = 0$, and so the image of $f_0 d$ is a subobject of $\text{Ker}(\epsilon') = \text{Im}(d')$. Hence by projectivity of P_1 we can find $f_1 : P_1 \to P_1'$ such that $f_0 d = d' f_1$. Let $p : T(P_0) \to F$ and $p' : T(P_0') \to F'$ be the cokernels of $T(d)$ and $T(d')$ respectively. Suppose that $g_0 : P_0 \to P_0'$ and $g_1 : P_1 \to P_1'$ are another pair of morphisms making (1) commutative. Let λ, $\mu : F \to F'$ be the morphisms induced by f_0, f_1 and g_0, g_1, respectively. Now $\epsilon'(f_0 - g_0) = 0$, and so again using projectivity of P_0 and exactness of the bottom row we obtain a morphism $h : P_0 \to P_1'$ such that $d'h = f_0 - g_0$. Then

$$\begin{aligned} (\lambda - \mu)p &= \lambda p - \mu p = p' T(f_0) - p' T(g_0) = p' T(f_0 - g_0) \\ &= p' T(d'h) = p' T(d') T(h) = 0. \end{aligned}$$

Therefore since p is an epimorphism, we must have $\lambda = \mu$. ∎

Theorem 5.2. *Let $\mathscr{P}$ be a full subcategory of a cocomplete abelian category $\mathscr{A}$, and suppose that the objects of $\mathscr{P}$ form a generating set of small projectives for $\mathscr{A}$. Let $T : \mathscr{P} \to \mathscr{B}$ be an additive functor into a cocomplete abelian category. Then T can be extended uniquely* (*up to natural equivalence*) *to a colimit preserving functor $\bar{T} : \mathscr{A} \to \mathscr{B}$.*

Proof. We first extend T to the subcategory of $\mathscr{A}$ consisting of all free objects; that is, objects of the form $\bigoplus_{i \in I} P_i$ where $P_i \in \mathscr{P}$ for all $i \in I$. We define $\bar{T}\left(\bigoplus_{i \in I} P_i\right) = \bigoplus_{i \in I} T(P_i)$. For a morphism $\alpha : \bigoplus_{i \in I} P_i \to \bigoplus_{j \in J} P_j$, let α_i be the composition with the ith injection into $\bigoplus_{i \in I} P_i$. By II, 16.1, since P_i is small we can write $\alpha_i = \sum_{j \in J} u_j p_j \alpha_i$ where u_j and p_j are the jth injection and projection, respectively, for the coproduct $\bigoplus_{j\in J} P_j$. We then define $\bar{T}(\alpha) : \bigoplus_{i\in I} T(P_i) \to \bigoplus_{j\in J} T(P_j)$ as the morphism which when composed with the ith injection into $\bigoplus_{i\in I} T(P_i)$ gives $\sum_{j\in J} v_j T(p_j \alpha_i)$, where v_j denotes the jth injection for $\bigoplus_{j\in J} T(P_j)$. The additive functorial properties of $\bar{T}$ as so far constructed follow from the additive functorial properties of T.

From now on the process resembles the construction of the zeroth (left) derived functor given in Chapters IV and V of [6]. For $A \in \mathscr{A}$ write an exact sequence

$$P_1 \xrightarrow{d} P_0 \to A \to 0 \tag{2}$$

where P_1 and P_0 are free. Define $\bar{T}(A)$ as $\text{Coker}(T(d))$. For a morphism $\alpha : A \to A'$, let $P_1' \xrightarrow{d'} P_0' \to A' \to 0$ be the sequence used to define $\bar{T}(A')$. Then by 5.1 we can find morphisms f_1 and f_0 making a commutative diagram

$$\begin{array}{ccccccc}
P_1 & \longrightarrow & P_0 & \longrightarrow & A & \longrightarrow & 0 \\
\downarrow{\scriptstyle f_1} & & \downarrow{\scriptstyle f_0} & & \downarrow{\scriptstyle \alpha} & & \\
P_1' & \longrightarrow & P_0' & \longrightarrow & A' & \longrightarrow & 0.
\end{array}$$

Define $\bar{T}(\alpha)$ as the morphism making the diagram

$$\begin{array}{ccccccc}
\bar{T}(P_1) & \longrightarrow & \bar{T}(P_0) & \longrightarrow & \bar{T}(A) & \longrightarrow & 0 \\
\downarrow{\scriptstyle \bar{T}(f_1)} & & \downarrow{\scriptstyle \bar{T}(f_0)} & & \downarrow{\scriptstyle \bar{T}(\alpha)} & & \\
\bar{T}(P_1') & \longrightarrow & \bar{T}(P_0') & \longrightarrow & \bar{T}(A') & \longrightarrow & 0
\end{array}$$

commutative. Then again by 5.1 we know that $\bar{T}(\alpha)$ is independent of the choice of f_0 and f_1, and in this way $\bar{T}$ is seen to be an additive functor from $\mathscr{A}$ to $\mathscr{B}$. Setting $A = A'$ and $\alpha = 1_A$ in the above discussion we see at this point that up to isomorphism $\bar{T}(A)$ is independent of the choice of the sequence (2) used to define it, and furthermore that this isomorphism is natural with respect to morphisms to and from A.

We now show that $\bar{T}$ is cokernel preserving. Let

$$0 \to A' \to A \to A'' \to 0 \tag{3}$$

be an exact sequence in $\mathscr{A}$, and take free resolutions $P_1' \to P_0' \to A' \to 0$ and

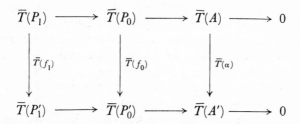

$P''_1 \to P''_0 \to A'' \to 0$ for A' and A''. We construct the following commutative diagram:

$$\begin{array}{ccccccc}
 & 0 & & 0 & & 0 & \\
 & \downarrow & & \downarrow & & \downarrow & \\
 & P'_1 & \longrightarrow & P'_0 & \longrightarrow & A' & \longrightarrow 0 \\
 & \downarrow & & \downarrow & & \downarrow & \\
 & P'_1 \oplus P''_1 & \longrightarrow & P'_0 \oplus P''_0 & \longrightarrow & A & \longrightarrow 0 \\
 & \downarrow & & \downarrow & & \downarrow & \\
 & P''_1 & \longrightarrow & P''_0 & \longrightarrow & A'' & \longrightarrow 0 \\
 & \downarrow & & \downarrow & & \downarrow & \\
 & 0 & & 0 & & 0 &
\end{array} \tag{4}$$

The middle column is a split exact sequence, and the morphism $P''_0 \to A$ is defined by projectivity of P''_0 and the epimorphism $A \to A''$. Taking the kernel of the morphism from the middle column to the right-hand column, we obtain a short exact sequence by the nine lemma (I, 16.1). If we repeat the above construction with the sequence of kernels replacing (3), and P'_1 and P''_1 replacing P'_0 and P''_0, respectively, we obtain the commutative diagram (4) with exact rows and columns. Hence we can use the middle row to define $\bar{T}(A)$. Applying $\bar{T}$ to (4), the left two columns will still be split exact sequences by additivity of $\bar{T}$. We then see from II, 12.2*, that $\bar{T}(A') \to \bar{T}(A) \to \bar{T}(A'') \to 0$ is exact. In other words $\bar{T}$ is cokernel preserving.

It now follows from II, 6.3*, that in order to show that $\bar{T}$ is colimit preserving it suffices to show that $\bar{T}$ preserves coproducts. Given a family $\{A_i\}_{i \in I}$ of objects in $\mathscr{A}$, choose a free resolution

$$P_1^i \xrightarrow{d^i} P_0^i \xrightarrow{\epsilon^i} A_i \to 0$$

for each $i \in I$. Then using the fact that coproducts are cokernel preserving (II, 12.2*), we see that

$$\bigoplus_{i \in I} P_1^i \xrightarrow{\oplus d^i} \bigoplus_{i \in I} P_0^i \xrightarrow{\oplus \epsilon^i} \bigoplus_{i \in I} A_i \longrightarrow 0$$

is a free resolution for $\bigoplus_{i \in I} A_i$. From this it follows that $\bar{T}$ preserves coproducts.

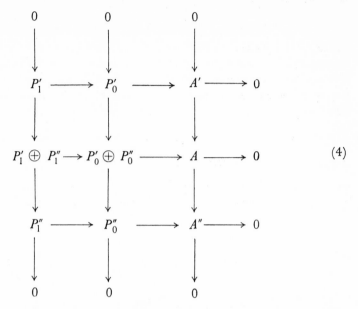

Finally, since the construction of $\bar{T}$ was forced at each step by the requirement that it be colimit preserving, we have the uniqueness assertion. ∎

Theorem 5.2 generalizes to functors of several variables (exercise 12).

Let $\mathscr{A}$ be a small additive category. Consider the functor from $\mathscr{A}$ to $(\mathscr{A}, \mathscr{G})$ which assigns to the object $A \in \mathscr{A}$ the functor $H^A \in (\mathscr{A}, \mathscr{G})$, and to the morphism $A \rightarrow B$ the induced transformation $H^B \rightarrow H^A$. By 2.2 we see that this is a full, contravariant imbedding, and by 2.3 the image of $\mathscr{A}$ in $(\mathscr{A}, \mathscr{G})$ is a generating set of small projectives. Composing this functor with the duality functor on $\mathscr{A}$ gives us a full covariant imbedding from $\mathscr{A}^*$ into $(\mathscr{A}, \mathscr{G})$.

Theorem 5.3 (Freyd). *A category $\mathscr{B}$ is equivalent to a functor category of the form $(\mathscr{A}, \mathscr{G})$ for some small additive category $\mathscr{A}$ if and only if $\mathscr{B}$ is cocomplete abelian with a generating set of small projectives.*

Proof. We have already seen that $(\mathscr{A}, \mathscr{G})$ is cocomplete abelian, and by 2.3 the family $\{H^A\}_{A \in \mathscr{A}}$ form a generating set of small projectives. Conversely, suppose that $\mathscr{B}$ is cocomplete abelian and that $\mathscr{P}$ is a full subcategory of $\mathscr{B}$, the objects of which form a generating set of small projectives. Then $\mathscr{B}$ and $(\mathscr{P}^*, \mathscr{G})$ are cocomplete abelian categories each with a full subcategory whose objects form a generating set of projectives, and furthermore these subcategories are isomorphic. Theorem 5.2 then gives us functors $T: \mathscr{B} \rightarrow (\mathscr{P}^*, \mathscr{G})$ and $S: (\mathscr{P}^*, \mathscr{G}) \rightarrow \mathscr{B}$ extending this isomorphism, and moreover the uniqueness part of 5.2 shows that ST and TS are naturally equivalent to the identity functors on $\mathscr{B}$ and $(\mathscr{P}^*, \mathscr{G})$, respectively. Hence by II, 10.1, T is an equivalence of categories. ∎

Remark. If $\mathscr{B}$ has a small projective generator, then 5.3 gives another proof that $\mathscr{B}$ is equivalent to a category of modules (4.1).

Theorem 5.4. *Let $\mathscr{A}$ be a C_3 category with a full subcategory $\mathscr{P}$ whose objects form a generating set of projectives for $\mathscr{A}$. Let $T, S: \mathscr{A} \rightarrow \mathscr{B}$ be additive, covariant functors where $\mathscr{B}$ is an exact additive category, and suppose that T is colimit preserving. Denote the restrictions of T and S to $\mathscr{P}$ by $T|\mathscr{P}$ and $S|\mathscr{P}$. Then any natural transformation $\varphi: T|\mathscr{P} \rightarrow S|\mathscr{P}$ can be extended uniquely to a natural transformation $\bar{\varphi}: T \rightarrow S$.*

Proof. For a free object $\bigoplus_{i \in I} P_i$ in $\mathscr{A}$ we have the composition

$$T(\bigoplus P_i) = \bigoplus T(P_i) \rightarrow \bigoplus S(P_i) \rightarrow S(\bigoplus P_i).$$

Here the equality is a result of the fact that T is coproduct preserving, the middle morphism is $\bigoplus \varphi_{P_i}$, and the last morphism is the one which when composed with the ith injection into $\bigoplus S(P_i)$ gives S of the ith injection into $\bigoplus P_i$. Consider a morphism $f: \bigoplus_{i \in I} P_i \rightarrow \bigoplus_{j \in J} P_j$ where J is finite. Using the fact that a morphism from a coproduct to a product is determined by its coordinate morphisms, we obtain a commutative diagram

$$\begin{array}{ccccc} \bigoplus_{i\in I} T(P_i) = T\left(\bigoplus_{i\in I} P_i\right) & \to & T\left(\bigoplus_{j\in J} P_j\right) & & \\ \downarrow & & \downarrow & & \\ S\left(\bigoplus_{i\in I} P_i\right) & \to & S\left(\bigoplus_{j\in J} P_j\right) & = & \times_{j\in J} S(P_j) \end{array} \tag{5}$$

Now let A be any finitely generated object. This means we can find an exact sequence

$$P_1 \to P_0 \to A \to 0$$

where P_1 is free and P_0 is a finite free (that is, a coproduct of the form $\bigoplus_{j\in J} P$ with J finite). Using (5) we have a commutative diagram

$$\begin{array}{ccccccc} T(P_1) & \to & T(P_0) & \to & T(A) & \to & 0 \\ \downarrow & & \downarrow & & & & \\ S(P_1) & \to & S(P_0) & \to & S(A) & \to & 0 \end{array} \tag{6}$$

where the top row is exact since T is colimit preserving, and the bottom row is of order two by the additive functorial property of S. Hence we can find a unique morphism $\bar{\varphi}_A : T(A) \to S(A)$ making (6) commutative.

Let $A \to A'$ be any morphism where A and A' are finitely generated. Consider the diagram

$$\begin{array}{ccccc} P_0 & \to & A & \to & 0 \\ & & \downarrow & & \\ P_0' & \to & A' & \to & 0 \end{array} \tag{7}$$

where the top row was used to define $\bar{\varphi}_A$ and the bottom row was used to define $\bar{\varphi}_{A'}$. Since P_0 is projective we can find $P_0 \to P_0'$ making (7) commutative. Now $\bar{\varphi}$ as so far constructed induces a morphism from the diagram

$$\begin{array}{ccc} T(P_0) & \longrightarrow & T(A) \\ \downarrow & & \downarrow \\ T(P_0') & \longrightarrow & T(A') \end{array}$$

to the diagram

$$\begin{array}{ccc} S(P_0) & \longrightarrow & S(A) \\ \downarrow & & \downarrow \\ S(P_0') & \longrightarrow & S(A') \end{array}$$

Furthermore, in the resulting cube we see that all faces are commutative save possibly the face

$$\begin{array}{ccc} T(A) & \longrightarrow & T(A') \\ {\scriptstyle \bar{\varphi}_A}\downarrow & & \downarrow{\scriptstyle \bar{\varphi}_{A'}} \\ S(A) & \longrightarrow & S(A') \end{array} \qquad (8)$$

But since $T(P_0) \to T(A)$ is an epimorphism, it follows from II, 1.1, that (8) is also commutative. Thus $\bar{\varphi}$ as so far constructed is natural.

For a not necessarily finitely generated object A, we let $\{A_i\}$ be a representative set of finitely generated subobjects. Since $\mathscr{A}$ is C_3 we know by III, 1.4, that A is the direct limit of the corresponding direct system, and so since T is colimit preserving we see that $T(A)$ is the direct limit of the corresponding system of $T(A_i)$'s. The cocompatible family $\{T(A_i) \to S(A_i) \to (SA)\}$ then defines a morphism $\bar{\varphi}_A : T(A) \to S(A)$. Given $A \to A'$ we must show commutativity of (8). For each finitely generated subobject A_i of A, let $A'_i \to A'$ be the image of the composition $A_i \to A \to A'$. Then A'_i is a finitely generated subobject of A'. Hence, by what we have already shown, the diagram

$$\begin{array}{ccc} T(A_i) & \longrightarrow & T(A'_i) \\ \downarrow & & \downarrow \\ S(A_i) & \longrightarrow & S(A'_i) \end{array} \qquad (9_i)$$

is commutative for each i. Consider the morphism from the diagram (9_i) to the diagram (8) induced by the morphisms $A_i \to A$ and $A'_i \to A'$. Again we have a cube in which all faces are commutative save possibly (8). From this we see that for each i the composition $T(A_i) \to T(A) \to T(A') \to S(A')$ is the same as the composition $T(A_i) \to T(A) \to S(A) \to S(A')$. Since $T(A)$ is the direct limit of the $T(A_i)$'s, this proves the commutativity of (8) and establishes naturality of $\bar{\varphi}$.

Uniqueness of $\bar{\varphi}$ is clear since each step in the above construction was forced by the requirement that $\bar{\varphi}$ be natural. ▮

Corollary 5.5. *Under the assumptions of* 5.4, *if further S is colimit preserving and φ is a natural equivalence, then $\bar{\varphi}$ is a natural equivalence.* ▮

Theorem 5.4 and Corollary 5.5 can be generalized to functors of several variables (exercise 11).

Exercises

1. Use the fact that $\mathscr{G}$ has an injective cogenerator to find an exact, contravariant imbedding from $\mathscr{G}$ to $\mathscr{G}$. Hence show that any abelian category with an injective cogenerator admits an exact covariant group valued imbedding. Show similarly that the conclusion of 3.3 is valid under dual hypothesis.

2. Consider the diagram (1) of abelian groups in §1. Let $X \to A$ be the kernel of the composition $A \to B \to B''$. Then we have a morphism $X \to B'$ such that $X \to B' \to B = X \to A \to B$, and an epimorphism $X \to K''$ such that

$$X \to A \to A'' = X \to K'' \to A''.$$

Show that the connecting morphism $K'' \to F'$ is such that

$$X \to K'' \to F' = X \to B' \to F'.$$

Prove also that the connecting morphism is self-dual by showing that it satisfies the dual of the above relation.

3. If $\mathscr{A}$ is a small, exact, additive category and T is a projective in $(\mathscr{A}, \mathscr{G})$, then T is a kernel preserving functor. (Use 2.3 and II, 14.2.)

4. Let $\mathscr{A}$ be a small additive category with kernels and finite biproducts, and let $T: \mathscr{A} \to \mathscr{G}$ be a small projective in the functor category $(\mathscr{A}, \mathscr{G})$. Then T is naturally equivalent to H^B for some $B \in \mathscr{A}$. (Find a composition $T \to H^A \to T$ which is the identity for some $A \in \mathscr{A}$, and then use I, 18.5, and the full, contravariant, kernel preserving imbedding $\mathscr{A} \to (\mathscr{A}, \mathscr{G})$ which assigns the functor H^A to the object A.) This exercise is due to Freyd.

5. Let $\mathscr{A}$ and $\mathscr{B}$ be additive categories, and for $A \in \mathscr{A}$, $B \in \mathscr{B}$, let

$$H^A \otimes H^B : \mathscr{A} \times \mathscr{B} \to \mathscr{G}$$

be the bifunctor whose value on the pair (A', B') is $[A, A'] \otimes [B, B']$. (The tensor product of groups is defined in VI, exercise 3). Let T be an additive bifunctor from $\mathscr{A} \times \mathscr{B}$ to $\mathscr{G}$. Establish a natural equivalence

$$[H^A \otimes H^B, T] \approx T(A, B),$$

and hence show that in the case where $\mathscr{A}$ and $\mathscr{B}$ are small the family $\{H^A \otimes H^B\}_{\mathscr{A} \times \mathscr{B}}$ is a generating set of small projectives for the category $(\mathscr{A}, (\mathscr{B}, \mathscr{G}))$. Generalize this result to additive group valued functors of any number of variables.

6. In exercise 5 let $\mathscr{A}$ be the category of finitely generated abelian groups $\bar{\mathscr{G}}$ (II, exercise 17) and let $\mathscr{B}$ be a ring $\mathbf{R}$, or in other words an additive category with a single object B. In this case denote the functor $H^A \otimes H^B$ by $H^A \otimes \mathbf{R}$. The functor category $(\mathscr{B}, \mathscr{G})$ here is the module category ${}^{\mathbf{R}}\mathscr{G}$. Then by exercise 5 the category $(\bar{\mathscr{G}}, {}^{\mathbf{R}}\mathscr{G})$ has an injective cogenerator Q. In particular, let $\mathbf{R} = \mathbf{Z}_2$, where in general $\mathbf{Z}_n$ denotes the integers reduced modulo n. Consider the epimorphism $f: \mathbf{Z}_4 \to \mathbf{Z}_2$ in $\bar{\mathcal{G}}$ defined by $f(1) = 1$. Then f induces a natural transformation

$$\eta : H^{\mathbf{Z}_2} \otimes \mathbf{Z}_2 \to H^{\mathbf{Z}_4} \otimes \mathbf{Z}_2.$$

By evaluating η at $\mathbf{Z}_4 \in \bar{\mathcal{G}}$ show that η is not an epimorphism. Hence, since Q is a cogenerator the morphism

$$[H^{\mathbf{Z}_4} \otimes \mathbf{Z}_2, Q] \to [H^{\mathbf{Z}_2} \otimes \mathbf{Z}_2, Q]$$

is not an epimorphism. But by exercise 5 this is just $Q(\mathbf{Z}_4) \to Q(\mathbf{Z}_2)$. Hence an injective, module-valued functor need not be an epifunctor.

Show, however, that if the ring $\mathbf{R}$ is torsion free as an abelian group (so that tensoring with it over the integers is an exact functor) and $\mathcal{A}$ is any abelian category, then an injective in the functor category $(\mathcal{A}^{\mathbf{R}}, \mathcal{G})$ is a cokernel preserving functor.

7. Let $\mathcal{A}$ be a small abelian category with projectives. Suppose that $T: \mathcal{A} \to \mathcal{G}$ is an additive epifunctor and consider the transformation

$$\bigoplus_{P} {}^{[H^P, T]}H^P \to T$$

whose αth coordinate is α, where P runs through all projectives in $\mathcal{A}$. Show that this transformation is an epimorphism in the category $(\mathcal{A}, \mathcal{G})$.

8. Let $\mathbf{R}$ be a commutative ring and take $U = \mathbf{R} \oplus \mathbf{R}$ in 4.1. Under T the $\mathbf{R}$-module $\mathbf{R}$ corresponds to the Λ-module $[\mathbf{R} \oplus \mathbf{R}, \mathbf{R}]^{\mathbf{R}}$ where

$$\Lambda = [\mathbf{R} \oplus \mathbf{R}, \mathbf{R} \oplus \mathbf{R}]^{\mathbf{R}} .$$

Show that every nonzero element of $[\mathbf{R} \oplus \mathbf{R}, \mathbf{R}]$ has torsion, so that in particular $[\mathbf{R} \oplus \mathbf{R}, \mathbf{R}]$ cannot be free as a Λ-module. Hence the property of freedom of modules is not invariant under equivalences of categories.

9. The **center** of a ring $\mathbf{R}$ is defined as $\{c \in \mathbf{R} | cr = rc \text{ for all } r \in \mathbf{R}\}$. If A is any object in a C_2 additive category $\mathcal{A}$, then the center of $[A, A]$ is ring isomorphic to the center of $[{}^IA, {}^IA]$ for any set I. Hence if $\mathcal{A}$ is a C_2 abelian category and U and V are both projective generators for $\mathcal{A}$, then $[U, U]$ and $[V, V]$ have isomorphic centers. (Write $U \oplus M = {}^IV$ and $V \oplus N = {}^IU$ for some infinite set I and show from this that ${}^IU = {}^IV$.) Therefore if ${}^{\mathbf{R}}\mathcal{G}$ is equivalent to ${}^{\mathbf{S}}\mathcal{G}$, then $\mathbf{R}$ and $\mathbf{S}$ have isomorphic centers. In particular, if $\mathbf{R}$ and $\mathbf{S}$ are commutative rings, then ${}^{\mathbf{R}}\mathcal{G}$ is equivalent to ${}^{\mathbf{S}}\mathcal{G}$ if and only if $\mathbf{R}$ is isomorphic to $\mathbf{S}$ (Freyd).

10. If the functor S of 5.4 is limit preserving, then it suffices to assume that $\mathcal{A}$ is C_2 abelian. If S is coproduct preserving and $\mathcal{B}$ is C_2, then it suffices to assume that $\mathcal{A}$ is cocomplete abelian. (In either case show that the diagram (5) of 5.4 is commutative even when J is not a finite set. Hence there is no need to resort to direct limits in these cases.)

11. Using induction on n generalize 5.4 to the case of additive functors

$$T, S : \mathscr{A}_1 \times \mathscr{A}_2 \times \ldots \times \mathscr{A}_n \to \mathscr{B}$$

where each $\mathscr{A}$ is a C_3 category possessing a generating set of projectives.

12. Use induction on n to generalize 5.2 to functors of several variables where each of the variables comes from a cocomplete abelian category having a generating set of small projectives. (Theorem 5.3 insures that such categories are C_3, hence exercise 11 applies.)

13. A **group object** in a category $\mathscr{A}$ is an object $A \in \mathscr{A}$ together with a group structure on $[B, A]$ for each $B \in \mathscr{A}$, such that morphisms $B \to B'$ induce morphisms of groups $[B', A] \to [B, A]$. Thus, if A is a group object, then $[\ , A]$ can be considered as a contravariant, (nonabelian) group valued functor. If $\mathscr{A}$ has a zero, then the unit element for the group $[B, A]$ is necessarily the zero morphism 0_{BA}. If, furthermore, $\mathscr{A}$ has finite products, then using 2.2* we can find unique morphisms $m : A \times A \to A$ and $i : A \to A$ inducing multiplication and inversion on $[B, A]$ for all $B \in \mathscr{A}$. Then m and i satisfy the following rules:

(i) The diagram

$$\begin{array}{ccc} A \times A \times A & \xrightarrow{m \times 1} & A \times A \\ \big\downarrow{\scriptstyle 1 \times m} & & \big\downarrow{\scriptstyle m} \\ A \times A & \xrightarrow{m} & A \end{array}$$

is commutative.

(ii) The composition $A \xrightarrow{u_2} A \times A \xrightarrow{m} A$ is 1_A, where u_2 is the second injection into the product.

(iii) The composition $A \xrightarrow{\binom{i}{1}} A \times A \xrightarrow{m} A$ is zero.

Conversely, if $\mathscr{A}$ is a category with a zero and finite products, and $m : A \times A \to A$ and $i : A \to A$ are morphisms satisfying (i), (ii), and (iii), then the sets $[B, A]$ become groups in such a way as to make A a group object. It then follows from the corresponding facts about ordinary groups (which are the group objects in the category of sets) that the composition

$$A \xrightarrow{\binom{1}{i}} A \times A \xrightarrow{m} A$$

is zero, the composition

$$A \xrightarrow{u_1} A \times A \xrightarrow{m} A$$

is 1_A, and the "inverse" morphism i satisfying (iii) is unique.

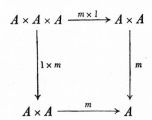

A morphism of group objects A_1 and A_2 is a morphism $f: A_1 \to A_2$ in $\mathscr{A}$ such that the induced morphism $[\ ,f]$ is a natural transformation of group valued functors. In this way the class $\mathscr{A}_G$ of group objects in $\mathscr{A}$ becomes a category. If $\mathscr{A}$ is Σ-complete, then so is $\mathscr{A}_G$. The corresponding statement for cocompleteness need not be true. If $\mathscr{A}$ has finite products and the "multiplications" on group objects A_1 and A_2 are m_1 and m_2, respectively, then $f: A_1 \to A_2$ is a morphism of group objects if and only if $fm_1 = m_2(f \times f)$.

If $\mathscr{A}$ is an additive category with finite products, then $\mathscr{A}_G$ is isomorphic to $\mathscr{A}$.

CHAPTER V

Adjoint Functors

Introduction

In this chapter we develop a theory of adjoint functors as introduced by Kan [24]. Theorem 3.1 gives a necessary and sufficient condition for a functor $T:\mathscr{A}\to\mathscr{B}$ to have a coadjoint. If $\mathscr{A}$ is a complete, locally small category with a cogenerator then this condition is simply that T be limit preserving (3.2).

If the inclusion functor $\mathscr{A}'\subset\mathscr{A}$ of a subcategory has a coadjoint R, then $\mathscr{A}'$ is called a coreflective subcategory of $\mathscr{A}$. In the case where $\mathscr{A}'$ is a full, coreflective subcategory of an abelian category and R is kernel preserving, it turns out that $\mathscr{A}'$ is abelian (5.3).

Let $\mathscr{M}$ be a full subcategory of a complete, locally small abelian category $\mathscr{A}$, and suppose that $\mathscr{M}$ is closed with respect to limits and subobjects. Suppose further that for every $M\in\mathscr{M}$ there is a monomorphism $M\to Q$ in $\mathscr{M}$ with Q injective in $\mathscr{A}$. Then $\mathscr{M}$ is called a monosubcategory of $\mathscr{A}$. A theory of monosubcategories is developed in §6. A certain subcategory of $\mathscr{M}$ will be shown to be abelian.

The last section gives a theory of projective classes in an abelian category. Under certain conditions it is shown that if $S:\mathscr{B}\to\mathscr{A}$ is a coadjoint for a faithful epifunctor T, then the projectives in $\mathscr{A}$ are precisely the objects of the form $S(P)$ where P is projective in $\mathscr{B}$.

The work in §3 and §6 is by Peter Freyd. Section 7 is due to Eilenberg and Moore [12].

1. Generalities

Recall that a covariant functor $T:\mathscr{A}\to\mathscr{B}$ is said to be an adjoint for the covariant functor $S:\mathscr{B}\to\mathscr{A}$ if there exists a natural equivalence of set-valued bifunctors (not necessarily unique)

$$\eta_{B,A}:[S(B),A]\to[B,T(A)]. \tag{1}$$

We say also that S is a coadjoint for T in this case. The adjoint situation given by the natural equivalence (1) will sometimes be described by the notation $(\eta; S, T; \mathscr{A}, \mathscr{B})$.

If $T_1, T_2 : \mathscr{A} \to \mathscr{B}$ are naturally equivalent functors, then it is immediate from definition that a functor $S : \mathscr{B} \to \mathscr{A}$ is a coadjoint for T_1 if and only if it is an adjoint for T_2. Also it is clear that $1_A : \mathscr{A} \to \mathscr{A}$ is a coadjoint for itself, and that if $S_2 : \mathscr{C} \to \mathscr{B}$ and $S_1 : \mathscr{B} \to \mathscr{A}$ are coadjoints for $T_2 : \mathscr{B} \to \mathscr{C}$ and $T_1 : \mathscr{A} \to \mathscr{B}$, respectively, then $S_1 S_2 : \mathscr{C} \to \mathscr{A}$ is a coadjoint for $T_2 T_1 : \mathscr{A} \to \mathscr{C}$.

Given the natural equivalence (1), for $B \in \mathscr{B}$ we denote by φ_B the morphism

$$\eta_{B,S(B)}(1_{S(B)}) : B \to TS(B). \tag{2}$$

Dually, for $A \in \mathscr{A}$ we denote by ψ_A the morphism

$$\eta^{-1}_{T(A),A}(1_{T(A)}) : ST(A) \to A. \tag{2*}$$

A morphism of the form $\alpha : S(B) \to A$ in $\mathscr{A}$ induces a commutative diagram

$$\begin{array}{ccc} [S(B), S(B)] & \xrightarrow{\eta} & [B, TS(B)] \\ \downarrow & & \downarrow \\ [S(B), A] & \xrightarrow{\eta} & [B, T(A)] \end{array}$$

which yields the equation

$$\eta(\alpha) = T(\alpha)\varphi_B. \tag{3}$$

Also a morphism $\gamma : A \to A'$ in $\mathscr{A}$ induces a commutative diagram

$$\begin{array}{ccc} [ST(A), A] & \xrightarrow{\eta} & [T(A), T(A)] \\ \downarrow & & \downarrow \\ [ST(A), A'] & \xrightarrow{\eta} & [T(A), T(A')] \end{array}$$

which gives us the equation

$$\gamma\psi_A = \eta^{-1}(T(\gamma)). \tag{4}$$

The duals of Eqs. (3) and (4) read

$$\eta^{-1}(\beta) = \psi_A S(\beta) \tag{3*}$$

$$\varphi_B \delta = \eta(S(\delta)) \tag{4*}$$

relative to respective morphisms $\beta : B \to T(A)$ and $\delta : B' \to B$ in $\mathscr{B}$.

Proposition 1.1. *Consider an adjoint situation $(\eta; S, T; \mathscr{A}, \mathscr{B})$. Given $\beta : B \to T(A)$ in $\mathscr{B}$, the morphism $\alpha = \eta^{-1}(\beta)$ is the unique morphism $S(B) \to A$ such that the diagram*

$$\begin{array}{ccc} B & \xrightarrow{\varphi_B} & TS(B) \\ & \searrow^{\beta} & \downarrow{\scriptstyle T(\alpha)} \\ & & T(A) \end{array}$$

is commutative. In particular, T is univalent on $[S(B), A]$. Furthermore, φ is a natural transformation from 1_B to TS; that is, relative to a morphism $\delta : B' \to B$ in $\mathscr{B}$, the diagram

$$\begin{array}{ccc} B' & \xrightarrow{\varphi_{B'}} & TS(B') \\ \downarrow{\scriptstyle \delta} & & \downarrow{\scriptstyle TS(\delta)} \\ B & \xrightarrow{\varphi_B} & TS(B) \end{array}$$

is commutative.

Proof. The first statement follows from (3), taking into account the fact that η is a 1–1 correspondence. To prove the statement regarding naturality of φ, we wish to show that

$$\varphi_B \delta = TS(\delta)\varphi_{B'}. \tag{5}$$

Using (3), the right side of (5) is $\eta(S(\delta))$. Hence Eq. (5) is equivalent to Eq. (4*). ▮

Proposition 1.2. *Given an adjoint situation $(\eta; S, T; \mathscr{A}, \mathscr{B})$, the following statements are equivalent.*

(a) *T is faithful.*
(b) *T reflects epimorphisms.*
(c) *If $\beta : B \to T(A)$ is an epimorphism, then $\alpha = \eta^{-1}(\beta)$ is an epimorphism.*
(d) *$\psi_A : ST(A) \to A$ is an epimorphism for all $A \in \mathscr{A}$.*

Proof. (a) ⇒ (*b*) follows from II, 7.1.

(b) ⇒ (c) If β is an epimorphism, then it follows from 1.1 that $T(\alpha)$ is an epimorphism. Since T reflects epimorphisms this means that α is an epimorphism.

(c) ⇒ (d) This follows by taking $\beta = 1_{T(A)}$.

(d) ⇒ (a) Suppose that $\alpha_1, \alpha_2 : A \to A'$ and $T(\alpha_1) = T(\alpha_2)$. Then using naturality of ψ we have

$$\alpha_1\psi_A = \psi_{A'}ST(\alpha_1) = \psi_{A'}ST(\alpha_2) = \alpha_2\psi_A.$$

Since ψ_A is an epimorphism this means $\alpha_1 = \alpha_2$. This shows that T is faithful. ▮

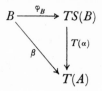

Proposition 1.3. *In an adjoint situation* $(\eta; S, T; \mathscr{A}, \mathscr{B})$ *we have*

$$(T\psi)(\varphi T) = 1_T. \tag{6}$$

If either T *or* S *is full, then* $T\psi$ *is a natural equivalence with inverse* φT *(and so by duality* $S\varphi$ *is also a natural equivalence with inverse* ψS*).*

Proof. Equation (6) follows from replacing α by ψ_A in Eq. (3).

Suppose now that T is full. Then $\varphi_{T(A)}$ can be written as $T(\alpha)$ for some $\alpha : A \to ST(A)$. Using (6) we have

$$\begin{aligned} T(1)\varphi_{T(A)} &= \varphi_{T(A)} = \varphi_{T(A)}T(\psi_A)\varphi_{T(A)} \\ &= T(\alpha)T(\psi_A)\varphi_{T(A)} = T(\alpha\psi_A)\varphi_{T(A)}. \end{aligned}$$

But then by 1.1 we must have $\alpha\psi_A = 1$. Hence $\varphi_{T(A)}T(\psi_A) = T(\alpha\psi_A) = 1$.

On the other hand, if S is full, we consider the composition of natural transformations of set valued functors of B,

$$[B, T(A)] \xrightarrow{S} [S(B), ST(A)] \xrightarrow{\eta} [B, TST(A)].$$

By 1.1*, S is univalent on $[B, T(A)]$; hence since S is also full, the first transformation is an equivalence. Therefore the composition is an equivalence, and so by IV, 2.2, the morphism $T(A) \to TST(A)$ which induces the transformation must be an isomorphism. But this morphism is just the image of $1_{T(A)}$ under the transformation, and is thus seen to be none other than $\varphi_{T(A)}$. ∎

We know from II, 12.1, that if $T : \mathscr{A} \to \mathscr{B}$ has a coadjoint, then T must be a limit preserving monofunctor. In particular, if $\mathscr{A}$ and $\mathscr{B}$ are categories with zero then T must be zero preserving. It then follows from Eq. (3) that η must be zero preserving. With regard to additivity we have the following proposition.

Proposition 1.4. *Consider an adjoint situation* $(\eta; S, T; \mathscr{A}, \mathscr{B})$. *If* $\mathscr{A}$ *and* $\mathscr{B}$ *are additive categories, then* T *is additive if and only if* η *is additive (that is, if and only if* η *is a natural equivalence of group valued bifunctors). Thus* T *is additive if and only if* S *is additive. In particular this will always be the case if either* $\mathscr{A}$ *or* $\mathscr{B}$ *has finite products.*

Proof. If T is additive, then for $\alpha_1, \alpha_2 : S(B) \to A$ we have, using (3),

$$\begin{aligned} \eta(\alpha_1 + \alpha_2) &= T(\alpha_1 + \alpha_2)\varphi_B = (T(\alpha_1) + T(\alpha_2))\varphi_B \\ &= T(\alpha_1)\varphi_B + T(\alpha_2)\varphi_B = \eta(\alpha_1) + \eta(\alpha_2). \end{aligned}$$

This shows that η is additive. A similar argument using Eq. (4) shows that if η is additive then so is T. It follows now by duality that S is additive if and only if η is additive. Therefore S is additive if and only if T is additive.

Suppose now that $\mathscr{A}$ has finite products. By II, 12.1, T must preserve finite products, and so by II, 6.4, T is additive. ∎

Consider an arbitrary family of categories $\{\mathscr{B}_i\}_{i\in I}$. The **product category** $\mathsf{X}_{i\in I}\, \mathscr{B}_i$ has for objects the class of all I-tuples (B_i) where $B_i \in \mathscr{B}_i$ for all $i \in I$. A morphism $\beta : (B_i) \rightarrow (B'_i)$ is a family of morphisms (β_i) where $\beta_i : B_i \rightarrow B'_i$. A morphism β in the product category is a monomorphism if and only if β_i is a monomorphism for all $i \in I$. In general, a limit for a diagram in the product category is obtained by projecting the diagram onto the ith category $\mathscr{B}_i$, taking a limit for the projection for each i, and then using the resulting family of limits to define a compatible system in $\mathsf{X}\, \mathscr{B}_i$. If each $\mathscr{B}_i$ is abelian then so is $\mathsf{X}\, \mathscr{B}_i$. A family of functors $T_i : \mathscr{A} \rightarrow \mathscr{B}_i$ determines a functor $T : \mathscr{A} \rightarrow \mathsf{X}_{i\in I}\, \mathscr{B}_i$ defined by $T(A) = (T_i(A))$ and $T(\alpha) = (T_i(\alpha))$. Conversely, any functor into the product category is determined by such a family.

A family of functors $T_i : \mathscr{A} \rightarrow \mathscr{B}_i$ will be called **collectively faithful** if for each pair of distinct morphisms $\alpha_1, \alpha_2 : A \rightarrow A'$ in $\mathscr{A}$ we have $T_i(\alpha_1) \neq T_i(\alpha_2)$ for some i. Thus $\{T_i\}$ is collectively faithful if and only if the associated functor T into the product category is faithful. Observe that a family of objects $\{U_i\}$ in $\mathscr{A}$ is a family of generators if and only if the family of functors $H^{U_i} : \mathscr{A} \rightarrow \mathscr{S}$ is collectively faithful.

A family of functors $S_i : \mathscr{B}_i \rightarrow \mathscr{A}$ is called **coproductive** if for each family of objects (B_i) with $B_i \in \mathscr{B}_i$ for each i, the coproduct $\bigoplus_{i\in I} S_i(B_i)$ is defined in $\mathscr{A}$. In this case we can define $S : \mathsf{X}_{i\in I}\, \mathscr{B}_i \rightarrow \mathscr{A}$ by taking $S((B_i)) = \bigoplus_{i\in I} S_i(B_i)$ and $S((\beta_i)) = \bigoplus S_i(\beta_i)$.

Proposition 1.5. *Let $T_i : \mathscr{A} \rightarrow \mathscr{B}_i$ be an adjoint for $S_i : \mathscr{B}_i \rightarrow \mathscr{A}$ for each $i \in I$, and suppose that the family $\{S_i\}$ is coproductive. Then the associated functor $T : \mathscr{A} \rightarrow \mathsf{X}\, \mathscr{B}_i$ is an adjoint for the associated functor $S : \mathsf{X}\, \mathscr{B}_i \rightarrow \mathscr{A}$. If U_i is a generator for $\mathscr{B}_i$ for each i and the family $\{T_i\}$ is collectively faithful, then $\{S_i(U_i)\}$ is a family of generators for $\mathscr{A}$. If $\mathscr{A}$ and the $\mathscr{B}_i$'s all have coproducts and U_i is a small object in $\mathscr{B}_i$ for each i, and if further the T_i's are all coproduct preserving and I is finite, then $\bigoplus_{i\in I} S_i(U_i)$ is a small object in $\mathscr{A}$.*

Proof. The assertion about adjointness follows from the sequence of natural equivalences

$$\begin{aligned} [S(B), A] &= \left[\bigoplus_{i\in I} S_i(B_i), A\right] \approx \mathsf{X}_{i\in I}\, [S_i(B_i), A] \approx \mathsf{X}_{i\in I}\, [B_i, T_i(A)] \\ &= [B, T(A)]. \end{aligned}$$

If $\{T_i\}$ is collectively faithful and U_i is a generator in $\mathscr{B}_i$ for each i, then it follows that the family of set valued functors $[U_i, T_i(\ )]$ is collectively faithful. Consequently, by adjointness the family of set valued functors $[S_i(U_i), \ ]$ is collectively faithful, or in other words $\{S_i(U_i)\}$ is a family of generators for $\mathscr{A}$.

Finally, suppose that U_i is small and T_i is coproduct preserving. Then smallness of $S_i(U_i)$ follows from the commutative diagram

$$\begin{array}{ccccc}
\left[S_i(U_i), \bigoplus_{k\in J} A_k\right] & \approx & \left[U_i, T_i(\bigoplus_{k\in J} A_k)\right] & = & \left[U_i, \bigoplus_{k\in J} T_i(A_k)\right] \\
\downarrow & & \downarrow & & \downarrow \\
\left[S_i(U_i), \bigoplus_{k\in K} A_k\right] & \approx & \left[U_i, T_i(\bigoplus_{k\in K} A_k)\right] & = & \left[U_i, \bigoplus_{k\in K} T_i(A_k)\right]
\end{array}$$

relative to a coproduct $\bigoplus_{k\in K} A_k$ in $\mathscr{A}$ and a subset J of K. Thus if I is finite, then $\bigoplus_{i\in I} S_i(U_i)$, being a finite coproduct of small objects, is itself small. ∎

2. Conjugate Transformations

Proposition 2.1. *Consider adjoint situations* $(\eta_1; S_1, T_1; \mathscr{A}, \mathscr{B})$ *and* $(\eta_2; S_2, T_2; \mathscr{A}, \mathscr{B})$ *and a natural transformation* $\mu : T_1 \to T_2$. *Then there is a unique natural transformation* $\lambda : S_2 \to S_1$ *such that for all* $A \in \mathscr{A}$ *and* $B \in \mathscr{B}$ *the diagram*

$$\begin{array}{ccc}
[S_1(B), A] & \xrightarrow{\eta_1} & [B, T_1(A)] \\
\downarrow & & \downarrow \\
[S_2(B), A] & \xrightarrow{\eta_2} & [B, T_2(A)]
\end{array} \qquad (1_{B,A})$$

is commutative.

Proof. For $B \in \mathscr{B}$ we consider the diagram

$$\begin{array}{ccc}
[S_1(B), S_1(B)] & \xrightarrow{\eta_1} & [B, T_1S_1(B)] \\
 & & \downarrow \\
[S_2(B), S_1(B)] & \xrightarrow{\eta_2} & [B, T_2S_1(B)].
\end{array}$$

Let 1 denote the identity morphism for $S_1(B)$. Define

$$\lambda_B = \eta_2^{-1}(\mu_{S_1(B)}\eta_1(1)).$$

This definition of λ_B is forced by the condition that $(1_{B,S_1(B)})$ be commutative, and so we already have the uniqueness assertion. Now let $\alpha \in [S_1(B), A]$. Place the diagram $(1_{B,A})$ over the diagram $(1_{B,S_1(B)})$ and join corresponding vertices by the morphisms induced by α. We obtain a cubical diagram, and using naturality of η_1, η_2, and μ we see that all its faces are commutative save possibly $(1_{B,S_1(B)})$ and $(1_{B,A})$. But $(1_{B,S_1(B)})$ is commutative as far as 1 is concerned. Hence $(1_{B,A})$ is commutative as far as α is concerned. Since this can be done for every $\alpha \in [S_1(B), A]$, this proves that $(1_{B,A})$ is commutative.

It remains to be shown that λ is a natural transformation. Given $B' \to B$ we must show that the diagram

$$\begin{array}{ccc} S_2(B') & \longrightarrow & S_2(B) \\ \downarrow{\scriptstyle \lambda_{B'}} & & \downarrow{\scriptstyle \lambda_B} \\ S_1(B') & \longrightarrow & S_1(B) \end{array} \tag{2}$$

is commutative. To this end place the diagram $(1_{B',S_1(B)})$ over the diagram $(1_{B,S_1(B)})$, joining corresponding vertices by the morphisms induced by $B' \to B$. Again we have a cubical diagram, and using the part of the theorem we have already proved, we see that all the faces are commutative save possibly the face

$$\begin{array}{ccc} [S_1(B), S_1(B)] & \longrightarrow & [S_1(B'), S_1(B)] \\ \downarrow & & \downarrow \\ [S_2(B), S_1(B)] & \longrightarrow & [S_2(B'), S_1(B)] \end{array} \tag{3}$$

But since η_2 is a one to one correspondence it follows that (3) is commutative also. Chasing 1 around (3) in both directions gives us the commutativity of (2). ∎

The transformations μ and λ of 2.1 are called **conjugate transformations** with respect to η_1 and η_2. Given adjoint situations $(\eta_i; S_i, T_i; \mathscr{A}, \mathscr{B})$ for $i = 1, 2, 3$, and transformations $\mu_1 : T_1 \to T_2$ and $\mu_2 : T_2 \to T_3$ with conjugates $\lambda_1 : S_2 \to S_1$ and $\lambda_2 : S_3 \to S_2$, respectively, it follows from definition that $\lambda_1\lambda_2$ is the conjugate of $\mu_2\mu_1$. Also in any situation $(\eta; S, T; \mathscr{A}, \mathscr{B})$ it is clear that 1_S is the conjugate of 1_T. Using these remarks and taking $T_1 = T_2 = T$ with $\mu = 1_T$ in 2.1 we obtain

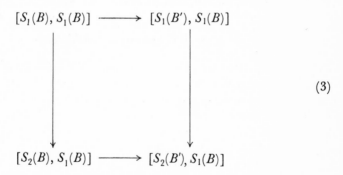

Corollary 2.2. *If S_1 and S_2 are coadjoints for a functor T, then S_1 and S_2 are naturally equivalent.* ▌

We can generalize the notion of adjoints to functors of several variables as follows. Let

$$T:\mathscr{C}_1 \times \mathscr{C}_2 \times \ldots \times \mathscr{C}_n \times \mathscr{A} \rightarrow \mathscr{B} \tag{4}$$

$$S:\mathscr{B} \times \mathscr{C}_1 \times \mathscr{C}_2 \times \ldots \times \mathscr{C}_n \rightarrow \mathscr{A} \tag{5}$$

be such that T is covariant in $\mathscr{A}$, S is covariant in $\mathscr{B}$, and for each i, $1 \leqslant i \leqslant n$, T has the opposite variance of S in $\mathscr{C}_i$. Then S is said to be the coadjoint of T if there is a natural equivalence

$$[S(B, C_1, C_2, \ldots, C_n), A] \approx [B, T(C_1, C_2, \ldots, C_n A)] \tag{6}$$

of $n+2$ variable set-valued functors.

Proposition 2.3. *The $n+1$ variable functor* (4) *has a coadjoint S if and only if each single variable partial functor of the form $T(C_1, C_2, \ldots, C_n, \quad): \mathscr{A} \rightarrow \mathscr{B}$ has a coadjoint. In this case for each i, T is limit preserving in $\mathscr{C}_i$ if and only if S is colimit preserving in $\mathscr{C}_i$.*

Proof. Using the discussion in the third paragraph of II, §9, the first statement is an immediate consequence of 2.1. The other statement follows easily from II, 5.1, in view of the natural equivalence (6). ▌

3. Existence of Adjoints

Let $T:\mathscr{A} \rightarrow \mathscr{B}$ be any covariant functor. We call a set of objects $\{S_i\}_{i \in I}$ in $\mathscr{A}$ a **solution set** with respect to T for an object $B \in \mathscr{B}$ if for any object $A \in \mathscr{A}$ and any morphism $B \rightarrow T(A)$ in $\mathscr{B}$ there are morphisms $B \rightarrow T(S_i)$ and $\alpha: S_i \rightarrow A$ for some i such that the diagram

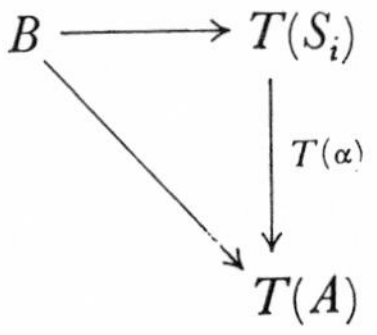

is commutative.

Theorem 3.1. *Consider a covariant functor $T:\mathscr{A} \rightarrow \mathscr{B}$ where $\mathscr{A}$ is complete and locally small. Then T has a coadjoint if and only if it is a limit preserving functor which admits a solution set for every object in $\mathscr{B}$.*

Proof. If T has a coadjoint S, then by II, 12.1, T must be limit preserving. Also we see from 1.1 that the single object $S(B)$ serves as a solution set for B in this case.

Conversely, let $T:\mathscr{A}\to\mathscr{B}$ be a limit preserving functor which admits solution sets for all objects in $\mathscr{B}$. Given $B\in\mathscr{B}$, let $\{S_i\}_{i\in I}$ be a solution set. Define

$$A_1 = \mathop{\mathsf{X}}_{i\in I} S_i^{[B,T(S_i)]}.$$

Then since T preserves limits we have

$$T(A_1) = \mathop{\mathsf{X}}_{i\in I} T(S_i)^{[B,T(S_i)]}.$$

Let $B\to T(A_1)$ be the morphism which when composed with the fth projection from the product gives f. This morphism has the property that for any $A\in\mathscr{A}$ and any morphism $B\to T(A)$, there is a morphism $\alpha_1 : A_1\to A$ such that the diagram

$$\begin{array}{ccc} B & \longrightarrow & T(A_1) \\ & \searrow & \downarrow{\scriptstyle T(\alpha_1)} \\ & & T(A) \end{array}$$

is commutative. Define $S(B)$ as the intersection of all subobjects $A'\to A_1$ such that $B\to T(A_1)$ factors through $T(A')\to T(A_1)$. Then since T is limit preserving, $B\to T(A_1)$ factors through $T(S(B))\to T(A_1)$. Now $S(B)$ still has the above factorization property of A_1; namely, given $\beta : B\to T(A)$, there is a morphism $\alpha : S(B)\to A$ such that the diagram

$$\begin{array}{ccc} B & \longrightarrow & T(S(B)) \\ & {\scriptstyle \beta}\searrow & \downarrow{\scriptstyle T(\alpha)} \\ & & T(A) \end{array} \qquad (1)$$

is commutative. Furthermore, in this case α is unique. For if α' is another such morphism, let $E\to S(B)$ be the equalizer of α and α'. Then since T is limit preserving, by II, 6.2, $T(E)\to T(S(B))$ is the equalizer of $T(\alpha)$ and $T(\alpha')$. Therefore $B\to T(S(B))$ factors through $T(E)\to T(S(B))$, and so E is one of the set of subobjects of A_1 of which $S(B)$ is the intersection. Therefore $E=S(B)$ and so $\alpha=\alpha'$.

For a morphism $\delta : B'\to B$ we define $S(\delta) : S(B')\to S(B)$ as the unique morphism making the diagram

$$\begin{array}{ccc} B' & \longrightarrow & T(S(B')) \\ \downarrow{\scriptstyle \delta} & & \downarrow{\scriptstyle T(S(\delta))} \\ B & \longrightarrow & T(S(B)) \end{array} \qquad (2)$$

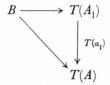

commutative. It follows from the uniqueness of $S(\delta)$ that S is a functor. By construction of S we have a 1–1 correspondence

$$[S(B), A] \to [B, T(A)].$$

The naturality of this correspondence in A and in B follows easily using the diagrams (1) and (2), respectively. Thus S is a coadjoint for T. ▌

Corollary 3.2. *If $\mathscr{A}$ is a complete and locally small category with a cogenerator, then $T : \mathscr{A} \to \mathscr{B}$ has a coadjoint if and only if it is limit preserving.*

Proof. Suppose that T is limit preserving, and let C be a cogenerator for $\mathscr{A}$. By 3.1 it suffices to find a solution set for every $B \in \mathscr{B}$. Given $\beta : B \to T(A)$, consider the pullback diagram in $\mathscr{A}$

$$\begin{array}{ccc} P & \xrightarrow{\tau} & C^{[B,\,T(C)]} \\ {\scriptstyle\alpha}\downarrow & & \downarrow{\scriptstyle\mu} \\ A & \xrightarrow{\lambda} & C^{[A,C]} \end{array}$$

where the composition of μ with the fth projection from $C^{[A,C]}$ gives the $(T(f)\beta)$th projection from $C^{[B,T(C)]}$, and the composition of λ with the fth projection from $C^{[A,C]}$ gives f. By II, 15.2*, λ is a monomorphism, hence so is τ. Now in $\mathscr{B}$ the diagram

$$\begin{array}{ccc} B & \longrightarrow & T(C)^{[B,\,T(C)]} \\ {\scriptstyle\beta}\downarrow & & \downarrow{\scriptstyle T(\mu)} \\ T(A) & \xrightarrow[T(\lambda)]{} & T(C)^{[A,C]} \end{array}$$

is commutative. Since T preserves pullbacks, this means that β factors through $T(\alpha)$. Therefore it suffices to take as a solution set for B the set of all subobjects of $C^{[B,T(C)]}$. ▌

4. Functor Categories

Proposition 4.1. *In an adjoint situation $(\eta; S, T; \mathscr{B}, \mathscr{C})$, consider the diagram of categories and covariant functors*

$$\begin{array}{ccc} \mathscr{B} & \underset{T}{\overset{S}{\rightleftarrows}} & \mathscr{C} \\ {\scriptstyle F}\nwarrow & & \nearrow{\scriptstyle G} \\ & \mathscr{A} & \end{array}$$

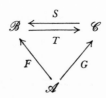

Then there is a one to one correspondence

$$\bar{\eta} : [SG, F] \to [G, TF]$$

which is natural in F and G.

Proof. For a natural transformation $\mu \in [SG, F]$, define $\bar{\eta}(\mu) \in [G, TF]$ by

$$\bar{\eta}(\mu)_A = \eta_{G(A),F(A)}(\mu_A)$$

for all $A \in \mathscr{A}$. To show that $\bar{\eta}(\mu)$ is a natural transformation we must show that given $A \to B$ in $\mathscr{A}$ we have a commutative diagram

$$\begin{array}{ccc} G(A) & \xrightarrow{\bar{\eta}(\mu)_A} & T(F(A)) \\ \downarrow & & \downarrow \\ G(B) & \xrightarrow{\bar{\eta}(\mu)_B} & T(F(B)) \end{array} \tag{1}$$

By naturality of μ we know that the diagram

$$\begin{array}{ccc} S(G(A)) & \xrightarrow{\mu_A} & F(A) \\ \downarrow & & \downarrow \\ S(G(B)) & \xrightarrow{\mu_B} & F(B) \end{array} \tag{2}$$

is commutative. Consider the diagram

$$\begin{array}{ccc} [S(G(A)), F(A)] & \xrightarrow{\eta} & [G(A), T(F(A))] \\ \downarrow & & \downarrow \\ [S(G(A)), F(B)] & \xrightarrow{\eta} & [G(A), T(F(B))] \\ \uparrow & & \uparrow \\ [S(G(B)), F(B)] & \xrightarrow{\eta} & [G(B), T(F(B))] \end{array} \tag{3}$$

which is commutative by naturality of η. Commutativity of (2) says that on the left-hand side of (3) the elements μ_A and μ_B are taken into the same element in the middle row. Therefore the same is true of $\bar{\eta}(\mu)_A$ and $\bar{\eta}(\mu)_B$ on the right-hand side. In other words (1) is commutative. Naturality of $\bar{\eta}$ in F and G then follows trivially from naturality of η. The inverse of $\bar{\eta}$ is constructed using η^{-1} just as $\bar{\eta}$ was constructed using η. ∎

Proposition 4.1 may be considered in the following way. If $T : \mathscr{B} \to \mathscr{C}$ is the adjoint of $S : \mathscr{C} \to \mathscr{B}$ and $\mathscr{A}$ is a small category, then the functor

$$T_0 : [\mathscr{A}, \mathscr{B}] \to [\mathscr{A}, \mathscr{C}]$$

defined by $T_0(F) = TF$ is the adjoint of the functor $S_0 : [\mathscr{A}, \mathscr{C}] \to [\mathscr{A}, \mathscr{B}]$ defined by $S_0(G) = SG$. If $\mathscr{A}$, $\mathscr{B}$, and $\mathscr{C}$ are additive categories, and T (and therefore S) is an additive functor, then the categories $[\mathscr{A}, \mathscr{B}]$ and $[\mathscr{A}, \mathscr{C}]$ may be replaced by $(\mathscr{A}, \mathscr{B})$ and $(\mathscr{A}, \mathscr{C})$, respectively.

5. Reflections

Consider a category $\mathscr{A}$, a subcategory $\mathscr{A}'$, and an object $A \in \mathscr{A}$. A **coreflection** for A in $\mathscr{A}'$ is an object $R(A) \in \mathscr{A}'$ together with a morphism

$$\rho_A : A \to R(A) \tag{1}$$

such that for every object $A' \in \mathscr{A}'$ and every morphism $A \to A'$ there exists a unique morphism $R(A) \to A'$ in $\mathscr{A}'$ making the diagram

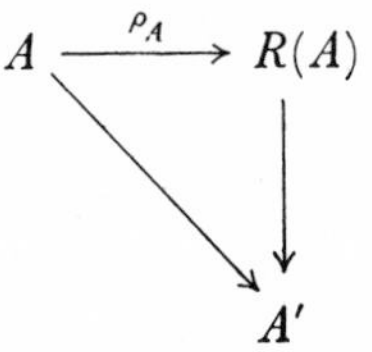

commutative. Equivalently, denoting by I the inclusion functor from $\mathscr{A}'$ to $\mathscr{A}$, (1) defines a coreflection for A if the function

$$[R(A), A']_{\mathscr{A}'} \to [A, I(A')]_{\mathscr{A}} \tag{2}$$

induced by ρ_A is a 1–1 correspondence for all $A' \in \mathscr{A}'$. From uniqueness of $R(A) \to A'$ it follows that any two coreflections for A are isomorphic in $\mathscr{A}'$. If $\mathscr{A}'$ is a full subcategory of $\mathscr{A}$, then every object of $\mathscr{A}$ which is in $\mathscr{A}'$ is its own coreflection via the identity morphism.

Dually, $R(A) \to A$ is called the **reflection** of A in $\mathscr{A}'$ if $R(A) \in \mathscr{A}'$ and if for any morphism $A' \to A$ with $A' \in \mathscr{A}'$ there is a unique morphism $A' \to R(A)$ in $\mathscr{A}'$ such that the diagram

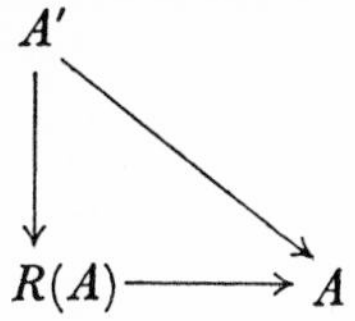

is commutative.

If every object in $\mathscr{A}$ has a coreflection (reflection) in $\mathscr{A}'$, then $\mathscr{A}'$ is called a **coreflective** (**reflective**) subcategory of $\mathscr{A}$. In this case R becomes a functor from $\mathscr{A}$ to $\mathscr{A}'$, called the **coreflector** (**reflector**) of $\mathscr{A}$ in $\mathscr{A}'$, by assigning to each morphism $\alpha : A \to B$ in $\mathscr{A}$ the unique morphism $R(\alpha) : R(A) \to R(B)$ in $\mathscr{A}'$ such that the diagram

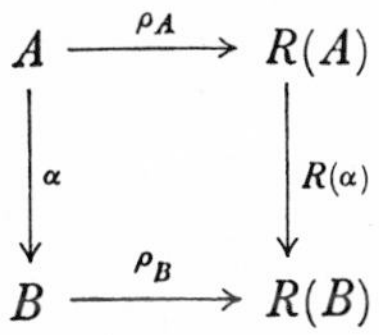

is commutative. It is then easy to check the naturality of (2) in both A and A'. In other words, if $R : \mathscr{A} \to \mathscr{A}'$ is a coreflector for $\mathscr{A}$ in $\mathscr{A}'$, then R is a coadjoint for the inclusion functor $I : \mathscr{A}' \to \mathscr{A}$. In this case ρ is simply the transformation φ described in §1. On the other hand, if the inclusion $I : \mathscr{A}' \to \mathscr{A}$ has a coadjoint R, then by 1.2, R is the coreflector of $\mathscr{A}$ in $\mathscr{A}'$.

Proposition 5.1. *Let $\mathscr{A}'$ be a full, coreflective subcategory of $\mathscr{A}$. If a diagram D in $\mathscr{A}'$ has a limit in $\mathscr{A}$, then it has a limit in $\mathscr{A}'$.*

Proof. Let $\{\alpha_i : L \to D_i\}$ be a limit for D in $\mathscr{A}$ and let $L' = R(L)$. Then by definition of coreflection we have morphisms $\alpha'_i : L' \to D_i$ such that $\alpha'_i \rho_L = \alpha_i$. Also, for an arrow m from i to j we have

$$D(m)\alpha'_i\rho_L = D(m)\alpha_i = \alpha_j = \alpha'_j\rho_L$$

and consequently $D(m)\alpha'_i = \alpha'_j$. The compatible family $\{\alpha'_i\}$ thus defines a morphism $\alpha : L' \to L$. For each i we have $\alpha_i\alpha\rho_L = \alpha'_i\rho_L = \alpha_i$, and consequently $\alpha\rho_L = 1_L$. We wish to show that $\rho_L\alpha = 1_{L'}$. Since $\mathscr{A}'$ is full we may assume that $\rho_{L'} = 1_{L'}$, in which case we must have $R(\rho_L) = 1_{L'}$. Then we have

$$\begin{aligned} \rho_L\alpha &= R(\alpha)\rho_{L'} = R(\alpha)R(\rho_L) \\ &= R(\alpha\rho_L) = R(1_L) = 1_{L'}. \end{aligned}$$

This proves that ρ_L is an isomorphism, and consequently $\{\alpha'_i\}$ is a limit for D in $\mathscr{A}'$. ▌

Proposition 5.2. *Let $\mathscr{A}'$ be a full, coreflective subcategory of $\mathscr{A}$. If D is a diagram in $\mathscr{A}'$ and $\{D_i \to L\}$ is a colimit for D in $\mathscr{A}$, then a colimit for D in $\mathscr{A}'$ is given by the family $\{D_i \to L \xrightarrow{\rho_L} R(L)\}$.*

Proof. Since $\mathscr{A}'$ is full we may assume that the restriction of R to $\mathscr{A}'$ is the identity functor, and that $\rho_{A'} = 1_{A'}$ for $\mathscr{A}' \in A'$. Now R, being a coadjoint, must preserve colimits. Consequently $\{R(D_i) \to R(L)\}$ is a colimit for RD in $\mathscr{A}'$. But using the assumption on R and ρ we have $RD = D$ and

$$R(D_i) \longrightarrow R(L) \;=\; D_i \longrightarrow L \xrightarrow{\rho_L} R(L)$$

as required. ▮

Of special interest is the case where $\mathscr{A}'$ is a full coreflective subcategory of an abelian category $\mathscr{A}$. By 5.1 and 5.2, $\mathscr{A}'$ has kernels, cokernels, and finite biproducts. A morphism in $\mathscr{A}'$ is a monomorphism in $\mathscr{A}'$ if and only if it is a monomorphism in $\mathscr{A}$. By II, 12.1*, the coreflector R is colimit preserving, and in particular cokernel preserving. If, on the other hand, R is kernel preserving, then the following has been observed by F. W. Lawvere.

Proposition 5.3. *Let $\mathscr{A}'$ be a full, coreflective subcategory of the abelian category $\mathscr{A}$, and suppose that the coreflector $R : \mathscr{A} \to \mathscr{A}'$ is kernel preserving. Then $\mathscr{A}'$ is an abelian category. Furthermore, if $\mathscr{A}$ is C_3, then so is $\mathscr{A}'$.*

Proof. To prove $\mathscr{A}'$ abelian it suffices to show that $\mathscr{A}'$ is normal and conormal (I, 20.1). By fullness we may assume as usual that the restriction of R to $\mathscr{A}'$ is the identity functor. Let $A_1 \to A_2$ be a monomorphism in $\mathscr{A}'$, hence in $\mathscr{A}$. Then $A_1 \to A_2$ is the kernel of some morphism $A_2 \to A_3$ in $\mathscr{A}$. By assumption on R this means that $R(A_1) \to R(A_2)$ is the kernel in $\mathscr{A}'$ of $R(A_2) \to R(A_3)$. But $R(A_1) \to R(A_2)$ is just $A_1 \to A_2$. This shows that $\mathscr{A}'$ is normal.

As for conormality, let $A_2 \to A_3$ be an epimorphism in $\mathscr{A}'$. Then its cokernel in $\mathscr{A}'$ is zero. By 5.2, this cokernel is the composition $A_3 \to A_4 \to R(A_4)$ where $A_3 \to A_4$ is the cokernel in $\mathscr{A}$. Hence $R(A_4) = 0$. Consider the sequence

$$A_1 \to A_2 \to I \to A_3 \to A_4$$

where I is the image of $A_2 \to A_3$ in $\mathscr{A}$ and $A_1 \to A_2$ is the kernel in either $\mathscr{A}$ or $\mathscr{A}'$. Then $R(I) \to R(A_3)$ is the kernel of $R(A_3) \to R(A_4)$ by assumption on R. But since $R(A_4) = 0$, this shows that $R(I) \to R(A_3)$ is an isomorphism. Since R is cokernel preserving, $R(A_2) \to R(I)$ is the cokernel in $\mathscr{A}'$ of $R(A_1) \to R(A_2)$. Since $R(A_2) \to R(I) \to R(A_3) = R(A_2) \to R(A_3) = A_2 \to A_3$ and

$$R(A_1) \to R(A_2) \;=\; A_1 \to A_2,$$

this establishes conormality for $\mathscr{A}'$.

Now suppose that $\mathscr{A}$ is C_3. To prove that $\mathscr{A}'$ is C_3, we must show that, given a monomorphism $D \to D'$ of direct systems in $\mathscr{A}'$, the induced morphism of the colimits in $\mathscr{A}'$ is a monomorphism. We know that the induced morphism

$L' \rightarrow L$ of the colimits in $\mathscr{A}$ is a monomorphism by C_3 for $\mathscr{A}$. But the induced morphism of the colimits in $\mathscr{A}'$ is just $R(L') \rightarrow R(L)$ which is a monomorphism since R is kernel preserving. Hence $\mathscr{A}'$ is C_3. ▌

Remark. We have proved in 5.3 that $\mathscr{A}'$ is an abelian category, but it is not true in general that $\mathscr{A}'$ is an abelian subcategory of $\mathscr{A}$. That is, it is not true that the inclusion of $\mathscr{A}'$ in $\mathscr{A}$ is an exact functor.

6. Monosubcategories

Throughout, $\mathscr{A}$ will denote a complete, locally small, abelian category, and $\mathscr{M}$ will denote a full subcategory of $\mathscr{A}$ satisfying the following axioms.

$\mathscr{M}_1$: $\mathscr{M}$ is a complete subcategory of $\mathscr{A}$.

$\mathscr{M}_2$: If $A \rightarrow B$ is a monomorphism in $\mathscr{A}$ and $B \in \mathscr{M}$, then $A \in \mathscr{M}$.

Axiom $\mathscr{M}_1$ says that $\mathscr{M}$ is a complete category, and the inclusion functor from $\mathscr{M}$ to $\mathscr{A}$ is limit preserving. Equivalently, the limit in $\mathscr{A}$ of every diagram in $\mathscr{M}$ is also in $\mathscr{M}$. Thus, in speaking of limits of diagrams in $\mathscr{M}$, it will not be necessary to specify whether the limit is to be considered in $\mathscr{A}$ or in $\mathscr{M}$. Likewise, since monomorphisms are characterized by having zero kernel, a morphism in $\mathscr{M}$ is a monomorphism in $\mathscr{M}$ if and only if it is a monomorphism in $\mathscr{A}$.

Proposition 6.1. *$\mathscr{M}$ is a coreflective subcategory of $\mathscr{A}$, and for each $A \in \mathscr{A}$ the coreflection is an epimorphism.*

Proof. Given $A \in \mathscr{A}$, let $\{M_i\}_{i \in I}$ be a representative set of quotient objects of A which are in $\mathscr{M}$. Let M be the image of the obvious morphism $A \rightarrow \underset{i \in I}{\times} M_i$. By $\mathscr{M}_1$, $\underset{i \in I}{\times} M_i$ is in $\mathscr{M}$ and so by $\mathscr{M}_2$, M is in $\mathscr{M}$. Given $A \rightarrow M'$ with $M' \in \mathscr{M}$, we wish to find a morphism $M \rightarrow M'$ such that the diagram

$$\begin{array}{ccc} A & \longrightarrow & M \\ & \searrow & \downarrow \\ & & M' \end{array} \qquad (1)$$

is commutative. By $\mathscr{M}_2$ we may suppose that $A \rightarrow M'$ is an epimorphism, hence we may assume that M' is M_k for some $k \in I$. The required morphism $M \rightarrow M'$ is then just the inclusion of M into the product composed with the kth projection. Since $A \rightarrow M$ is an epimorphism, the morphism $M \rightarrow M'$ making (1) commutative is unique. Hence $A \rightarrow M$ is the coreflection of A in $\mathscr{M}$. ▌

Throughout the remainder of the section we assume that $\mathscr{M}$ satisfies the following additional axiom.

$\mathscr{M}_3$: For each $M \in \mathscr{M}$ there is a monomorphism $M \rightarrow Q$ in $\mathscr{M}$ such that Q is injective considered as an object in $\mathscr{A}$.

We shall call $\mathcal{M}$ a **monosubcategory** of $\mathcal{A}$ if it satisfies the axioms $\mathcal{M}_1$, $\mathcal{M}_2$, and $\mathcal{M}_3$.

Lemma 6.2. *Let*

$$0 \to M \to A \to N \to 0$$

be an exact sequence in $\mathcal{A}$, and let M and N be in $\mathcal{M}$. Then $A \in \mathcal{M}$.

Proof. Let $M \to Q$ be as in $\mathcal{M}_3$, and form the pushout diagram (I, 20.3*)

$$\begin{array}{ccccccccc}
0 & \longrightarrow & M & \longrightarrow & A & \longrightarrow & N & \longrightarrow & 0 \\
 & & \downarrow & & \downarrow & & \| & & \\
0 & \longrightarrow & Q & \longrightarrow & P & \longrightarrow & N & \longrightarrow & 0
\end{array}$$

Since Q is injective, the lower sequence splits; that is, $P = Q \oplus N$. Now Q and N are in $\mathcal{M}$, hence by $\mathcal{M}_1$, so is $Q \oplus N$. Since $M \to Q$ is a monomorphism, by I, 20.2*, $A \to P$ is also a monomorphism. Therefore by $\mathcal{M}_2$, A is in $\mathcal{M}$. ∎

We shall call an object $T \in \mathcal{A}$ a **torsion object** with respect to $\mathcal{M}$ if the coreflection of T in $\mathcal{M}$ is 0. Equivalently, T is a torsion object if $[T, M] = 0$ for all $M \in \mathcal{M}$.

Proposition 6.3. *Given $A \in \mathcal{A}$, let $T \to A$ be the kernel of the coreflection $A \to M$. Then T is a torsion object. Furthermore, any morphism $T' \to A$ with T' a torsion object factors uniquely through $T \to A$.*

Proof. To show that T is torsion, we form the pushout diagram

$$\begin{array}{ccccccccc}
0 & \longrightarrow & T & \longrightarrow & A & \longrightarrow & M & \longrightarrow & 0 \\
 & & \downarrow & & \downarrow & & \| & & \\
0 & \longrightarrow & N & \longrightarrow & P & \longrightarrow & M & \longrightarrow & 0
\end{array}$$

where $T \to N$ is any morphism with $N \in \mathcal{M}$. By 6.2, P is in $\mathcal{M}$, and so we have an induced morphism $M \to P$ such that $A \to M \to P = A \to P$. Therefore $T \to N \to P = T \to A \to P = T \to A \to M \to P = 0$, and so since $N \to P$ is a monomorphism, $T \to N$ is zero. This proves that T is torsion. Now if T' is torsion, then for any morphism $T' \to A$ we have $T' \to A \to M = 0$; hence $T' \to A$ factors uniquely through the kernel $T \to A$. ∎

Consider an exact sequence in $\mathcal{A}$

$$0 \to L \to M \to N \to 0 \tag{2}$$

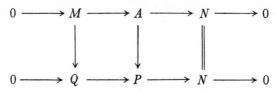

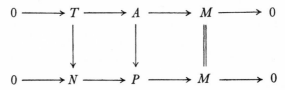

where L and M are in $\mathcal{M}$. We shall call $L \to M$ a **pure monomorphism** if $N \in \mathcal{M}$. We shall call L a **pure object** if every monomorphism from L to an object of $\mathcal{M}$ is pure. If $L \in \mathcal{M}$ is injective in $\mathcal{A}$, then L is necessarily pure. For in this case the sequence (2) splits, so N is a subobject of M, and consequently N is in $\mathscr{M}$ by $\mathscr{M}_2$.

Let us denote the full subcategory of $\mathscr{M}$ consisting of all pure objects by $\mathscr{L}$.

Lemma 6.4. *Let*

$$0 \to L \to M \to N \to 0$$

be an exact sequence in $\mathscr{A}$. *If* $N \in \mathscr{M}$ *and* $M \in \mathscr{L}$, *then* $L \in \mathscr{L}$.

Proof. Let $L \to M'$ be a monomorphism with $M' \in \mathscr{M}$. Form the pushout diagram (I, 20.3*)

$$\begin{array}{ccccccccc}
 & & 0 & & 0 & & & & \\
 & & \downarrow & & \downarrow & & & & \\
0 & \longrightarrow & L & \longrightarrow & M & \longrightarrow & N & \longrightarrow & 0 \\
 & & \downarrow & & \downarrow & & \| & & \\
0 & \longrightarrow & M' & \longrightarrow & P & \longrightarrow & N & \longrightarrow & 0 \\
 & & \downarrow & & \downarrow & & & & \\
 & & N' & = & N' & & & & \\
 & & \downarrow & & \downarrow & & & & \\
 & & 0 & & 0 & & & &
\end{array}$$

Since M' and N are in $\mathscr{M}$, by 6.2, so is P. But then since M is pure, $N' \in \mathscr{M}$. This proves that L is pure. ▮

Lemma 6.5. *Let*

$$0 \to M \to R \to T \to 0$$

be an exact sequence in $\mathscr{A}$ *with* $M \in \mathscr{M}$, $R \in \mathscr{L}$, *and* T *torsion. Then* $M \to R$ *is the coreflection of* M *in* $\mathscr{L}$.

Proof. Let $M \to L$ be any morphism with $L \in \mathscr{L}$. Form the commutative diagram with exact rows in $\mathscr{A}$

$$\begin{array}{ccccccccc}
0 & \longrightarrow & M & \longrightarrow & R & \longrightarrow & T & \longrightarrow & 0 \\
 & & \downarrow & & \downarrow & & \downarrow & & \\
0 & \longrightarrow & L & \longrightarrow & Q & \longrightarrow & F & \longrightarrow & 0
\end{array}$$

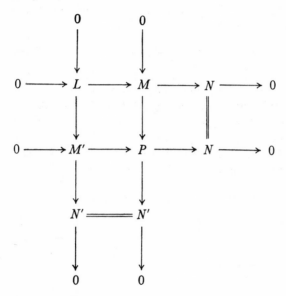

where the bottom row is defined by $\mathscr{M}_3$ and $R \to Q$ can be defined by injectivity of Q. Since $L \in \mathscr{L}$ and $Q \in \mathscr{M}$ we have $F \in \mathscr{M}$. But since T is torsion, $T \to F$ is zero. Therefore $R \to Q \to F$ is zero and so $R \to Q$ factors through $L \to Q$. Since $L \to Q$ is a monomorphism we must then have

$$M \to R \to L = M \to L. \tag{3}$$

Now suppose that there were two morphisms $R \to L$ satisfying (3), and let d be their difference. Then $M \to R \xrightarrow{d} L$ is zero, and hence d factors through $R \to T$. But again since T is torsion and $L \in \mathscr{M}$, the morphism $T \to L$ must be zero. Hence d is zero. This proves that $R \to L$ is unique, and so $M \to R$ is the coreflection of M in $\mathscr{L}$. ▌

Lemma 6.6. *$\mathscr{L}$ is a coreflective subcategory of $\mathscr{A}$. If $M \in \mathscr{M}$, then the coreflection $M \to R$ is a monomorphism.*

Proof. Since $\mathscr{M}$ is a coreflective subcategory of $\mathscr{A}$ (6.1), it suffices to prove that $\mathscr{L}$ is a coreflective subcategory of $\mathscr{M}$. For $M \in \mathscr{M}$, take an exact sequence $0 \to M \to Q \to A \to 0$ where $Q \in \mathscr{M}$ is injective in $\mathscr{A}$. Consider also the exact sequence $0 \to T \to A \to N \to 0$ where $A \to N$ is the coreflection of A in $\mathscr{M}$, so that by 6.3, T is a torsion object. Forming the pullback of $Q \to A$ and $T \to A$, by I, 16.3, we get a commutative diagram with exact rows and columns

$$
\begin{array}{ccccccccc}
 & & & & 0 & & 0 & & \\
 & & & & \downarrow & & \downarrow & & \\
0 & \to & M & \to & R & \to & T & \to & 0 \\
 & & \| & & \downarrow & & \downarrow & & \\
0 & \to & M & \to & Q & \to & A & \to & 0 \\
 & & & & \downarrow & & \downarrow & & \\
 & & & & N & = & N & & \\
 & & & & \downarrow & & \downarrow & & \\
 & & & & 0 & & 0 & &
\end{array}
$$

Since $Q \in \mathscr{L}$ and $N \in \mathscr{M}$, by 6.4, $R \in \mathscr{L}$. Therefore by 6.5, $M \to R$ is the coreflection of M in $\mathscr{L}$. ▌

Lemma 6.7. *If $A' \to A$ is a monomorphism in $\mathscr{A}$, then so is the induced morphism $R' \to R$ of the coreflections in $\mathscr{L}$.*

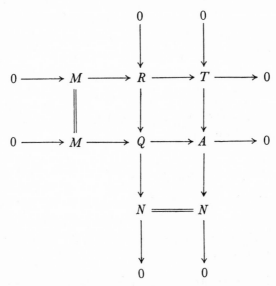

Proof. Form the diagram

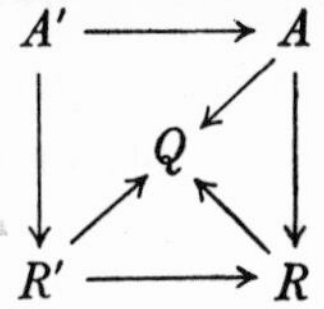

where $R' \to Q$ is a monomorphism with $Q \in \mathscr{M}$ injective in $\mathscr{A}$, $A \to Q$ is defined so that $A' \to A \to Q = A' \to R' \to Q$, and $R \to Q$ is defined so that

$$A \to Q = A \to R \to Q$$

(which is possible since $Q \in \mathscr{L}$ and $A \to R$ is the coreflection of A in $\mathscr{L}$). Then we have

$$\begin{aligned} A' \to R' \to Q &= A' \to A \to Q \\ &= A' \to A \to R \to Q \\ &= A' \to R' \to R \to Q. \end{aligned}$$

But then since $Q \in \mathscr{L}$ and $A' \to R'$ is the coreflection of A' in $\mathscr{L}$, we must have $R' \to Q = R' \to R \to Q$. Therefore since $R' \to Q$ is a monomorphism, the same is true of $R' \to R$. ▌

Theorem 6.8. *$\mathscr{L}$ is a coreflective subcategory of $\mathscr{A}$ and the coreflector $R : \mathscr{A} \to \mathscr{L}$ is an exact, colimit preserving functor. Hence $\mathscr{L}$ is a complete abelian category. Furthermore, $\mathscr{L}$ has injectives. If $\mathscr{A}$ is cocomplete (C_3), then so is $\mathscr{L}$. If $\mathscr{A}$ has a generator, then $\mathscr{L}$ has a generator and an injective cogenerator.*

Proof. We begin by showing that $\mathscr{L}$ is normal. Let $L' \to L$ be a monomorphism in $\mathscr{L}$. Let $L \to M$ be its cokernel in $\mathscr{A}$ and let $M \to R(M)$ be the coreflection of M in $\mathscr{L}$. Since $L' \in \mathscr{L}$ we must have $M \in \mathscr{M}$, and so $M \to R(M)$ is a monomorphism by 6.6. Therefore since $L' \to L$ is the kernel of $L \to M$ it is also the kernel of $L \to M \to R(M)$. This shows that $\mathscr{L}$ is normal.

We can now show that R is kernel preserving. Consider an exact sequence $0 \to A' \to A \to A''$ in $\mathscr{A}$, and let $A \to I \to A''$ be the factorization in $\mathscr{A}$ of $A \to A''$ through its image. Since R is cokernel preserving, $R(A) \to R(I)$ is the cokernel of $R(A') \to R(A)$ in $\mathscr{L}$. But then, since by 6.7, $R(A') \to R(A)$ is a monomorphism and since $\mathscr{L}$ is normal, we see that $R(A') \to R(A)$ is the kernel of $R(A) \to R(I)$. Now again by 6.7, $R(I) \to R(A'')$ is a monomorphism. Hence $R(A') \to R(A)$ is the kernel of $R(A) \to R(I) \to R(A'') = R(A) \to R(A'')$. Therefore R is kernel preserving.

It now follows from 5.1, 5.2, and 5.3 that $\mathscr{L}$ is a complete abelian category, cocomplete (C_3) if $\mathscr{A}$ is cocomplete (C_3). By $\mathscr{M}_3$ and the fact that an injective in $\mathscr{A}$ is necessarily injective in $\mathscr{L}$ we see that $\mathscr{L}$ has injective resolutions. From 1.5 we see that if U is a generator for $\mathscr{A}$, then $R(U)$ is a generator for $\mathscr{L}$. In this case it follows from III, 3.3, that $\mathscr{L}$ also has an injective cogenerator. ▌

7. Projective Classes

Throughout this section all categories will be abelian.

Consider a category $\mathscr{A}$ and a class $\mathscr{E}$ of epimorphisms in $\mathscr{A}$. We will say that an object $P \in \mathscr{A}$ is **$\mathscr{E}$-projective** if $[P, \alpha]$is an epimorphism for every $\alpha \in \mathscr{E}$. The class of all $\mathscr{E}$-projectives will be denoted by $\mathscr{P}(\mathscr{E})$. On the other hand starting with a class $\mathscr{P}$of objects in $\mathscr{A}$ we let $\mathscr{E}(\mathscr{P})$ denote all epimorphisms α in $\mathscr{A}$ such that $[P, \alpha]$ is an epimorphism for all $P \in \mathscr{P}$. If $\mathscr{E}' \subset \mathscr{E}$ then $\mathscr{P}(\mathscr{E}') \supset \mathscr{P}(\mathscr{E})$, and if $\mathscr{P}' \subset \mathscr{P}$ then $\mathscr{E}(\mathscr{P}') \supset \mathscr{E}(\mathscr{P})$. Also we have $\mathscr{E}(\mathscr{P}(\mathscr{E})) \supset \mathscr{E}$ for any class of epimorphisms $\mathscr{E}$ and $\mathscr{P}(\mathscr{E}(\mathscr{P})) \supset \mathscr{P}$ for any class of objects $\mathscr{P}$. It then follows that $\mathscr{P}(\mathscr{E}(\mathscr{P}(\mathscr{E}))) = \mathscr{P}(\mathscr{E})$ and $\mathscr{E}(\mathscr{P}(\mathscr{E}(\mathscr{P}))) = \mathscr{E}(\mathscr{P})$. A class of the form $\mathscr{E}(\mathscr{P})$ will be called a **closed class** of epimorphisms.

Denoting by ø the empty class, the class $\mathscr{P}(ø)$ is the class of all objects in $\mathscr{A}$, and $\mathscr{E}_0 = \mathscr{E}(\mathscr{P}(ø))$ is the class of all retractions. On the other hand, the class $\mathscr{E}_1 = \mathscr{E}(ø)$ is the class of all epimorphisms in $\mathscr{A}$ and $\mathscr{P}(\mathscr{E}(ø))$ is the class of ordinary projectives.

If $P \in \mathscr{P}(\mathscr{E})$ and P' is a retract of P, then it is easy to see that P' is also in $\mathscr{P}(\mathscr{E})$. Also if $\beta\alpha \in \mathscr{E}(\mathscr{P})$, then we must have $\beta \in \mathscr{E}(\mathscr{P})$.

A class of epimorphisms $\mathscr{E}$ will be called a **projective class** if it is closed, and if for every object $A \in \mathscr{A}$ there is a morphism $\alpha : P \to A$ such that $\alpha \in \mathscr{E}$ and $P \in \mathscr{P}(\mathscr{E})$. The class $\mathscr{E}_0$ is clearly a projective class, whereas the class $\mathscr{E}_1$ is a projective class if and only if $\mathscr{A}$ has projectives.

Lemma 7.1. *If $\mathscr{E}$ is a projective class and $\alpha : A \to B$ is such that $[P, \alpha]$ is an epimorphism for all $P \in \mathscr{P}(\mathscr{E})$, then $\alpha \in \mathscr{E}$.*

Proof. Since $\mathscr{E}$ is closed, it suffices to show that α is an epimorphism. Let $f: P \to B$ be an epimorphism with $P \in \mathscr{P}(\mathscr{E})$. Since $[P, \alpha]$ is an epimorphism we can find $g \in [P, A]$ such that $\alpha g = f$. This shows that α is an epimorphism. ∎

Theorem 7.2. *Consider an adjoint situation $(\eta : S, T; \mathscr{A}, \mathscr{B})$ with T faithful, and let $\mathscr{E}$ be a projective class in $\mathscr{B}$. Let $T^{-1}(\mathscr{E})$ be the class of all morphisms α in $\mathscr{A}$ such that $T(\alpha) \in \mathscr{E}$. Then $T^{-1}(\mathscr{E})$ is a projective class in $\mathscr{A}$, and the $T^{-1}(\mathscr{E})$-projectives are the objects of the form $S(P)$ and their retracts, where P is the $\mathscr{E}$-projective.*

Proof. Observe that since T is faithful, if $T(\alpha) \in \mathscr{E}$ then α must be an epimorphism. Let P be $\mathscr{E}$-projective. Then $[P, T(\alpha)]$ is an epimorphism for all $\alpha \in T^{-1}(\mathscr{E})$. Using η this means that $[S(P), \alpha]$ is an epimorphism for all $\alpha \in T^{-1}(\mathscr{E})$. Hence $S(P)$ is $T^{-1}(\mathscr{E})$-projective. Now let $\alpha \in \mathscr{E}(\mathscr{P}(T^{-1}(\mathscr{E})))$. Then $[S(P), \alpha]$ is an epimorphism for all $P \in \mathscr{P}(\mathscr{E})$. Therefore $[P, T(\alpha)]$ is an epimorphism for all $P \in \mathscr{P}(\mathscr{E})$, and so by 7.1, $T(\alpha) \in \mathscr{E}$. Therefore $\alpha \in T^{-1}(\mathscr{E})$, and so $T^{-1}(\mathscr{E})$ is closed.

Given $A \in \mathscr{A}$, let $\beta : P \to T(A)$ be in $\mathscr{E}$ with $P \in \mathscr{P}(\mathscr{E})$. Then letting $\alpha = \eta^{-1}(\beta) : S(P) \to A$, we see from 1.1 that $T(\alpha) \in \mathscr{E}$. Hence $\alpha \in T^{-1}(\mathscr{E})$, and so since $S(P)$ is $T^{-1}(\mathscr{E})$-projective, this shows that $T^{-1}(\mathscr{E})$ is a projective class. Also if A is $T^{-1}(\mathscr{E})$-projective, then α must be a retraction, or in other words A is a retract of $S(P)$. Thus the $T^{-1}(\mathscr{E})$-projectives are as stated. ▌

Proposition 7.3. *Under the hypothesis of* 7.2 *suppose further that there is a functor* $R : \mathscr{A} \to \mathscr{B}$ *with the following properties:*

1. *There is a natural equivalence* $\mu : RS \to 1_{\mathscr{B}}$.
2. *If* $\alpha : S(P) \to A$ *is such that* $R(\alpha)$ *is an isomorphism and* P *and* A *are* $\mathscr{E}$ *and* $T^{-1}(\mathscr{E})$*-projective, respectively, then* α *is an isomorphism.*

Then any $T^{-1}(\mathscr{E})$*-projective is isomorphic to an object of the form* $S(P)$ *where* P *is* $\mathscr{E}$*-projective.*

Proof. Let A be $T^{-1}(\mathscr{E})$-projective. By 7.2 we can find a composition $A \to S(P) \to A$ which is the identity, where P is $\mathscr{E}$-projective. Applying R, we see that $R(A)$ is a retract of $RS(P) \approx P$. Hence $R(A)$ is $\mathscr{E}$-projective, and so we need only show $SR(A) \approx A$. Now $\psi_A = \eta^{-1}(1_{T(A)}) : ST(A) \to A$ is in $T^{-1}(\mathscr{E})$, hence we can find $\gamma : A \to ST(A)$ such that $\psi_A \gamma = 1_A$. Let α denote the composition

$$SR(A) \xrightarrow{SR(\gamma)} SRST(A) \xrightarrow{S\mu T} ST(A) \xrightarrow{\psi_A} A. \tag{1}$$

Using naturality of μ, we have the following commutative diagram:

$$\begin{array}{ccc} RSRS & \xrightarrow{\mu RS} & RS \\ {\scriptstyle RS\mu}\downarrow & & \downarrow{\scriptstyle \mu} \\ RS & \xrightarrow{\mu} & 1_{\mathscr{B}} \end{array}$$

Since μ is a natural equivalence, it follows that $\mu RS = RS\mu$. Also we have the commutative diagram

$$\begin{array}{ccc} RSR(A) & \xrightarrow{(\mu R)_A} & R(A) \\ {\scriptstyle RSR(\gamma)}\downarrow & & \downarrow{\scriptstyle R(\gamma)} \\ RSRST(A) & \xrightarrow{(\mu RST)_A} & RST(A) \end{array}$$

Applying R to (1), we obtain

$$\begin{aligned} R(\alpha) &= R(\psi_A)(RS\mu T)_A RSR(\gamma) \\ &= R(\psi_A)(\mu RST)_A RSR(\gamma) \\ &= R(\psi_A)R(\gamma)(\mu R)_A = R(\psi_A \gamma)(\mu R)_A. \end{aligned}$$

This shows that $R(\alpha)$ is an isomorphism, and so α is an isomorphism by condition 2. ▌

Consider a family of categories $\{\mathscr{B}_i\}_{i\in I}$, and for each $i \in I$ let $\mathscr{E}_i$ be a projective class in $\mathscr{B}_i$. Then $\mathop{\times}\limits_{i\in I} \mathscr{E}_i$ is a projective class in $\mathop{\times}\limits_{i\in I} \mathscr{B}_i$, and

$$\mathscr{P}\left(\mathop{\times}_{i\in I} \mathscr{E}_i\right) = \mathop{\times}_{i\in I} \mathscr{P}(\mathscr{E}_i).$$

Using 1.5, we then have

Corollary 7.4. *For each $i \in I$, let $T_i : \mathscr{A} \to \mathscr{B}_i$ be an adjoint for $S_i : \mathscr{B}_i \to \mathscr{A}$ and let $\mathscr{E}_i$ be a projective class for $\mathscr{B}_i$. Suppose that $\{T_i\}$ is collectively faithful and that $\{S_i\}$ is coproductive. Then $\bigcap\limits_{i\in I} T_i^{-1}(\mathscr{E}_i)$ is a projective class in $\mathscr{A}$ whose projectives are the objects of the form $\bigoplus\limits_{i\in I} S_i(P_i)$ and their retracts, where P_i is $\mathscr{E}_i$-projective for all $i \in I$.* ▮

Corollary 7.5. *Under the hypothesis of 7.4, suppose further that there are functors $R_i : \mathscr{A} \to \mathscr{B}_i$ with the following properties:*

1. *$R_j S_i = 0$ for $j \neq i$, $R_i S_i$ is naturally equivalent to 1_{B_i} for each $i \in I$, and each R preserves coproducts of the form $\bigoplus\limits_{i\in I} S_i(B_i)$.*
2. *If $\alpha : \bigoplus\limits_{i\in I} S_i(P_i) \to A$ is such that $R_i(\alpha)$ is an isomorphism for all $i \in I$ and P_i and A are $\mathscr{E}_i$ and $\bigcap\limits_{i\in I} T_i^{-1}(\mathscr{E}_i)$-projective respectively, then α is an isomorphism.*

Then any $\bigcap\limits_{i\in I} T_i^{-1}(\mathscr{E}_i)$-projective is isomorphic to an object of the form $\bigoplus\limits_{i\in I} S_i(P_i)$ where P_i is $\mathscr{E}_i$-projective for all $i \in I$. ▮

We say that a family of functors $R_i : \mathscr{A} \to \mathscr{B}_i$ **collectively preserves nonzero objects** if for each $A \neq 0$ in $\mathscr{A}$ we have $R_i(A) \neq 0$ in $\mathscr{B}_i$ for some i.

Corollary 7.6. *Let $T_i : \mathscr{A} \to \mathscr{B}_i$ be a collectively faithful system of exact functors, and let $S_i : \mathscr{B}_i \to \mathscr{A}$ be a coproductive family of coadjoints. If each $\mathscr{B}_i$ has projectives, then $\mathscr{A}$ has projectives, and the projectives in $\mathscr{A}$ are the objects of the form $\bigoplus\limits_{i\in I} S_i(P_i)$ and their retracts, where P_i is projective in $\mathscr{B}_i$ for each i.*

If, furthermore, there is a family of cokernel preserving functors $R_i : \mathscr{A} \to \mathscr{B}_i$ which collectively preserves nonzero objects and which satisfies condition 1 of 7.5, then the projectives in $\mathscr{A}$ are precisely the objects of the form $\bigoplus\limits_{i\in I} S_i(P_i)$.

Proof. If each T_i is exact, then taking $\mathscr{E}_i$ to be the family of all epimorphisms in $\mathscr{B}_i$ for each i, we see that $\bigcap\limits_{i\in I} T_i^{-1}(\mathscr{E}_i)$ is the class of all epimorphisms in $\mathscr{A}$. Consequently, the first statement follows from 7.4.

To prove the second statement, it suffices to show that the family R_i satisfies condition 2 of 7.5. Consider the functor $R : \mathscr{A} \to \mathop{\times}\limits_{i\in I} \mathscr{B}_i$ associated with the family R_i. Then R preserves nonzero objects and is cokernel preserving. We show that if $\alpha : A \to P$ is a morphism in $\mathscr{A}$ such that P is projective and $R(\alpha)$ is an isomorphism, then α is an isomorphism. Since R is cokernel preserving, we have $R(\text{Coker } \alpha) = \text{Coker}(R(\alpha)) = 0$ since $R(\alpha)$ is an isomorphism. Hence $\text{Coker}(\alpha)$ is 0, and so α is an epimorphism. But then since P is projective, the sequence

$$0 \to \text{Ker}(\alpha) \to A \xrightarrow{\alpha} P \to 0 \tag{2}$$

splits. Applying R to (2) we still have a split exact sequence, and so again using the fact that $R(\alpha)$ is an isomorphism, we see that $R(\text{Ker}(\alpha)) = 0$. Consequently, $\text{Ker}(\alpha) = 0$, and so α is an isomorphism. ▌

Exercises

1. Given functors $T : \mathscr{A} \to \mathscr{B}$ and $S : \mathscr{B} \to \mathscr{A}$ and natural transformations $\psi : ST \to 1_{\mathscr{A}}$ and $\varphi : 1_{\mathscr{B}} \to TS$ satisfying the relations $(T\psi)(\varphi T) = 1_T$ and $(\psi S)(S\varphi) = 1_S$, show that there is an adjoint situation $(\eta; S, T; \mathscr{A}, \mathscr{B})$ such that φ and ψ are the transformations defined in §1 (cf. 1.3).

2. Let $T : \mathscr{A} \to \mathscr{B}$ and $S : \mathscr{B} \to \mathscr{A}$ be such that $ST \approx 1_{\mathscr{A}}$. Then T reflects limits and colimits. In particular, this is true if T is the inclusion functor of a full, coreflective subcategory.

3. Let $\mathscr{A}'$ be a full, coreflective subcategory of the abelian category $\mathscr{A}$, and suppose that the coreflector $R : \mathscr{A} \to \mathscr{A}'$ is kernel preserving. Then an object $Q \in \mathscr{A}'$ is injective in $\mathscr{A}'$ if and only if it is injective in $\mathscr{A}$. In particular, if $\mathscr{M}$ is a monosubcategory of $\mathscr{A}$ and $\mathscr{L}$ is the subcategory of pure objects, then an object is injective in $\mathscr{L}$ if and only if it is injective in $\mathscr{A}$.

4. If $\mathscr{M}$ is a monosubcategory of $\mathscr{A}$ and if $M \to Q$ is an injective envelope with $M \in \mathscr{M}$, then $Q \in \mathscr{M}$. Hence if $M \in \mathscr{M}$ has an injective envelope, then the coreflection $M \to R$ of M in $\mathscr{L}$ is an essential extension. (Examine the construction of the coreflection for M given in 6.6.)

5. Let $\mathscr{E}$ be a class of epimorphisms in an abelian category $\mathscr{A}$, and let $\mathscr{M}(\mathscr{E})$ denote the class of all monomorphisms which are kernels of members of $\mathscr{E}$. Also let $\mathscr{E}(\mathscr{M}(\mathscr{E}))$ denote all epimorphisms which are cokernels of members of $\mathscr{M}(\mathscr{E})$. Following Buchsbaum [4] we call $\mathscr{E}$ an h.f. class under the following conditions:

(i) $\mathscr{E} = \mathscr{E}(\mathscr{M}(\mathscr{E}))$.
(ii) All retractions are in $\mathscr{E}$ (and hence all coretractions are in $\mathscr{M}(\mathscr{E})$).
(iii) If $\alpha, \beta \in \mathscr{E}$, and $\beta\alpha$ is defined, then $\beta\alpha \in \mathscr{E}$.
(iv) If $\gamma, \delta \in \mathscr{M}(\mathscr{E})$, and $\delta\gamma$ is defined, then $\delta\gamma \in \mathscr{M}(\mathscr{E})$.
(v) If α is an epimorphism and $\beta\alpha \in \mathscr{E}$, then $\beta \in \mathscr{E}$.
(vi) If δ is a monomorphism and $\delta\gamma \in \mathscr{M}(\mathscr{E})$, then $\gamma \in \mathscr{M}(\mathscr{E})$.

Any closed class in $\mathscr{A}$ is an h.f. class. (Use I, 16.2, in verifying axioms (iv) and (vi).) On the other hand, if $\mathscr{E}$ is an h.f. class in $\mathscr{A}$ such that for every object $A \in \mathscr{A}$ there is an epimorphism $\alpha : P \to A$ with $\alpha \in \mathscr{E}$ and $P \in \mathscr{P}(\mathscr{E})$, then $\mathscr{E}$ is a projective class. (If $\gamma : A' \to A$ has the property that $[P, \gamma]$ is an epimorphism for all $P \in \mathscr{P}(\mathscr{E})$, then form the pullback diagram

$$\begin{array}{ccc} P' & \longrightarrow & A' \\ \big\downarrow & & \big\downarrow{\scriptstyle \gamma} \\ P & \xrightarrow{\ \alpha\ } & A \end{array}$$

and show that $P' \to P$ is a retraction.)

[CHAPTER VI]

Applications of Adjoint Functors

Introduction

It is first shown that under certain conditions, completeness in a category implies cocompleteness (1.1). In §2 it is proved that any **R**-module valued functor which has a coadjoint is naturally equivalent to a morphism functor represented by some **R**-object. The converse problem of showing that morphism functors have coadjoints leads to the definition of the tensor product. We establish its existence under two different assumptions on the category (3.1 and 3.2). The tensor product then helps in showing that the existence of a projective generator is still another property which a functor category $(\mathscr{A}, \mathscr{B})$ inherits from the codomain category $\mathscr{B}$. This fact is due to Freyd.

In §5 we establish the existence of 0th derived and coderived functors for group-valued functors from small abelian categories. In §6 we show that the category of monofunctors $\mathscr{M}(\mathscr{A}, \mathscr{G})$ is a monosubcategory of $(\mathscr{A}, \mathscr{G})$. The subcategory of kernel preserving functors $\mathscr{L}(\mathscr{A}, \mathscr{G})$ coincides with the category of pure objects. In particular it follows that $\mathscr{L}(\mathscr{A}, \mathscr{B})$ is abelian. This paves the way to the full imbedding theorem 7.2.

The chapter is concluded with a section on complexes, and an application of the projective class theory of V, §7 to the hyperhomology theory of Cartan-Eilenberg [6, Chapter XVII].

Sections 1, 2, 5 and 6, as well as Theorem 3.2 are due to Peter Freyd. The existence of coderived functors and the abelianness of $\mathscr{L}(\mathscr{A}, \mathscr{B})$ modulo certain set theoretic conditions on the categories $\mathscr{A}$ and $\mathscr{B}$ were first shown by Gabriel [17]. An alternative proof of 6.2 can be given using Gabriel's work. The section on complexes is due to Eilenberg and Moore [12].

1. Application to Limits

Consider a diagram category $[\Sigma, \mathscr{B}]$ where $\mathscr{B}$ is any category and Σ is any diagram scheme. For $B \in \mathscr{B}$ let $I(B)$ be the diagram which has B at every vertex and 1_B at every arrow. Dualizing the discussion of II, §12, we see that $\mathscr{B}$ is Σ-cocomplete if and only if the functor $I : \mathscr{B} \to [\Sigma, \mathscr{B}]$ has a coadjoint $L : [\Sigma, \mathscr{B}] \to \mathscr{B}$. Now I is clearly limit preserving. Consequently, we have as an immediate application of V, 3.2:

Theorem 1.1. *Let $\mathscr{B}$ be a complete, locally small category with a cogenerator. Then $\mathscr{B}$ is cocomplete.* ▮

Using II, 15.1*, we have

Corollary 1.2. *Let $\mathscr{B}$ be a complete, exact category with a cogenerator. Then $\mathscr{B}$ is cocomplete.* ▮

2. Module-Valued Adjoints

Lemma 2.1. *Let $\mathbf{R}$ be a ring and $\mathscr{A}$ an additive category. If a functor $T : \mathscr{A} \to \mathscr{G}^{\mathbf{R}}$ has a coadjoint, then for some $C \in {}^{\mathbf{R}}\mathscr{A}$ we have a natural equivalence $T \approx H^C$.*

Proof. Consider an adjoint situation $(\eta; S, T; \mathscr{A}, \mathscr{G}^{\mathbf{R}})$. Then by V, 1.4, S is additive, and so $C = S(\mathbf{R})$ can be regarded as a left $\mathbf{R}$-object by means of left operations of $\mathbf{R}$ on itself. Then for $A \in \mathscr{A}$ we have

$$H^C(A) = [S(\mathbf{R}), A] \overset{\eta}{\approx} [\mathbf{R}, T(A)] \approx T(A)$$

where the middle isomorphism preserves addition by V, 1.4, and $\mathbf{R}$-module structure by naturality of η, and the right-hand isomorphism is a natural equivalence of right $\mathbf{R}$-modules (II, exercise 12). ▮

Theorem 2.2. *Let $\mathscr{A}$ be a complete, locally small, additive category with a cogenerator, and let $\mathbf{R}$ be a ring. Suppose that $T : \mathscr{A} \to \mathscr{G}^{\mathbf{R}}$ is a covariant, limit preserving functor. Then for some $C \in {}^{\mathbf{R}}\mathscr{A}$ we have a natural equivalence $T \approx H^C$.*

Proof. This follows immediately from 2.1 and V, 3.2. ▮

Theorem 2.2*. *Let $\mathscr{A}$ be a cocomplete, colocally small, additive category with a generator, and let $\mathbf{R}$ be a ring. Suppose that $T : \mathscr{A} \to \mathscr{G}^{\mathbf{R}}$ is a contravariant, limit preserving functor. Then for some $C \in \mathscr{A}^{\mathbf{R}}$ we have a natural equivalence $T \approx H_C$.* ▮

Theorems 2.2 and 2.2* generalize theorems of C. Watts [34].

3. The Tensor Product

We now turn to the converse of 2.1. Under two sets of conditions on the category $\mathscr{A}$ we will prove that if $C \in {}^{\mathbf{R}}\mathscr{A}$, then the functor $H^C : \mathscr{A} \to \mathscr{G}^{\mathbf{R}}$ has a coadjoint. In the first case we shall construct the coadjoint directly without applying any general existence theorem. The second case will be an application of V, 3.1.

Theorem 3.1. *Let $\mathscr{A}$ be a cocomplete abelian category and let $\mathbf{R}$ be any ring. Then we have an additive, colimit preserving, covariant bifunctor $\mathscr{G}^{\mathbf{R}} \times {}^{\mathbf{R}}\mathscr{A} \to \mathscr{A}$, whose value on the pair (M, C) we denote by $M \otimes_{\mathbf{R}} C$, and a natural equivalence of trifunctors*

$$\eta = \eta_{M,C,A} : [M, [C, A]_{\mathscr{A}}]^{\mathbf{R}} \to [M \otimes_{\mathbf{R}} C, A]_{\mathscr{A}} \tag{1}$$

where $M \in \mathscr{G}^{\mathbf{R}}$, $C \in {}^{\mathbf{R}}\mathscr{A}$, and $A \in \mathscr{A}$.

Proof. By V, 2.3, it suffices to construct a coadjoint for the functor $H^C : \mathscr{A} \to \mathscr{G}^{\mathbf{R}}$ for each $C \in {}^{\mathbf{R}}\mathscr{A}$. Now a left $\mathbf{R}$-object C can be considered as a functor into $\mathscr{A}$ from the full subcategory of $\mathscr{G}^{\mathbf{R}}$ consisting of the single object $\mathbf{R}$. In other words we are in a position to apply IV, 5.2. That theorem gives us a unique colimit preserving functor from $\mathscr{G}^{\mathbf{R}}$ to $\mathscr{A}$, whose value on the right $\mathbf{R}$-module M we denote by $M \otimes_{\mathbf{R}} C$, such that $\mathbf{R} \otimes_{\mathbf{R}} C = C$ as left $\mathbf{R}$-objects. Explicitly we can define $M \otimes_{\mathbf{R}} C$ as follows. We first take the exact sequence of right $\mathbf{R}$-modules

$${}^{K}\mathbf{R} \xrightarrow{\lambda} {}^{M}\mathbf{R} \xrightarrow{\pi} M \to 0$$

where the mth coordinate of π is the unique right $\mathbf{R}$-module morphism $\varphi_m : \mathbf{R} \to M$ such that $\varphi_m(1) = m$, K is the set of elements in the kernel of π, and λ is the right $\mathbf{R}$-module morphism whose kth coordinate is $\varphi_k : \mathbf{R} \to {}^{M}\mathbf{R}$ where $\varphi_k(1) = k$. Then $M \otimes_{\mathbf{R}} C$ is the cokernel of the induced morphism ${}^{K}C \to {}^{M}C$. If $\mu : M \to M'$ then we have the morphism ${}^{M}\mathbf{R} \to {}^{M'}\mathbf{R}$ which is such that composition with the mth injection into ${}^{M}\mathbf{R}$ yields the $\mu(m)$th injection into ${}^{M'}\mathbf{R}$. The morphism $\mu \otimes_{\mathbf{R}} C$ is then the unique morphism making the diagram

$$\begin{array}{ccc} {}^{M}C & \longrightarrow & M \otimes_{\mathbf{R}} C \\ \downarrow & & \downarrow {\scriptstyle \mu \otimes_{\mathbf{R}} C} \\ {}^{M'}C & \longrightarrow & M' \otimes_{\mathbf{R}} C \end{array}$$

commutative.

We now define the transformation (1). A right $\mathbf{R}$-module morphism $f: M \to [C, A]$ determines a morphism $\bar{\eta}(f) : {}^{M}C \to A$, and using the fact that f is additive and commutes with operations by $\mathbf{R}$ we see that the composition ${}^{K}C \to {}^{M}C \to A$ is zero. Hence $\bar{\eta}(f)$ induces a morphism $\eta(f) : M \otimes_{\mathbf{R}} C \to A$. On the other hand, given $g : M \otimes_{\mathbf{R}} C \to A$ we can compose g with ${}^{M}C \to M \otimes_{\mathbf{R}} C$ to get a morphism $\bar{g} : {}^{M}C \to A$. Then $\bar{g}$ determines the function

$$\eta'(g) : M \to [C, A]$$

such that $\eta'(g)(m)$ is just the mth coordinate of $\bar{g}$. That $\eta'(g)$ is a right $\mathbf{R}$-module morphism comes from the fact that the composition ${}^{K}C \to {}^{M}C \to A$ is zero. It is then easy to check that η and η' are inverses of each other.

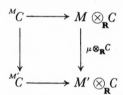

To show that η is natural in M, we must prove commutativity of the diagram

$$\begin{array}{ccc} [M', [C, A]]^{\mathbf{R}} & \longrightarrow & [M' \otimes_{\mathbf{R}} C, A] \\ \big\downarrow & & \big\downarrow \\ [M, [C, A]]^{\mathbf{R}} & \longrightarrow & [M \otimes_{\mathbf{R}} C, A] \end{array} \tag{2}$$

relative to a morphism $\mu : M \to M'$ of right $\mathbf{R}$-modules. Commutativity of (2) amounts to showing that relative to an $\mathbf{R}$-module morphism $f : M' \to [C, A]$ we have a commutative diagram

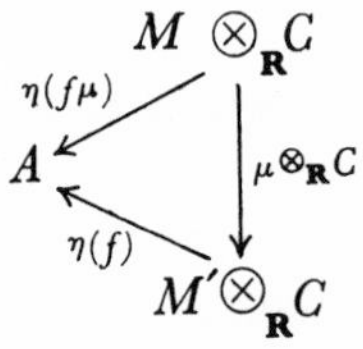

(3)

Commutativity of (3) comes from the diagram

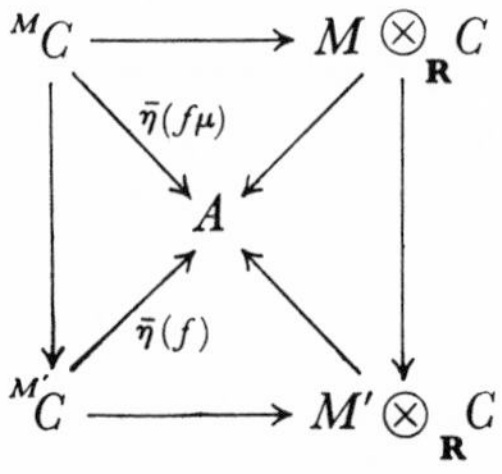

in which the square and each triangle save possibly (3) is commutative. Since ${}^{M}C \to M \otimes_{\mathbf{R}} C$ is an epimorphism it follows that (3) is commutative also. This establishes naturality of η in M. Naturality in A is simpler and is left to the reader. ▌

Theorem 3.2. *Let $\mathscr{A}$ be a complete, locally small, colocally small, additive category with coproducts. Then the conclusions of* 3.1 *are valid.*

Proof. For fixed $C \in {}^{\mathbf{R}}\mathscr{A}$ the functor $H^{C} : \mathscr{A} \to \mathscr{G}^{\mathbf{R}}$ is limit preserving. Hence by V, 3.1, to show that it has a coadjoint it suffices to find a solution set in $\mathscr{A}$ for each right $\mathbf{R}$-module M. That is, we wish to find a set of objects $\{A_i\}$ in $\mathscr{A}$

such that any morphism $f: M \to [C, A]$ of right **R**-modules admits a factorization of the form

$$M \xrightarrow{g} [C, A_i] \xrightarrow{[C,\alpha]} [C, A]$$

for some morphism $\alpha : A_i \to A$ in $\mathscr{A}$ and some morphism g of **R**-modules. Let $\{A_i\}$ be the set of all quotient objects of ${}^M C$. Consider the morphism ${}^M C \to A$ whose mth coordinate is $f(m)$, and let

$${}^M C \xrightarrow{p} I \xrightarrow{\alpha} A$$

be the factorization through its image. Our hypothesis assures that the image exists and that p is an epimorphism (I, §10). Thus I is one of the A_i. If we define g by $g(m) = pu_m$ where u_m is the mth injection into ${}^M C$, then it follows immediately from the fact that f is an **R**-module morphism and $[C, \alpha]$ is an **R**-module monomorphism that g is an **R**-module morphism. This proves that $\{A_i\}$ is a solution set. ▮

When $\mathscr{A}$ is a category satisfying conditions dual to 3.1 or 3.2, we can define the **symbolic morphism functor** from ${}^{\mathbf{R}}\mathscr{G} \times {}^{\mathbf{R}}\mathscr{A}$ to $\mathscr{A}$ whose value on the pair (M, C) we denote by ${}^{\mathbf{R}}\{M, C\}$. For fixed C it is defined by means of the duality

$${}^{\mathbf{R}}\{M, C\} = (M \otimes_{\mathbf{R}^*} C^*)^*.$$

We thus have a natural equivalence

$${}^{\mathbf{R}}[M, [A, C]_{\mathscr{A}}] \approx [A, {}^{\mathbf{R}}\{M, C\}]_{\mathscr{A}}. \tag{4}$$

It follows that the symbolic morphism functor has the same limit preserving properties as the ordinary morphism functor. The natural equivalence $\mathbf{R} \otimes_{\mathbf{R}} C \approx C$ of left **R**-objects dualizes to a natural equivalence ${}^{\mathbf{R}}\{R, C\} \approx C$. In the case where $\mathscr{A}$ is the category of abelian groups, ${}^{\mathbf{R}}\{M, C\}$ is the same as ${}^{\mathbf{R}}[M, C]$ (exercise 9).

If C is a right **R**-object and M is a left **R**-module, then we define

$$C \otimes_{\mathbf{R}} M = M \otimes_{\mathbf{R}^*} C.$$

When $\mathbf{R} = \mathbf{Z}$ we shall denote $M \otimes_{\mathbf{Z}} C = C \otimes_{\mathbf{Z}} M$ simply by $M \otimes C$.

4. Functor Categories

Let $\mathscr{A}$ be a small, additive category and let $\mathscr{B}$ be a cocomplete abelian category. Let us denote

$$S_A(B)(A') = [A, A'] \otimes B$$

where $A, A' \in \mathscr{A}$ and $B \in \mathscr{B}$. We consider S as a functor from $\mathscr{A} \times \mathscr{B}$ to the functor category $(\mathscr{A}, \mathscr{B})$. Thus, for fixed A, $S_A : \mathscr{B} \to (\mathscr{A}, \mathscr{B})$. Recall also the functor $E : (\mathscr{A}, \mathscr{B}) \times \mathscr{A} \to \mathscr{B}$ given by $E(T, A) = T(A)$. Holding A fixed we obtain the evaluation functor $E_A : (\mathscr{A}, \mathscr{B}) \to \mathscr{B}$ (II, §11).

Theorem 4.1. *Let $\mathscr{A}$ be a small, additive category and let $\mathscr{B}$ be a cocomplete abelian category. Then $S : \mathscr{A} \times \mathscr{B} \to (\mathscr{A}, \mathscr{B})$ is a coadjoint for $E : (\mathscr{A}, \mathscr{B}) \times \mathscr{A} \to \mathscr{B}$. If U_A is a generator in $\mathscr{B}$ for each $A \in \mathscr{A}$, then $\bigoplus_{A \in \mathscr{A}} S_A(U_A)$ is a generator for $(\mathscr{A}, \mathscr{B})$. If, on the other hand, U_A is small for each $A \in \mathscr{A}$ and $\mathscr{A}$ has only a finite number of objects, then $\bigoplus_{A \in \mathscr{A}} S_A(U_A)$ is a small object in $(\mathscr{A}, \mathscr{B})$.*

If $\mathscr{E}$ is a projective class in $\mathscr{B}$ and $\mathscr{E}(\mathscr{A}, \mathscr{B})$ is the class of morphisms in $(\mathscr{A}, \mathscr{B})$ which are pointwise in $\mathscr{E}$, then $\mathscr{E}(\mathscr{A}, \mathscr{B})$ is a projective class in $(\mathscr{A}, \mathscr{B})$. The $\mathscr{E}(\mathscr{A}, \mathscr{B})$-projectives are the functors of the form $\bigoplus_{A \in \mathscr{A}} S_A(P_A)$ and their retracts, where P_A is $\mathscr{E}$-projective for each $A \in \mathscr{A}$. In particular, if $\mathscr{B}$ has projectives, then so does $(\mathscr{A}, \mathscr{B})$.

Proof. In V, 4.1, let $\mathscr{C}$ be the category $\mathscr{G}$, let T be H^B, and let G be H^A. Then using IV, 2.1, we have natural equivalences

$$\begin{aligned}[S_A(B), F] &= [H^A \otimes B, F] \approx [H^A, H^B F] \approx H^B F(A) \\ &= [B, F(A)] = [B, E_A(F)]. \end{aligned} \tag{1}$$

This shows the required adjointness. Since the evaluation functors are collectively faithful and coproduct preserving, the statements concerning generators and small objects follow from V, 1.5. The statements concerning projective classes follow from V, 7.4, and V, 7.6. ▌

Applying IV, 4.1, we obtain:

Corollary 4.2. *Let $\mathscr{A}$ be an additive category with only a finite number of objects, and let $\mathbf{R}$ be a ring. For each $A \in \mathscr{A}$ let n_A be an integer > 0. Then $\bigoplus_{A \in \mathscr{A}} S_A(\mathbf{R}^{n_A})$ is a small projective generator for $(\mathscr{A}, \mathscr{G}^{\mathbf{R}})$. Consequently, $(\mathscr{A}, \mathscr{G}^{\mathbf{R}})$ is equivalent to the category of right modules over the ring of endomorphisms of $\bigoplus_{A \in \mathscr{A}} S_A(\mathbf{R}^{n_A})$.* ▌

If $\mathscr{B}$ is complete abelian, then we can apply duality to $\mathscr{A}$ and $\mathscr{B}$ to obtain functors $J_{A,B} : \mathscr{A} \to \mathscr{B}$, defined by

$$J_{A,B}(A') = [A', A] \otimes B^* = \{[A', A], B\}.$$

Dualizing (1), we obtain a natural equivalence

$$[F, J_{A,B}] \approx [F(A), B]$$

where $F \in (\mathscr{A}, \mathscr{B})$. From 4.1* it follows that if Q is an injective cogenerator for $\mathscr{B}$, then $\mathsf{X}_{A \in \mathscr{A}} J_{A,Q}$ is an injective cogenerator for $(\mathscr{A}, \mathscr{B})$. In the case where $\mathscr{B}$ is the category of abelian groups, the functor $J_{A,B}$ is the same as that defined in IV, §3. This follows from the fact that here the symbolic morphism functor coincides with the ordinary morphism functor (exercise 9).

Let S and S' be sets, and consider a function $f : S \to S'$. Letting B be an object in a category $\mathscr{B}$ with coproducts, we have the morphism ${}^f B : {}^S B \to {}^{S'} B$ which is such that when composed with the sth injection in ${}^S B$ yields the $f(s)$th injection into ${}^{S'}B$. On the other hand, a morphism $\beta : B \to B'$ yields the morphism ${}^{S}\beta : {}^{S}B \to {}^{S}B'$. In this way, ${}^{S}B$ can be regarded as the value of a two variable functor from $\mathscr{S} \times \mathscr{B}$ to $\mathscr{B}$. Furthermore, we have a natural equivalence of trifunctors

$$[S, [B, C]_{\mathscr{B}}]_{\mathscr{S}} \approx [{}^{S}B, C]_{\mathscr{B}}.$$

For this reason we define the tensor product $S \otimes_{\mathscr{S}} B$ of a set S with an object B as ${}^{S}B$. If $\mathscr{A}$ is any small category (not necessarily additive), we can define as before

$$S_A(B)(A') = [A, A'] \otimes_{\mathscr{S}} B.$$

Thus, S_A may be considered as a functor from B to the category of not necessarily additive functors $[\mathscr{A}, \mathscr{B}]$.

Theorem 4.3. *Let $\mathscr{A}$ be a small category, and let $\mathscr{B}$ be a category with coproducts. Then $S : \mathscr{A} \times \mathscr{B} \to [\mathscr{A}, \mathscr{B}]$ is a coadjoint for $E : [\mathscr{A}, \mathscr{B}] \times \mathscr{A} \to \mathscr{B}$. If U_A is a generator in $\mathscr{B}$ for each $A \in \mathscr{A}$, then $\bigoplus_{A \in \mathscr{A}} S_A(U_A)$ is a generator for $[\mathscr{A}, \mathscr{B}]$. If, on the other hand, U_A is small for each $A \in \mathscr{A}$ and $\mathscr{A}$ has only a finite number of objects, then $\bigoplus_{A \in \mathscr{A}} S_A(U_A)$ is a small object in $[\mathscr{A}, \mathscr{B}]$.*

Suppose further that $\mathscr{B}$ is abelian, and let $\mathscr{E}$ be a projective class in $\mathscr{B}$. If $\mathscr{E}[\mathscr{A}, \mathscr{B}]$ is the class of morphisms in $[\mathscr{A}, \mathscr{B}]$ which are pointwise in $\mathscr{E}$, then $\mathscr{E}[\mathscr{A}, \mathscr{B}]$ is a projective class in $[\mathscr{A}, \mathscr{B}]$. The $\mathscr{E}[\mathscr{A}, \mathscr{B}]$-projectives are the functors of the form $\bigoplus_{A \in \mathscr{A}} S_A(P_A)$ and their retracts, where P_A is $\mathscr{E}$-projective for all $A \in \mathscr{A}$. In particular, if $\mathscr{B}$ has projectives, then so does $[\mathscr{A}, \mathscr{B}]$.

Proof. The proof is identical to that of 4.1, except that we must take $\mathscr{C}$ to be $\mathscr{S}$ instead of $\mathscr{G}$ in establishing adjointness. ▌

Corollary 4.4. *Let $\mathscr{A}$ be a category with only a finite number of objects, and let $\mathbf{R}$ be a ring. For each $A \in \mathscr{A}$ let n_A be an integer > 0. Then $\bigoplus_{A \in \mathscr{A}} S_A(\mathbf{R}^{n_A})$ is a small projective generator for $[\mathscr{A}, \mathscr{G}^{\mathbf{R}}]$. Consequently, $[\mathscr{A}, \mathscr{G}^{\mathbf{R}}]$ is equivalent to the category of right modules over the ring of endomorphisms of $\bigoplus_{A \in \mathscr{A}} S_A(\mathbf{R}^{n_A})$.* ▌

5. Derived Functors

Throughout this section $\mathscr{A}$ and $\mathscr{B}$ will denote abelian categories, and all functors will be additive.

Consider a covariant functor $T : \mathscr{A} \to \mathscr{B}$. The **0th derived functor** of T is a natural transformation $L_0 T \to T$ such that $L_0 T : \mathscr{A} \to \mathscr{B}$ is a cokernel preserving functor, and such that any other natural transformation from a cokernel preserving functor to T factors uniquely through $L_0 T \to T$. If T is contravariant, then $L_0 T \to T$ is the 0th derived functor of T if $(L_0 T)_* \to T_*$ is the 0th derived functor of the covariant functor T_*.

If $\mathscr{A}$ is a small category, then the 0th derived functor of the covariant functor T is simply the reflection of T in the full subcategory $\mathscr{R}(\mathscr{A}, \mathscr{B})$ of $(\mathscr{A}, \mathscr{B})$ consisting of all cokernel preserving functors. Thus, to show the existence of 0th derived functors for all covariant functors $T: \mathscr{A} \to \mathscr{B}$ is equivalent to showing that $\mathscr{R}(\mathscr{A}, \mathscr{B})$ is a reflective subcategory of $(\mathscr{A}, \mathscr{B})$.

Dually we say that a natural transformation $T \to R^0 T$ is the **0th coderived functor** of T if the corresponding transformation $(R^0 T)_*^* \to T_*^*$ is the 0th derived functor of T_*^*. Thus $T \to R^0 T$ is the 0th coderived functor of T if and only if $R^0 T$ is kernel preserving, and every natural transformation from T to a kernel preserving functor factors uniquely through $T \to R^0 T$. When $\mathscr{A}$ is small, the 0th coderived functor for the covariant functor T is just the coreflection of T in the full subcategory $\mathscr{L}(\mathscr{A}, \mathscr{B})$ of $(\mathscr{A}, \mathscr{B})$ consisting of all kernel preserving functors.

If $\mathscr{A}$ is a small category, we let $|\mathscr{A}|$ denote the cardinal number of the set of all morphisms in $\mathscr{A}$. Also, if $T: \mathscr{A} \to \mathscr{G}$, we let $|T|$ denote the cardinal number of the disjoint union of sets $\bigcup_{A \in \mathscr{A}} T(A)$.

Lemma 5.1. *Let $\mathscr{C}$ be a class of exact sequences in a small category $\mathscr{A}$, and let $\mathscr{C}(\mathscr{A}, \mathscr{G})$ denote the full subcategory of $(\mathscr{A}, \mathscr{G})$ consisting of all those functors which preserve exact sequences in $\mathscr{C}$. Let $T_0 \subset F$ where $F \in \mathscr{C}(\mathscr{A}, \mathscr{G})$, and let ρ be any infinite cardinal number such that $\rho \geqslant \max(|\mathscr{A}|, |T_0|)$. Then there is a subfunctor $T \subset F$ such that $T \in \mathscr{C}(\mathscr{A}, \mathscr{G})$, $T_0 \subset T$, and $|T| \leqslant \rho$.*

Proof. For each morphism $\alpha: A \to A_1$ in $\mathscr{A}$, choose a function $f_\alpha: F(A_1) \to F(A)$ such that

$$\begin{aligned} f_\alpha(z) &= 0 \qquad \text{for} \quad z \notin \operatorname{Im}(F(\alpha)) \\ F(\alpha)(f_\alpha(z)) &= z \qquad \text{for} \quad z \in \operatorname{Im}(F(\alpha)). \end{aligned}$$

We define subfunctors $T_n \subset F$ inductively as follows. Given $T_n \subset F$ and $A \in \mathscr{A}$, let S_A be the subset of $F(A)$ defined by the following set theoretic union:

$$S_A = \bigcup_{A_1 \in \mathscr{A}} \left(\bigcup_{\alpha \in [A, A_1]} f_\alpha(T_n(A_1)) \right).$$

By taking $\alpha = 1_A$, we see in particular that $S_A \supset T_n(A)$. If we assume that $|T_n| \leqslant \rho$, then using the fact that $\rho^2 = \rho$ we see that the disjoint union of sets $\bigcup_{A \in \mathscr{A}} S_A$ has cardinal number $\leqslant \rho$. We define T_{n+1} as the subfunctor of F generated by the family $\{S_A\}_{A \in \mathscr{A}}$ (see II, exercise 6). Then $T_{n+1} \supset T_n$, and it is not difficult to see that $|T_{n+1}| \leqslant \rho$ (II, exercise 6). Now define $T = \bigcup_{n \geqslant 0} T_n$. Then $|T| \leqslant \rho$ since $|T_n| \leqslant \rho$ for all n, and furthermore $T_0 \subset T$. We show that $T \in \mathscr{C}(\mathscr{A}, \mathscr{B})$.

Consider an exact sequence $A' \xrightarrow{\alpha} A \xrightarrow{\beta} A''$ in $\mathscr{C}$. We wish to show that $T(A') \to T(A) \to T(A'')$ is exact in $\mathscr{G}$. Suppose that $z \in T(A)$ and $T(\beta)(z) = 0$. For some n we have $z \in T_n(A) \subset F(A)$. Now $T(\beta)(z) = 0$ implies $F(\beta)(z) = 0$, and so since $F \in \mathscr{C}(\mathscr{A}, \mathscr{B})$ we have $z = F(\alpha)(y)$ for some $y \in F(A')$. We may assume $y = f_\alpha(z)$. Then by construction of T_{n+1} we have $y \in T_{n+1}(A') \subset T(A')$. Hence $z = T(\alpha)(y)$ as required. ∎

Theorem 5.2. *Let $\mathscr{A}$ be a small category, and let $\mathscr{C}$ be a class of exact sequences of the form*

$$A' \to A \to A'' \to 0 \tag{1}$$

in $\mathscr{A}$. Then $\mathscr{C}(\mathscr{A}, \mathscr{G})$ is a reflective subcategory of $(\mathscr{A}, \mathscr{G})$.

Proof. It follows from II, 12.4*, that $\mathscr{C}(\mathscr{A}, \mathscr{G})$ is a cocomplete subcategory of $(\mathscr{A}, \mathscr{G})$. In particular, this means that an epimorphism in $\mathscr{C}(\mathscr{A}, \mathscr{G})$ is a necessarily an epimorphism in $(\mathscr{A}, \mathscr{G})$. Consequently, since $(\mathscr{A}, \mathscr{G})$ is colocally small, the same is true of $\mathscr{C}(\mathscr{A}, \mathscr{G})$. Therefore by V, 3.2*, to show that $\mathscr{C}(\mathscr{A}, \mathscr{G})$ is a reflective subcategory of $(\mathscr{A}, \mathscr{G})$, it suffices to show that $\mathscr{C}(\mathscr{A}, \mathscr{G})$ has a generator. Let ρ be any infinite cardinal number $\geqslant |\mathscr{A}|$. Then it follows from 5.1 that for $F \in \mathscr{C}(\mathscr{A}, \mathscr{G})$, $A \in \mathscr{A}$, and $x \in F(A)$, there is a subfunctor $T \subset F$ such that $x \in T(A)$, $T \in \mathscr{C}(\mathscr{A}, \mathscr{G})$, and $|T| \leqslant \rho$. Now by identifying naturally equivalent functors and using the fact that $\mathscr{A}$ is a set, it is not difficult to see that $\{T \mid |T| \leqslant \rho\}$ is a set. It then follows from the above that $\{T \mid T \in \mathscr{C}(\mathscr{A}, \mathscr{G})$ and $|T| \leqslant \rho\}$ is a set of generators for $\mathscr{C}(\mathscr{A}, \mathscr{G})$. ∎

Taking $\mathscr{C}$ to be the class of all sequences of the form (1), we obtain:

Corollary 5.3. *If $\mathscr{A}$ is a small category, then every functor $T: \mathscr{A} \to \mathscr{G}$ has a 0th derived functor.* ∎

Theorem 5.4. *Let $\mathscr{A}$ be a small category, and let $\mathscr{C}$ be a class of exact sequences of the form*

$$0 \to A' \to A \to A''$$

in $\mathscr{A}$. Then $\mathscr{C}(\mathscr{A}, \mathscr{G})$ is a coreflective subcategory of $(\mathscr{A}, \mathscr{G})$.

Proof. By II, 12.4, $\mathscr{C}(\mathscr{A}, \mathscr{G})$ is a complete subcategory of $(\mathscr{A}, \mathscr{G})$, and in particular is locally small. Therefore by V, 3.1, to show that $\mathscr{C}(\mathscr{A}, \mathscr{G})$ is a coreflective subcategory of $(\mathscr{A}, \mathscr{G})$, it suffices to find a solution set in $\mathscr{C}(\mathscr{A}, \mathscr{G})$ for each object $S \in (\mathscr{A}, \mathscr{B})$. Let ρ be any infinite cardinal number $\geqslant \max(|\mathscr{A}|, |S|)$. Consider a morphism $S \to F$ where $F \in \mathscr{C}(\mathscr{A}, \mathscr{G})$, and let T_0 be its image. Then $|T_0| \leqslant |S| \leqslant \rho$, and so by 5.1 we can find a subfunctor $T \subset F$ such that $T_0 \subset T$ and $|T| \leqslant \rho$. This shows that as a solution set for S we may take $\{T \mid T \in \mathscr{C}(\mathscr{A}, \mathscr{G})$ and $|T| \leqslant \rho\}$. ∎

Corollary 5.5. *If $\mathscr{A}$ is a small category, then every functor $T: \mathscr{A} \to \mathscr{G}$ has a 0th coderived functor.* ∎

The results of this section generalize to group valued functors of several variables (exercise 12). Furthermore, a simple trick enables us to replace $\mathscr{G}$ by $\mathscr{G}^{\mathbf{R}}$ throughout (exercise 18). In the case where $\mathscr{A}$ has projectives (injectives), we can construct derived (coderived) functors using the techniques of Cartan and Eilenberg [6] (exercise 15).

6. The Category of Kernel Preserving Functors

Lemma 6.1. *Let*

$$0 \to T' \to T \to T'' \to 0 \tag{1}$$

be an exact sequence of functors between two abelian categories.

(i) *If T' is kernel preserving and T is a monofunctor, then T'' is a monofunctor.*
(ii) *If T'' is a monofunctor and T is kernel preserving, then T' is kernel preserving.*

Proof. The proof is a simple exercise in chasing the three by three diagram which arises from evaluating (1) on an exact sequence $0 \to A \to B \to C \to 0$ in the domain category. ∎

Supposing that $\mathscr{A}$ is a small abelian category, let $\mathscr{M}(\mathscr{A}, \mathscr{G})$ be the full subcategory of $(\mathscr{A}, \mathscr{G})$ consisting of all monofunctors. Then by II, 12.4, $\mathscr{M}(\mathscr{A}, \mathscr{G})$ is a complete subcategory of $(\mathscr{A}, \mathscr{G})$. In other words the axiom $\mathscr{M}_1$ of V, §6, is satisfied. Since a subfunctor of a monofunctor is necessarily a monofunctor, axiom $\mathscr{M}_2$ is satisfied as well. Also by IV, 2.4, and IV, 2.5, the injective envelope of a monofunctor is an exact functor. Consequently, $\mathscr{M}_3$ is satisfied. Now by 6.1, (i), any kernel preserving functor is pure with respect to $\mathscr{M}(\mathscr{A}, \mathscr{G})$. On the other hand, if T is a pure functor, consider the exact sequence

$$0 \to T \to Q \to M \to 0$$

where $T \to Q$ is the injective envelope of T. Since T is a monofunctor, Q is exact, and since T is pure, M is a monofunctor. Therefore by 6.1, (ii), T is kernel preserving. In other words the category $\mathscr{L}$ consisting of all pure objects is precisely the category $\mathscr{L}(\mathscr{A}, \mathscr{G})$ of all kernel preserving functors. Hence by V, 6.8, we have

Theorem 6.2. *Let $\mathscr{A}$ be a small abelian category. Then $\mathscr{L}(\mathscr{A}, \mathscr{G})$ is a coreflective subcategory of $(\mathscr{A}, \mathscr{G})$. The coreflector $R^0 : (\mathscr{A}, \mathscr{G}) \to \mathscr{L}(\mathscr{A}, \mathscr{G})$ is an exact, colimit preserving functor. $\mathscr{L}(\mathscr{A}, \mathscr{G})$ is a complete, C_3 abelian category with a generator and an injective cogenerator.* ∎

Remark 1. By 5.5 we already know that $\mathscr{L}(\mathscr{A}, \mathscr{G})$ is coreflective. By C_3 for $\mathscr{G}$, the colimit of a direct system of kernel preserving functors is kernel preserving. Thus C_3 for $\mathscr{L}(\mathscr{A}, \mathscr{G})$ follows immediately from C_3 for $(\mathscr{A}, \mathscr{G})$. Also, since $\bigoplus_{A \in \mathscr{A}} H^A$ is a generator for $(\mathscr{A}, \mathscr{G})$ (IV, 2.3) and is also kernel preserving, it serves as a generator for $\mathscr{L}(\mathscr{A}, \mathscr{G})$. The strength of 6.2 lies in the fact that $\mathscr{L}(\mathscr{A}, \mathscr{G})$ is abelian.

Remark 2. A projective functor in $(\mathscr{A}, \mathscr{G})$, although necessarily kernel preserving (IV, exercise 3), is not necessarily projective in $\mathscr{L}(\mathscr{A}, \mathscr{G})$. In particular, $\bigoplus_{A \in \mathscr{A}} H^A$ is not in general a projective in $\mathscr{L}(\mathscr{A}, \mathscr{G})$. However, if $\mathscr{A}$ has injective resolutions, then we can show that $\mathscr{L}(\mathscr{A}, \mathscr{G})$ has a projective generator (exercise 17).

7. The Full Imbedding Theorem

Lemma 7.1. *Let $\mathscr{A}$ be any small abelian category. Then the contravariant functor $H: \mathscr{A} \to \mathscr{L}(\mathscr{A}, \mathscr{G})$ defined by $H(A) = H^A$ is a full, exact imbedding.*

Proof. We have seen in IV, 2.2, that H is a full imbedding. Let C be a cogenerator for $\mathscr{L}(\mathscr{A}, \mathscr{G})$. Such exists by 6.2. Let $0 \to A' \to A \to A'' \to 0$ be an exact sequence in $\mathscr{A}$. We wish to show that the sequence

$$0 \to H^{A''} \to H^A \to H^{A'} \to 0$$

is exact in $\mathscr{L}(\mathscr{A}, \mathscr{G})$. We know that $H^{A''} \to H^A$ is the kernel of $H^A \to H^{A'}$ in $(\mathscr{A}, \mathscr{G})$, hence also in $\mathscr{L}(\mathscr{A}, \mathscr{G})$. Consequently, it suffices to show that $H^A \to H^{A'}$ is an epimorphism in $\mathscr{L}(\mathscr{A}, \mathscr{G})$. Since C is a cogenerator for $\mathscr{L}(\mathscr{A}, \mathscr{G})$ it suffices to show that $[H^{A'}, C] \to [H^A, C]$ is a monomorphism. But by IV, 2.1, this last is equivalent to $C(A') \to C(A)$, which is a monomorphism since C is kernel preserving. ▮

Theorem 7.2. *Every small abelian category $\mathscr{A}$ admits a full, exact (covariant) imbedding into a category $\mathscr{G}^{\mathbf{R}}$ of modules over an appropriate ring $\mathbf{R}$.*

Proof. By 7.1 and 6.2 we know that $\mathscr{A}$ admits a full, exact, contravariant imbedding into a complete abelian category possessing an injective cogenerator. Composing this imbedding with the duality functor on its codomain, we obtain a full, exact, covariant imbedding S from $\mathscr{A}$ to a cocomplete abelian category possessing a projective generator. Since $\mathscr{A}$ is small, by taking the coproduct of sufficiently many copies of the projective generator we can arrange that every object in the image of S is finitely (in fact, singly) generated. Then if we compose S with the functor T of IV, 4.1, we obtain the required imbedding. ▮

As a consequence of 7.2 we have:

Metatheorem 7.3. *Let $\mathscr{A}$ be any abelian category. If a theorem is of the form "p implies q" where p is a categorical statement about a diagram in $\mathscr{A}$ over a finite scheme Σ and q states that a finite number of additional morphisms exist between objects over designated vertices in the diagram so as to make some categorical statement true of the extended diagram, and if the theorem is true when $\mathscr{A} = \mathscr{G}^{\mathbf{R}}$ for every ring $\mathbf{R}$, then the theorem is true for any abelian category $\mathscr{A}$.* ▮

(Cf. IV, Metatheorem 2.8.)

8. Complexes

Throughout this section $\mathscr{A}$ will denote an abelian category. A **complex** X in $\mathscr{A}$ is a sequence of morphisms in $\mathscr{A}$

$$\cdots \longrightarrow X_{n+1} \xrightarrow{d_{n+1}} X_n \xrightarrow{d_n} X_{n-1} \longrightarrow \cdots \qquad (-\infty < n < \infty)$$

such that $d_n d_{n+1} = 0$ for all integers n. The class $\mathscr{C}(\mathscr{A})$ of all complexes in $\mathscr{A}$ becomes a category by defining a morphism $f: X \to X'$ of complexes as a family of morphisms $f_n : X_n \to X'_n$ such that $d'_n f_n = f_{n-1} d_n$ for all n. (Actually $\mathscr{C}(\mathscr{A})$ can be viewed as the category of additive functors to $\mathscr{A}$ from an appropriate additive category. See II, exercise 16.) We have additive functors $C_n, B_n, Z_n, B'_n, Z'_n, : \mathscr{C}(\mathscr{A}) \to \mathscr{A}$ which are defined for each integer n as follows:

$$\begin{aligned} C_n(X) &= X_n \\ B_n(X) &= \mathrm{Im}(d_{n+1}) \\ Z_n(X) &= \mathrm{Ker}(d_n) \\ B'_n(X) &= \mathrm{Coim}(d_n) \\ Z'_n(X) &= \mathrm{Coker}(d_{n+1}). \end{aligned}$$

Observe that $B_n = B'_{n+1}$. The distinction is made only to facilitate duality.

The relation $d_n d_{n+1} = 0$ shows that $B_n \subset Z_n$, and so we can define further $H_n : \mathscr{C}(\mathscr{A}) \to \mathscr{A}$ by $H_n(X) = Z_n(X)/B_n(X)$. The first Noether isomorphism theorem (I, 16.2) then gives us an exact, commutative diagram of functors and natural transformations for each n,

$$\begin{array}{ccccccccc} & & & & 0 & & 0 & & \\ & & & & \downarrow & & \downarrow & & \\ 0 & \longrightarrow & B_n & \longrightarrow & Z_n & \longrightarrow & H_n & \longrightarrow & 0 \\ & & \| & & \downarrow & & \downarrow & & \\ 0 & \longrightarrow & B_n & \longrightarrow & C_n & \longrightarrow & Z'_n & \longrightarrow & 0 \\ & & & & \downarrow & & \downarrow & & \\ & & & & B'_n & = & B'_n & & \\ & & & & \downarrow & & \downarrow & & \\ & & & & 0 & & 0 & & \end{array} \qquad (1)$$

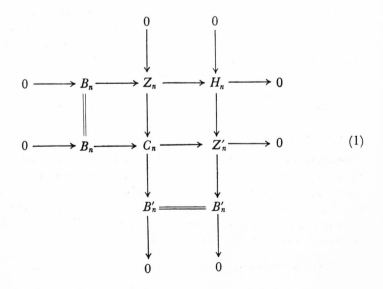

In the dual category $\mathscr{A}^*$, a complex X in $\mathscr{A}$ becomes a complex X^* if we set $(X^*)_n = (X_{-n})^*$. We have $Z_n(X^*) = (Z'_{-n}(X))^*$ and $Z'_n(X^*) = (Z_{-n}(X))^*$, with similar relations holding for the B's. It follows from (1) that

$$H_n(X^*) = (H_{-n}(X))^*.$$

Consider the composition $Z'_n \to B'_n \approx B_{n-1} \to Z_{n-1}$. Since $B_{n-1} \to Z_{n-1}$ is a monomorphism it follows from (1) that the kernel of this composition is $H_n \to Z'_n$. Similarly since $Z'_n \to B'_n$ is an epimorphism we see that the cokernel is $Z_{n-1} \to H_{n-1}$. That is, we have an exact sequence

$$0 \to H_n \to Z'_n \to Z_{n-1} \to H_{n-1} \to 0 \tag{2}$$

for each n. Now it follows from II, 12.2, that Z_n is limit preserving and Z'_n is colimit preserving. Hence, given an exact sequence of complexes

$$0 \to X' \to X \to X'' \to 0, \tag{3}$$

using (2) we obtain a commutative diagram

$$\begin{array}{ccccccccc}
 & & 0 & & 0 & & 0 & & \\
 & & \downarrow & & \downarrow & & \downarrow & & \\
 & & H_n(X') & \longrightarrow & H_n(X) & \longrightarrow & H_n(X'') & & \\
 & & \downarrow & & \downarrow & & \downarrow & & \\
 & & Z'_n(X') & \longrightarrow & Z'_n(X) & \longrightarrow & Z'_n(X'') & \longrightarrow & 0 \\
 & & \downarrow & & \downarrow & & \downarrow & & \\
0 & \longrightarrow & Z_{n-1}(X') & \longrightarrow & Z_{n-1}(X) & \longrightarrow & Z_{n-1}(X'') & & \\
 & & \downarrow & & \downarrow & & \downarrow & & \\
 & & H_{n-1}(X') & \longrightarrow & H_{n-1}(X) & \longrightarrow & H_{n-1}(X'') & & \\
 & & \downarrow & & \downarrow & & \downarrow & & \\
 & & 0 & & 0 & & 0 & &
\end{array} \tag{4}$$

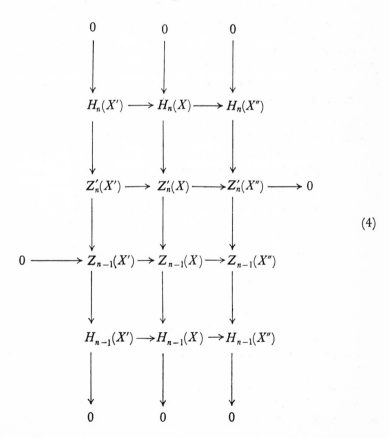

where the columns and middle two rows are exact. There results a connecting morphism $\delta_n : H_n(X'') \to H_{n-1}(X')$ which is such that the sequence

$$H_n(X') \to H_n(X) \to H_n(X'') \xrightarrow{\delta} H_{n-1}(X') \to H_{n-1}(X) \to H_{n-1}(X'') \qquad (5)$$

is exact (IV, §1). Since the connecting morphism of a diagram of the form (4) is self-dual (IV, exercise 2), it follows that the connecting morphism relative to the dual of the exact sequence (3) is simply δ considered as a morphism in the dual category. Observe that if any two of the complexes in the sequence (3) is exact (so that $H_n = 0$ for all n), then by the exact sequence (5) the third complex must also be exact. Also the exactness of (5) shows in particular that the functors H_n are half exact.

Consider the functor $S_n : \mathscr{A} \to \mathscr{C}(\mathscr{A})$ defined by $S_n(A)_n = S_n(A)_{n-1} = A$ with $d_n = 1_A$, $S_n(A)_i = 0$ for $i \neq n,\ n-1$, and $S_n(\alpha)_n = S_n(\alpha)_{n-1} = \alpha$. Then there is an obvious one to one correspondence

$$[S_n(A),\, X]_{\mathscr{C}(\mathscr{A})} \approx [A,\, X_n]_{\mathscr{A}}$$

which is natural in A and X. That is, S_n is a coadjoint for C_n. Since a family $\{S_n(A_n)\}_{n\in\mathbf{Z}}$ involves only a finite number (two, at most) of objects in each dimension n, it follows that the family $\{S_n\}$ is coproductive. Also the family $\{C_n\}$ is collectively faithful. Hence by V, 7.4, if $\mathscr{E}$ is a projective class in $\mathscr{A}$ and $\mathscr{E}\mathscr{C}(\mathscr{A})$ is the class of morphisms in $\mathscr{C}(\mathscr{A})$ which are pointwise in $\mathscr{E}$, then $\mathscr{E}\mathscr{C}(\mathscr{A})$ is a projective class in $\mathscr{C}(\mathscr{A})$. We are going to show that the $\mathscr{E}\mathscr{C}(\mathscr{A})$-projectives are precisely the objects of the form $\bigoplus_{n\in\mathbf{Z}} S_n(P_n)$ where P_n is $\mathscr{E}$-projective. In the first place it is clear that the functors $B_{n-1} : \mathscr{C}(\mathscr{A}) \to \mathscr{A}$ satisfy condition (1) of V, 7.5. To show that condition (2) is also satisfied we remark first that any $\mathscr{E}\mathscr{C}(\mathscr{A})$-projective X, being a retract of an object of the form $\bigoplus_{n\in\mathbf{Z}} S_n(P_n)$, must be an exact complex. That is, $B_n(X) = Z_n(X)$. Now if $\alpha : X \to Y$ is a morphism of $\mathscr{E}\mathscr{C}(\mathscr{A})$-projectives such that $B_n(\alpha)$ is an isomorphism for all n, an application of the five lemma to the exact commutative diagram

$$\begin{array}{ccccccccc}
0 & \longrightarrow & B_n(X) & \longrightarrow & X_n & \longrightarrow & B_{n-1}(X) & \longrightarrow & 0 \\
 & & \downarrow & & \downarrow & & \downarrow & & \\
0 & \longrightarrow & B_n(Y) & \longrightarrow & Y_n & \longrightarrow & B_{n-1}(Y) & \longrightarrow & 0
\end{array}$$

shows that α must be an isomorphism. Hence the desired result follows from V, 7.5.

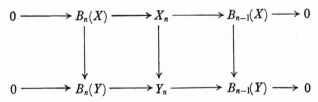

Now consider the functor $S'_n : \mathscr{A} \to \mathscr{C}(\mathscr{A})$ defined by $S'_n(A)_n = A$, $S'_n(A)_i = 0$ for $i \neq n$, and $S'_n(\alpha)_n = \alpha$. Then it is easy to see that S'_n is a coadjoint for Z_n. Again, since a family $\{S_n(A_n)\}_{n\in\mathbf{Z}} \cup \{S'_n(A'_n)\}_{n\in\mathbf{Z}}$ involves at most three nonzero objects in each dimension, it follows that the family $\{S_n\} \cup \{S'_n\}$ is coproductive. Thus by V, 7.4, if $\mathscr{E}$ is a projective class in $\mathscr{A}$ and $\mathscr{E}\mathscr{C}(\mathscr{A})'$ is the class of morphisms α in $\mathscr{C}(\mathscr{A})$ such that $C_n(\alpha)$ and $Z_n(\alpha)$ are in $\mathscr{E}$ for all $n \in \mathbf{Z}$, then $\mathscr{E}\mathscr{C}(\mathscr{A})'$ is a projective class in $\mathscr{C}(\mathscr{A})$. We are going to show that the $\mathscr{E}\mathscr{C}(\mathscr{A})'$-projectives are precisely the objects of the form $\bigoplus_{n\in\mathbf{Z}} S_n(P_n) \oplus S'_n(P'_n)$ where P_n and P'_n are $\mathscr{E}$-projective.

Let $X = \bigoplus_{n\in\mathbf{Z}} S_n(A_n) \oplus S'_n(A'_n)$. Then we have natural isomorphisms

$$C_m(X) \approx A_{m+1} \oplus A_m \oplus A'_m \tag{6}$$
$$Z_m(X) \approx A_{m+1} \oplus A'_m \tag{7}$$
$$B_m(X) \approx A_{m+1} \tag{8}$$
$$Z'_m(X) \approx A_m \oplus A'_m \tag{9}$$
$$H_m(X) \approx A'_m. \tag{10}$$

In particular, (8) and (10) show that the family $\{B_{n-1}\} \cup \{H_n\}$ satisfies condition (1) of V, 7.5. Now if $\alpha : X \to Y$ is a morphism in $\mathscr{C}(\mathscr{A})$ such that $B_n(\alpha)$ and $H_n(\alpha)$ are isomorphisms for all n (X and Y do not have to be $\mathscr{E}\mathscr{C}(\mathscr{A})'$-projective here), then applying the five lemma to the exact sequence

$$0 \to H_n \to Z'_n \to B_{n-1} \to 0$$

we see that $Z'_n(\alpha)$ is an isomorphism. Hence another application of the five lemma to the sequence

$$0 \to B_n \to C_n \to Z'_n \to 0$$

yields that α is an isomorphism. Thus condition (2) of V, 7.5, is satisfied, and so the $\mathscr{E}\mathscr{C}(\mathscr{A})'$-projectives are as stated.

Finally, we consider the case where $\mathscr{E} = \mathscr{E}_1$, where we suppose that $\mathscr{A}$ has projective resolutions. Starting with a complex X in $\mathscr{C}(\mathscr{A})$ we can find an exact sequence

$$0 \to K^1 \to X^0 \to X \to 0$$

where X^0 is $\mathscr{E}\mathscr{C}(\mathscr{A})'$-projective and $X^0 \to X$ is in $\mathscr{E}\mathscr{C}(\mathscr{A})'$. Thus the sequences

$$0 \to C_n(K^1) \to C_n(X^0) \to C_n(X) \to 0 \tag{11}$$

and

$$0 \to Z_n(K^1) \to Z_n(X^0) \to Z_n(X) \to 0 \tag{12}$$

are exact for all n. An application of the nine lemma (I, 16.1*) to the exact sequence

$$0 \to Z_n \to C_n \to B_{n-1} \to 0 \tag{13}$$

then shows that

$$0 \to B_n(K^1) \to B_n(X^0) \to B_n(X) \to 0 \tag{14}$$

is exact for all n. Hence by the exact sequences

$$0 \to B_n \to Z_n \to H_n \to 0 \tag{15}$$

and

$$0 \to B_n \to C_n \to Z'_n \to 0 \tag{16}$$

we see that the sequences

$$0 \to Z'_n(K^1) \to Z'_n(X^0) \to Z'_n(X) \to 0 \tag{17}$$

and

$$0 \to H_n(K^1) \to H_n(X^0) \to H_n(X) \to 0 \tag{18}$$

are exact. We can then replace X by K^1 and repeat the process. By such an iterative procedure we obtain an $\mathscr{E}\mathscr{C}(\mathscr{A})'$-projective resolution

$$\ldots \to X^{i+1} \to X^i \to X^{i-1} \to \ldots \to X^1 \to X^0 \to X \to 0. \tag{19}$$

Using Eqs. (6)–(10) and exact sequences (14), (17), and (18), we see that if we apply the functors C_n B_n, Z_n, Z'_n, and H_n to (19), we obtain projective resolutions in $\mathscr{A}$ for $C_n(X)$, $B_n(X)$, $Z_n(X)$, $Z'_n(X)$, and $H_n(X)$ respectively. Thus we have shown that every complex in $\mathscr{A}$ has a projective resolution in the sense of Cartan and Eilenberg [6, p. 363]. Conversely, suppose that we are given an order 2 sequence (19) which is such that when we apply H_n and B_n, we obtain projective resolutions for $H_n(X)$ and $B_n(X)$, respectively, for all n. Using (13), (15), and (16), we see that if we apply Z_n, C_n, and Z'_n to (19), we obtain exact sequences. From (15) we can write $Z_n(X^i) = B_n(X^i) \oplus H_n(X^i)$ since $H_n(X^i)$ is projective. Then from (13) we can find a coretraction $u : B_{n-1}(X^i) \to C_n(X^i)$ since $B_{n-1}(X^i)$ is projective, and we can write

$$\begin{aligned} X^i_n = C_n(X^i) &= Z_n(X^i) \oplus B_{n-1}(X^i) \\ &= B_n(X^i) \oplus H_n(X^i) \oplus B_{n-1}(X^i). \end{aligned} \tag{20}$$

If we compose $X^i_n \to X^i_{n-1}$ with either of the inclusions $B_n(X^i) \to X^i_n$ and $H_n(X^i) \to X^i_n$, we obtain 0 since both are subobjects of $Z_n(X^i)$. On the other hand, we have

$$\begin{aligned} B_{n-1}(X^i) \xrightarrow{u} X^i_n \to X^i_{n-1} &= B_{n-1}(X^i) \xrightarrow{u} X^i_n \to B_{n-1}(X^i) \to X^i_{n-1} \\ &= B_{n-1}(X^i) \to X^i_{n-1}. \end{aligned}$$

Therefore it follows from (20) that

$$X^i = \bigoplus_{n \in \mathbf{Z}} S_n(B_{n-1}(X^i)) \oplus S'_n(H_n(X^i)).$$

Consequently, X^i is $\mathscr{E}\mathscr{C}(\mathscr{A})'$-projective for all $i \geqslant 0$.

Exercises

1. Let $\mathbf{R}$ be an integral domain. An $\mathbf{R}$-module A is called **torsion free** if $ra = 0$ for $r \in \mathbf{R}$ and $a \in A$ implies that one of r or a is zero. Show that the injective envelope of a torsion free $\mathbf{R}$-module is torsion free. Hence, show that the full subcategory $\mathscr{M}$ of ${}^{\mathbf{R}}\mathscr{G}$ consisting of all torsion free modules is a mono-subcategory of ${}^{\mathbf{R}}\mathscr{G}$, and further that A is pure with respect to $\mathscr{M}$ if and only if A is torsion free and divisible (use II, exercise 18). Consequently, the category

$\mathcal{A}$ of torsion free and divisible **R**-modules is abelian, and in particular the category of torsion free, injective abelian groups is abelian. Show directly that $\mathcal{A}$ is isomorphic to the category of vector spaces over the field of quotients of **R**.

2. Use the Tietze extension theorem [25, p. 242] to show that the category $\mathcal{CHT}$ of compact Hausdorff spaces has an injective cogenerator. Also use the Tychonoff product theorem [25, p. 143] and II, 2.4, to show that $\mathcal{CHT}$ is a complete subcategory of the category $\mathcal{HT}$ of all Hausdorff spaces. Consequently, $\mathcal{CHT}$ is a coreflective subcategory of $\mathcal{HT}$.

3. Let A be a right **R**-module and B a left **R**-module. Let F be the free abelian group generated by pairs (a, b) with $a \in A$ and $b \in B$, and let G be the subgroup of F generated by elements of the form

$$(a + a', b) - (a, b) - (a', b)$$
$$(a, b + b') - (a, b) - (a, b')$$
$$(ar, b) - (a, rb) \qquad\qquad (r \in \mathbf{R}).$$

Then define $A \otimes_{\mathbf{R}} B$ as the quotient group F/G, and for morphisms $\alpha : A \to A_1$ and $\beta : B \to B_1$ define $\alpha \otimes_{\mathbf{R}} \beta$ in the obvious way so as to make $\otimes_{\mathbf{R}}$ into an additive covariant bifunctor from $\mathcal{G}^{\mathbf{R}} \times {}^{\mathbf{R}}\mathcal{G}$ to $\mathcal{G}$. For $A \in \mathcal{G}^{\mathbf{R}}$, $B \in {}^{\mathbf{R}}\mathcal{G}^{\mathbf{S}}$, and $C \in \mathcal{G}^{\mathbf{S}}$ establish a natural equivalence of trifunctors

$$[A, [B, C]^{\mathbf{S}}]^{\mathbf{R}} \approx [A \otimes_{\mathbf{R}} B, C]^{\mathbf{S}}$$

thereby showing that the above definition of tensor product is a special case of the one given in the text.

4. Establish a natural equivalence of trifunctors

$$M \otimes_{\mathbf{S}} (N \otimes_{\mathbf{R}} C) \approx (M \otimes_{\mathbf{S}} N) \otimes_{\mathbf{R}} C$$

for $M \in \mathcal{G}^{\mathbf{S}}$, $N \in {}^{\mathbf{S}}\mathcal{G}^{\mathbf{R}}$, and $C \in {}^{\mathbf{R}}\mathcal{A}$, where **R** and **S** are any rings and $\mathcal{A}$ is a cocomplete abelian category.

5. Consider a covariant additive functor $S : {}^{\mathbf{R}}\mathcal{G} \to \mathcal{A}$ where $\mathcal{A}$ is cocomplete abelian. Then $S(\mathbf{R})$ is a right **R**-object in $\mathcal{A}$, and so we can consider the covariant colimit preserving functor $T : {}^{\mathbf{R}}\mathcal{G} \to \mathcal{A}$ defined by

$$T(M) = S(\mathbf{R}) \otimes_{\mathbf{R}} M.$$

Apply IV, 5.4, to find a natural transformation $T \to S$ which is a natural equivalence in the case where S is colimit preserving. Hence the covariant colimit preserving functors from ${}^{\mathbf{R}}\mathcal{G}$ to $\mathcal{A}$ are precisely those given by tensoring with a fixed left **R**-object in $\mathcal{A}$. This generalizes results due independently to Watts [34] and Eilenberg [9].

6. Let $\mathcal{A}$ be a cocomplete abelian category and let $S : {}^{\mathbf{R}}\mathcal{G} \to \mathcal{A}$ be any additive functor. If C is a right **R**-object in $\mathcal{A}$, use IV, 5.4, to establish a one-to-one correspondence

$$[C \otimes_{\mathbf{R}}, S] \approx [C, S(\mathbf{R})]^{\mathbf{R}}.$$

Show that this is an isomorphism of groups and is natural in C and in S.

7. Let $T: \mathscr{G}^{\mathbf{R}} \times {}^{\mathbf{R}}\mathscr{G} \to \mathscr{G}$ be a covariant colimit preserving bifunctor. Use the generalization of IV, 5.4 (IV, exercise 11), to produce a natural equivalence

$$T(A, B) \approx A \otimes_{\mathbf{R}} T(\mathbf{R}, \mathbf{R}) \otimes_{\mathbf{R}} B.$$

Hence T is naturally equivalent as a bifunctor to the tensor product if and only if T is colimit preserving and $T(\mathbf{R}, \mathbf{R})$ is isomorphic to $\mathbf{R}$ as a left $\mathbf{R}$, right $\mathbf{R}$-bimodule.

8. Let $T: \mathscr{G} \times \mathscr{G} \to \mathscr{G}$ be a limit preserving bifunctor, contravariant in the first variable and covariant in the second variable. Then by 2.1, for fixed $A \in \mathscr{G}$ we have a natural equivalence of the functors of B

$$T(A, B) \approx [M(A), B] \tag{1}$$

for some $M(A) \in \mathscr{G}$. Using IV, 2.2, M can be considered as a functor in such a way that (1) becomes a natural equivalence of bifunctors, and M is colimit preserving. Suppose that T has the property that $T(\mathbf{Z}, B)$ is an exact functor of B. Then $M(\mathbf{Z})$ is a projective group, hence free (see, for example, [6, I, 5.3]). Hence, if $T(\mathbf{Z}, \mathbf{Z}) \approx \mathbf{Z}$, then $M(\mathbf{Z}) \approx \mathbf{Z}$, and so M is naturally equivalent to the identity functor on $\mathscr{G}$. In other words, T is naturally equivalent as a bifunctor to [,] if and only if T is limit preserving, $T(\mathbf{Z}, \mathbf{Z}) \approx \mathbf{Z}$, and $T(\mathbf{Z},\ )$ is exact. (This exercise was suggested by Michael Shub.)

9. For $M, C \in {}^{\mathbf{R}}\mathscr{G}$ and $A \in \mathscr{G}$, establish a natural equivalence of trifunctors

$${}^{\mathbf{R}}[M, [A, C]] \approx [A, {}^{\mathbf{R}}[M, C]]$$

to show that in this case the symbolic morphism functor ${}^{\mathbf{R}}\{M, C\}$ is the same as the ordinary morphism functor ${}^{\mathbf{R}}[M, C]$.

10. Let $\mathscr{A}$ be a small additive category and let $\mathscr{B}$ be a locally small abelian category which is complete and cocomplete. Then the existence of a coadjoint for $E_A: (\mathscr{A}, \mathscr{B}) \to \mathscr{B}$ could be established using V, 3.1, as follows. For $B \in \mathscr{B}$ take as a solution set the set of all additive functors $T: \mathscr{A} \to \mathscr{B}$ such that for each $A_1 \in \mathscr{A}$ the object $T(A_1)$ is a quotient object of ${}^{[A,A_1]}B$. Given $f: B \to S(A)$, define $I(A_1)$ as the image of the morphism ${}^{[A,A_1]}B \to S(A_1)$ whose αth coordinate is $S(\alpha)f$. Show that I is a subfunctor of S (hence is additive) and that f factors through $I(A) \to T(A)$ (Freyd).

11. The discussion in §6 applies if $\mathscr{G}$ is replaced by any complete abelian category $\mathscr{B}$ which has the following property: If $T: \mathscr{A} \to \mathscr{B}$ is a monofunctor, then there is a monomorphism $T \to Q$ with Q kernel preserving and injective in $(\mathscr{A}, \mathscr{B})$. Hence if $\mathscr{A}$ has projectives, apply duality and IV, exercise 7, to show that the reflector $L_0: (\mathscr{A}, \mathscr{G}) \to \mathscr{R}(\mathscr{A}, \mathscr{G})$ is an exact, limit preserving functor and that $\mathscr{R}(\mathscr{A}, \mathscr{G})$ is a complete and cocomplete abelian category with a cogenerator and a projective generator.

12. Generalize the results of §5 to functors of several variables

$$T: \mathscr{A}_1 \times \mathscr{A}_2 \times \ldots \times \mathscr{A}_n \to \mathscr{G}$$

where each $\mathscr{A}_i$ is a small abelian category.

13. Let $F: \mathscr{A} \to \mathscr{G}$ be an additive covariant functor where $\mathscr{A}$ is a small abelian category. For $A \in \mathscr{A}$ let $T(A)$ be the set of $x \in F(A)$ such that $F(\alpha)(x) = 0$ for some monomorphism α. Use I, 20.2* to show first that $T(A)$ is a subgroup of $F(A)$ and second that T is a subfunctor of F. Hence show that T is the maximal torsion subobject of F with respect to $\mathscr{M}(\mathscr{A}, \mathscr{G})$. In the case where there exists a monomorphism $A \to Q$ with Q injective, show that $T(A)$ is the kernel of $F(A) \to F(Q)$ (Freyd).

14. Let $F: \mathscr{A} \to \mathscr{G}$ be covariant and additive where $\mathscr{A}$ is an abelian category with projectives. For each $A \in \mathscr{A}$ choose an epimorphism $P_A \to A$ with P_A projective. Then the reflection R of F in the category of epifunctors is given by

$$R(A) = \mathrm{Im}(F(P_A) \to F(A)).$$

In particular, if $F = H^B$, then $R(A)$ is the set of all $\alpha \in [B, A]$ such that α factors through a projective (Freyd).

15. Let $\mathscr{A}$ be an abelian category with projectives. Then V, 5.2, and V, 5.4, are valid if the category $\mathscr{P}$ is replaced by the full subcategory of $\mathscr{A}$ consisting of all projective objects and the expression "colimit preserving" is replaced by "cokernel preserving." (The proofs are identical, except that here there is no need to deal with coproducts of members of $\mathscr{P}$ since every object in $\mathscr{A}$ is already the quotient of a member of $\mathscr{P}$.) It follows that if $T: \mathscr{A} \to \mathscr{B}$ is an additive functor where $\mathscr{B}$ is abelian, then the unique cokernel preserving extension $\bar{T}: \mathscr{A} \to \mathscr{B}$ of $T|\mathscr{P}$ is the derived functor of T. Furthermore we have an equivalence of categories $\mathscr{R}(\mathscr{A}, \mathscr{B}) \approx (\mathscr{P}, \mathscr{B})$, showing that $\mathscr{R}(\mathscr{A}, \mathscr{B})$ is an abelian category possessing the completeness and generation properties of $\mathscr{B}$ (cf. exercise 11).

The above generalizes to functors of several variables by remarking that the above analogues of V, 5.2, and V, 5.4, also generalize to functors of several variables (cf. V, exercises 11 and 12).

16. Let $\mathscr{A}$ and $\mathscr{B}$ be abelian categories and suppose that $\mathscr{A}$ has injectives. Show that an additive functor $T: \mathscr{A} \to \mathscr{B}$ is a torsion object with respect to $\mathscr{M}(\mathscr{A}, \mathscr{B})$ if and only if $T(Q) = 0$ for every injective $Q \in \mathscr{A}$. (Use exercise 15*.)

17. Let $\mathscr{A}$ be a small abelian category with injectives. Use exercise 16 and IV, 2.1, to show that if $Q \in \mathscr{A}$ is injective, then H^Q is projective in $\mathscr{L}(\mathscr{A}, \mathscr{G})$. Hence show that $\bigoplus_Q H^Q$ is a projective generator for $\mathscr{L}(\mathscr{A}, \mathscr{G})$, where Q runs through all injectives in $\mathscr{A}$.

18. Consider an additive functor $T: \mathscr{A} \to {}^{\mathbf{R}}\mathscr{B}$ where $\mathscr{A}$ and $\mathscr{B}$ are abelian, and let $\bar{T}$ be the group valued functor obtained by composing T with the forgetful functor from ${}^{\mathbf{R}}\mathscr{B}$ to $\mathscr{B}$. Let $R^0\bar{T}$ be the 0th coderived functor of $\bar{T}$. An element $r \in \mathbf{R}$ induces a natural transformation from $\bar{T}$ to $\bar{T}$ which in turn induces a natural transformation from $R^0\bar{T}$ to $R^0\bar{T}$. Show that in this way $R^0\bar{T}$ can be considered as a functor with values in ${}^{\mathbf{R}}\mathscr{B}$, and as such it is the 0th coderived functor of T.

19. Let $\mathscr{A}$ be an abelian category. Given an epimorphism $L \to L''$ in $\mathscr{L}(\mathscr{A}, \mathscr{G})$ and a morphism $H^A \to L''$, show that these can be put into a commutative diagram

$$\begin{array}{ccc} H^B & \longrightarrow & H^A \\ \downarrow & & \downarrow \\ L & \longrightarrow & L'' \end{array}$$

where $A \to B$ is a monomorphism in $\mathscr{A}$ and hence $H^B \to H^A$ is an epimorphism in $\mathscr{L}(\mathscr{A}, \mathscr{G})$. (Use exercise 13 and IV, 2.1.) Then, letting $L'' = H^A$ and taking $H^A \to L''$ as the identity on H^A, show that if

$$0 \to H^C \to L \to H^A \to 0$$

is a short exact sequence in $\mathscr{L}(\mathscr{A}, \mathscr{G})$, then L is representable. (Show that $H^B \oplus H^C \to L$ is an epimorphism in $\mathscr{L}(\mathscr{A}, \mathscr{G})$ and hence form a 3×3 exact commutative diagram in which all functors are representable functors save possibly L) (Freyd).

20. Given a ring $\mathbf{R}$ and an $\mathbf{R}$-module M, let $|M|$ denote the cardinal number of the underlying set of M. Let ρ be any infinite cardinal number $> |\mathbf{R}|$. The full subcategory of $\mathscr{G}^{\mathbf{R}}$ consisting of all modules M such that $|M| < \rho$ is an abelian category with coproducts indexed over sets of cardinal number $< \rho$. Hence if $\mathscr{B}$ is an abelian category with coproducts indexed over sets of cardinal number $< \rho$, then the tensor product $M \otimes_{\mathbf{R}} C$ can be constructed as in 3.1 for any $\mathbf{R}$-object C and any $\mathbf{R}$-module M such that $|M| < \rho$. Thus, if $\mathscr{A}$ is a small additive category such that $[A, A'] < \rho$ for all pairs $A, A' \in \mathscr{A}$, then coadjoints S_A for the evaluation functors $E_A : (\mathscr{A}, \mathscr{B}) \to \mathscr{B}$ can be constructed.

If ρ is any infinite cardinal and $\mathscr{A}$ is any small category such that $|[A, A']| < \rho$ for all $A, A' \in \mathscr{A}$, and if $\mathscr{B}$ is any category with coproducts indexed over sets of cardinal number $< \rho$, then coadjoints can be constructed for $E_A : [\mathscr{A}, \mathscr{B}] \to \mathscr{B}$.

21. Let $\mathscr{A}$ be a C_1 category. Then the functors $B_n, Z_n, B'_n, Z'_n, H_n : \mathscr{C}(\mathscr{A}) \to \mathscr{A}$ are all coproduct preserving.

22. Given an exact sequence of complexes in an abelian category

$$0 \to X' \to X \to X'' \to 0,$$

let δ denote the composition $Z_n(X'') \to H_n(X'') \to H_{n-1}(X')$. Show that the sequence

$$0 \to Z_n(X') \to Z_n(X) \to Z_n(X'') \xrightarrow{\delta} H_{n-1}(X') \to H_{n-1}(X) \to H_{n-1}(X'')$$

is exact.

CHAPTER VII

Extensions

Introduction

An **extension** (or 1-fold extension) of an object A by an object C in an abelian category is a short exact sequence $0 \to A \to B \to C \to 0$. Two such extensions are called **equivalent** if there is a morphism from one to the other with identity morphisms on A and C at the ends. In 1934, Baer [2] defined an addition on the class $\text{Ext}^1(C, A)$ of equivalence classes of extensions of an abelian group A by an abelian group C in such a way that $\text{Ext}^1(C, A)$ became an abelian group. In [6] Cartan and Eilenberg gave a definition of a connected sequence of group valued bifunctors $\{\text{Ext}^n(C, A)\}_{n \geqslant 0}$ which was valid in any abelian category having either projectives or injectives. Then Yoneda [35] showed that the groups $\text{Ext}^n(C, A)$ could be defined in terms of equivalence classes of n-fold extensions of A by C: that is, exact sequences of the form

$$0 \to A \to B_{n-1} \to B_{n-2} \to \dots \to B_1 \to B_0 \to C \to 0.$$

This enabled one to define the connected sequence of group valued functors $\{\text{Ext}^n\}$ for arbitrary abelian categories. The trickiest thing was to prove the exactness of the connected sequence without the use of projectives or injectives. This was done by Steven Schanuel and is presented here in 4.1 and 5.2. A proof of this was sketched also by Buchsbaum in [4].

The presentation of the material in this chapter owes much to a course in homological algebra given by Saunders MacLane at the University of Chicago during the summer of 1959. An appendix relating the Baer–Yoneda definition of Ext to the Cartan–Eilenberg definition has been included at the end of the chapter. A generalization of the theory by Buchsbaum is outlined in exercise 5.

1. Ext^1

All categories in this chapter will be abelian.

We begin with a few notational remarks. We shall suppress subscripts on identity morphisms whenever there is no ambiguity, writing 1 in place of 1_A. As in I, §17, the morphism $\Delta : A \to A \oplus A$ is the one represented by the matrix $\begin{pmatrix}1\\1\end{pmatrix}$ and $\nabla : A \oplus A \to A$ by the matrix $(1, 1)$. The morphism $\tau : A \oplus A \to A \oplus A$ is given by the matrix $\begin{pmatrix}0 & 1\\1 & 0\end{pmatrix}$. If $\alpha : A \to B$ and $\alpha' : A' \to B'$, then $\alpha \oplus \alpha' : A \oplus A' \to B \oplus B'$ is represented by the matrix $\begin{pmatrix}\alpha & 0\\0 & \alpha'\end{pmatrix}$. Given two short exact sequences

$$E : 0 \to A \xrightarrow{\mu} B \xrightarrow{\lambda} C \to 0$$

$$E' : 0 \to A' \xrightarrow{\mu'} B' \xrightarrow{\lambda'} C' \to 0$$

the sequence

$$0 \longrightarrow A \oplus A' \xrightarrow{\mu \oplus \mu'} B \oplus B' \xrightarrow{\lambda \oplus \lambda'} C \oplus C' \longrightarrow 0$$

will be denoted by $E \oplus E'$. A similar definition can be made for the coproduct of two exact sequences of any length. A **morphism** from the sequence E to the sequence E' is a commutative diagram

$$\begin{array}{ccccccccc} 0 & \longrightarrow & A & \longrightarrow & B & \longrightarrow & C & \longrightarrow & 0 \\ & & \downarrow{\scriptstyle \alpha} & & \downarrow{\scriptstyle \beta} & & \downarrow{\scriptstyle \gamma} & & \\ 0 & \longrightarrow & A' & \longrightarrow & B' & \longrightarrow & C' & \longrightarrow & 0 \end{array}$$

and is denoted by (α, β, γ).

For fixed objects A and C, consider the class of all exact sequences of the form $E : 0 \to A \to B \to C \to 0$. We shall say that E is equivalent to E':

$$0 \to A \to B' \to C \to 0$$

if there is a morphism $(1, \beta, 1) : E \to E'$. By the five lemma we see that β must be an isomorphism, hence we have indeed an equivalence relation. However β is not usually unique. If E is equivalent to E' we shall abuse the notation by writing $E = E'$.

Given a diagram of the form

$$\begin{array}{ccccccccc} & & & & & & C' & & \\ & & & & & & \downarrow{\scriptstyle \gamma} & & \\ E{:}0 & \longrightarrow & A & \longrightarrow & B & \longrightarrow & C & \longrightarrow & 0 \end{array}$$

with E exact, by I, 20.3, we can imbed this in a commutative diagram

$$\begin{array}{ccccccccc}
\bar{E}: 0 & \longrightarrow & A & \longrightarrow & \bar{B} & \longrightarrow & C' & \longrightarrow & 0 \\
 & & \| & & \downarrow{\scriptstyle \bar{\beta}} & & \downarrow{\scriptstyle \gamma} & & \\
E: 0 & \longrightarrow & A & \longrightarrow & B & \longrightarrow & C & \longrightarrow & 0
\end{array} \qquad (1)$$

with $\bar{E}$ exact. In fact, it suffices to take the right-hand square as a pullback, and define $A \to \bar{B}$ as the morphism induced by the given morphism $A \to B$ and the zero morphism from A to C'.

Lemma 1.1. *Given a morphism* $(\alpha, \beta, \gamma) : E' \to E$ *of short exact sequences, we can find a commutative diagram*

$$\begin{array}{ccccccccc}
E': 0 & \longrightarrow & A' & \longrightarrow & B' & \longrightarrow & C' & \longrightarrow & 0 \\
 & & \downarrow{\scriptstyle \alpha} & & \downarrow{\scriptstyle \beta'} & & \| & & \\
\bar{E}: 0 & \longrightarrow & A & \longrightarrow & \bar{B} & \longrightarrow & C' & \longrightarrow & 0 \\
 & & \| & & \downarrow{\scriptstyle \bar{\beta}} & & \downarrow{\scriptstyle \gamma} & & \\
E: 0 & \longrightarrow & A & \longrightarrow & B & \longrightarrow & C & \longrightarrow & 0
\end{array} \qquad (2)$$

where $\bar{E}$ *is exact and* $\bar{\beta}\beta' = \beta$.

Proof. We form $\bar{E}$ as in (1). Then β' can be defined from the pullback property of (1) so as to make the northeast corner of (2) commutative, and so that $\bar{\beta}\beta' = \beta$. That the northwest corner is commutative follows from the fact that both compositions yield the same thing when composed with both $\bar{B} \to C'$ and $\bar{B} \to B$. ▌

Corollary 1.2. *The sequence* $\bar{E}$ *satisfying* (1) *is unique.*

Proof. This follows immediately by replacing α by 1_A in 1.1. ▌

In view of 1.2 we shall denote the sequence $\bar{E}$ of (1) by $E\gamma$. Dually, given a morphism $\alpha : A \to A'$, the sequence αE is defined by the commutative diagram

$$\begin{array}{ccccccccc}
E: 0 & \longrightarrow & A & \longrightarrow & B & \longrightarrow & C & \longrightarrow & 0 \\
 & & \downarrow{\scriptstyle \alpha} & & \downarrow & & \| & & \\
\alpha E: 0 & \longrightarrow & A' & \longrightarrow & \bar{B} & \longrightarrow & C & \longrightarrow & 0
\end{array}$$

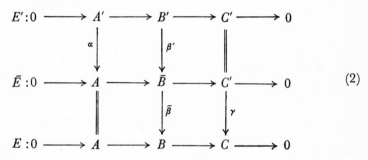

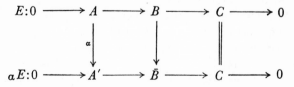

Thus a morphism $(\alpha, \beta, 1) : E \to E'$ expresses the fact that $E' = \alpha E$. It will not usually be necessary to give a name to the middle morphism (which is not unique in any case). Therefore we shall write $(\alpha, \ , 1) : E \to \alpha E$ and $(1, \ , \gamma) : \gamma E \to E$. Lemma 1.1 then says that given a morphism $(\alpha, \ , \gamma) : E' \to E$ we can find a factorization

$$E' \xrightarrow{(\alpha, \ ,1)} \bar{E} \xrightarrow{(1, \ ,\gamma)} E.$$

Hence $\alpha E' = \bar{E} = E\gamma$.

Lemma 1.3. *The following are true whenever either side is defined.*

(i) $1E = E$ (i*) $E1 = E$

(ii) $(\alpha'\alpha)E = \alpha'(\alpha E)$ (ii*) $E(\gamma\gamma') = (E\gamma)\gamma'$.

(iii) $(\alpha E)\gamma = \alpha(E\gamma)$.

Proof. (i) and (ii) are obvious. To prove (iii) we consider the composition

$$E\gamma \xrightarrow{(1, \ ,\gamma)} E \xrightarrow{(\alpha, \ ,1)} \alpha E.$$

Applying 1.1, this can be rewritten as

$$E\gamma \xrightarrow{(\alpha, \ ,1)} \bar{E} \xrightarrow{(1, \ ,\gamma)} \alpha E$$

which shows that $\alpha(E\gamma) = \bar{E} = (\alpha E)\gamma$. ▮

Lemma 1. 3 enables us to write $\alpha'\alpha E$, $E\gamma\gamma'$, and $\alpha E\gamma$ without ambiguity.

Let $\mathrm{Ext}^1_{\mathscr{A}}(C, A)$ denote the class of equivalence classes of short exact sequences of the type

$$0 \to A \to B \to C \to 0.$$

When no confusion can arise we shall write $\mathrm{Ext}^1(C, A)$. A logical difficulty (apart from the commonplace one that the members of $\mathrm{Ext}^1(C, A)$ may not be sets) arises from the fact that $\mathrm{Ext}^1(C, A)$ may not be a set. Of course if $\mathscr{A}$ is small, then $\mathrm{Ext}^1(C, A)$ will be a set. Likewise it can be shown that $\mathrm{Ext}^1(C, A)$ is a set if $\mathscr{A}$ has projectives or injectives (see the appendix to this chapter), or if $\mathscr{A}$ has a generator or a cogenerator (exercise 1). However, in order not to restrict ourselves to any particular class of abelian categories, we introduce at this point the notion of a **big abelian group**. This is defined in the same way as an ordinary abelian group, except that the underlying class need not be a set. We are prevented from talking about "the category of big abelian groups" because the class of morphisms between a given pair of big groups need not be a set. Nevertheless this will not keep us from talking about kernels, cokernels, images, exact sequences, etc., for big abelian groups. These are defined in the same set theoretic terms in which the corresponding notions for ordinary abelian groups can be described. Nor will we be very inhibited in speaking of a big group valued functor from a category, and a natural transformation of two such functors. In fact, it is precisely the aim of this section to show that Ext^1

is a big group valued bifunctor. Henceforth in the chapter the term group will be understood to mean big group.

We define an addition in $\mathrm{Ext}^1(C, A)$ by the rule

$$E + E' = \nabla(E \oplus E')\Delta$$

and proceed to show that $+$ makes $\mathrm{Ext}^1(C, A)$ an abelian group. In the following lemma we make use of the easy relation

$$\alpha\nabla = \nabla(\alpha \oplus \alpha) \tag{3}$$

and the relation

$$\alpha + \alpha' = \nabla(\alpha \oplus \alpha')\Delta \tag{4}$$

of I, 18.3.

Lemma 1.4. *The following are true whenever either side is defined.*

(i) $(\alpha \oplus \alpha')(E \oplus E') = \alpha E \oplus \alpha' E'$

(ii) $(\alpha + \alpha')E = \alpha E + \alpha' E$

(iii) $\alpha(E + E') = \alpha E + \alpha E'$

(i*) $(E \oplus E')(\gamma \oplus \gamma') = E\gamma \oplus E'\gamma'$

(ii*) $E(\gamma + \gamma') = E\gamma + E\gamma'$

(iii*) $(E + E')\gamma = E\gamma + E'\gamma.$

Proof. The proof of (i) is trivial. To prove (ii) we observe the morphism $(\Delta, \Delta, \Delta) : E \to E \oplus E$ which shows that $\Delta E = (E \oplus E)\Delta$. Then using (i) and Eq. (4) we have

$$\begin{aligned}(\alpha + \alpha')E &= \nabla(\alpha \oplus \alpha')\Delta E = \nabla(\alpha \oplus \alpha')(E \oplus E)\Delta \\ &= \nabla(\alpha E \oplus \alpha' E)\Delta = \alpha E + \alpha' E.\end{aligned}$$

For (iii) we use (i) and Eq. (3) to obtain

$$\begin{aligned}\alpha(E + E') &= \alpha\nabla(E \oplus E')\Delta = \nabla(\alpha \oplus \alpha)(E \oplus E')\Delta \\ &= \nabla(\alpha E \oplus \alpha E')\Delta = \alpha E + \alpha E'. \quad \blacksquare\end{aligned}$$

Theorem 1.5. *The operation* $+$ *gives* $\mathrm{Ext}^1(C, A)$ *the structure of an abelian group.*

Proof. We first prove associativity. We have

$$\begin{aligned}E + (E' + E'') &= E + \nabla(E' \oplus E'')\Delta = \nabla(E \oplus \nabla(E' \oplus E'')\Delta)\Delta \\ &= \nabla((1 \oplus \nabla)(E \oplus (E' \oplus E''))(1 \oplus \Delta))\Delta \\ &= \nabla(1 \oplus \nabla)(E \oplus (E' \oplus E''))(1 \oplus \Delta)\Delta.\end{aligned} \tag{5}$$

Similarly, we have

$$(E + E') + E'' = \nabla(\nabla \oplus 1)((E \oplus E') \oplus E'')(\Delta \oplus 1)\Delta. \tag{6}$$

If we identify $E \oplus (E' \oplus E'')$ and $(E \oplus E') \oplus E''$ in the obvious way, it is easy to show that $\nabla(1 \oplus \nabla) = \nabla(\nabla \oplus 1)$ and $(1 \oplus \Delta)\Delta = (\Delta \oplus 1)\Delta$. Hence associativity follows from (5) and (6).

Next we prove commutativity. The morphism

$$E \oplus E' \xrightarrow{(\tau,\tau,\tau)} E' \oplus E$$

shows that $\tau(E \oplus E') = (E' \oplus E)\tau$. Also it is clear that $\nabla\tau = \nabla$ and $\tau\Delta = \Delta$. Hence

$$\begin{aligned} E + E' &= \nabla(E \oplus E')\Delta = \nabla\tau(E \oplus E')\Delta = \nabla(E' \oplus E)\tau\Delta \\ &= \nabla(E' \oplus E)\Delta = E' + E. \end{aligned}$$

Now we show that the split exact sequence

$$E_0 : 0 \to A \to A \oplus C \to C \to 0$$

acts as a zero element for $\mathrm{Ext}^1(C, A)$. Consider an arbitrary sequence

$$E : 0 \to A \xrightarrow{\mu} B \xrightarrow{\lambda} C \to 0 \tag{7}$$

and form the diagram

$$\begin{array}{ccccccccc}
E_0 \oplus E: 0 & \longrightarrow & A \oplus A & \longrightarrow & (A \oplus C) \oplus B & \longrightarrow & C \oplus C & \longrightarrow & 0 \\
 & & \downarrow{\scriptstyle\nabla} & & \downarrow{\scriptstyle\gamma} & & \Vert & & \\
0 & \longrightarrow & A & \xrightarrow{\alpha} & C \oplus B & \xrightarrow{\delta} & C \oplus C & \longrightarrow & 0 \\
 & & \Vert & & \uparrow{\scriptstyle\beta} & & \uparrow{\scriptstyle\Delta} & & \\
E: 0 & \longrightarrow & A & \xrightarrow{\mu} & B & \xrightarrow{\lambda} & C & \longrightarrow & 0
\end{array}$$

The morphism α is defined by the matrix $\begin{pmatrix} 0 \\ \mu \end{pmatrix}$, δ by means of the matrix $\begin{pmatrix} 1 & 0 \\ 0 & \lambda \end{pmatrix}$, γ by means of the matrix $\begin{pmatrix} 0 & 1 & 0 \\ \mu & 0 & 1 \end{pmatrix}$, and β by means of the matrix $\begin{pmatrix} \lambda \\ 1 \end{pmatrix}$. Then commutativity of the diagram comes from a few simple matrix multiplications, and the middle row, being the coproduct of E with the sequence $0 \to 0 \to C = C \to 0$, is exact. This shows that $E = E_0 + E$ as required.

Finally we show the existence of an additive inverse for each sequenc e(7).

First we prove that $0E = E_0$. This follows from the commutative diagram

$$\begin{array}{ccccccccc} E:0 & \longrightarrow & A & \longrightarrow & B & \xrightarrow{\lambda} & C & \longrightarrow & 0 \\ & & \downarrow{\scriptstyle 0} & & \downarrow{\scriptstyle \beta} & & \| & & \\ E_0:0 & \longrightarrow & A & \longrightarrow & A \oplus C & \longrightarrow & C & \longrightarrow & 0 \end{array}$$

where β is represented by the matrix $\begin{pmatrix} 0 \\ \lambda \end{pmatrix}$. Then we have, using 1.4, (ii),

$$E_0 = 0E = (1 + (-1))E = 1E + (-1)E = E + (-1)E.$$

Therefore $(-1)E$ acts as an additive inverse for E. ▌

When there can be no danger of confusion we shall write 0 in place of E_0. Given a morphism $\alpha : A \to A'$, we define a function

$$\hat{\alpha} = \mathrm{Ext}^1(C, \alpha) : \mathrm{Ext}^1(C, A) \to \mathrm{Ext}^1(C, A')$$

by the relation $\hat{\alpha}(E) = \alpha E$. Similarly, if $\gamma : C' \to C$ we define

$$\hat{\gamma} = \mathrm{Ext}^1(\gamma, A) : \mathrm{Ext}^1(C, A) \to \mathrm{Ext}^1(C', A)$$

by $\hat{\gamma}(E) = E\gamma$. Then by 1.3, 1.4, and 1.5 we see that Ext^1 is an additive group valued bifunctor, contravariant in the first variable and covariant in the second.

2. The Exact Sequence (Special Case)

Consider any exact sequence

$$E : 0 \to A \to B \to C \to 0$$

and any object X. Then we have a function

$$\theta : [X, C] \to \mathrm{Ext}^1(X, A)$$

defined by $\theta(\gamma) = E\gamma$. It follows from 1.4 that θ is a group morphism. If $Y \to X$ is any morphism, then by 1.3 we get a commutative diagram

$$\begin{array}{ccc} [X, C] & \xrightarrow{\theta} & \mathrm{Ext}^1(X, A) \\ \downarrow & & \downarrow \\ [Y, C] & \xrightarrow{\theta} & \mathrm{Ext}^1(Y, A) \end{array} \qquad (1)$$

In other words, θ is a natural transformation from H_C to $\mathrm{Ext}^1(\ ,A)$. Furthermore, using 1.1, a commutative diagram

$$\begin{array}{ccccccccc} 0 & \longrightarrow & A & \longrightarrow & B & \longrightarrow & C & \longrightarrow & 0 \\ & & \downarrow & & \downarrow & & \downarrow & & \\ 0 & \longrightarrow & A' & \longrightarrow & B' & \longrightarrow & C' & \longrightarrow & 0 \end{array} \tag{2}$$

with exact rows induces a commutative diagram

$$\begin{array}{ccc} [X, C] & \longrightarrow & \mathrm{Ext}^1(X, A) \\ \downarrow & & \downarrow \\ [X, C'] & \longrightarrow & \mathrm{Ext}^1(X, A') \end{array} \tag{3}$$

The morphism θ is called the **covariant connecting morphism** at X relative to the short exact sequence E. Dually, one obtains a contravariant connecting morphism

$$\theta : [A, X] \to \mathrm{Ext}^1(C, X)$$

defined by $\theta(\alpha) = \alpha E$. Diagrams dual to (1) and (3) relative to morphisms $X \to Y$ and commutative diagrams (2) are obtained in this case.

The proof of the following lemma is left to the reader.

Lemma 2.1. *Given a diagram of the form*

$$\begin{array}{ccccccccc} & & & & & & X & & \\ & & & & & & \downarrow{\scriptstyle\gamma} & & \\ E:0 & \longrightarrow & A & \longrightarrow & B & \longrightarrow & C & \longrightarrow & 0 \end{array}$$

with E exact, then γ can be factored through $B \to C$ if and only if $E\gamma = 0$. ∎

Proposition 2.2. *Relative to an exact sequence*

$$0 \to A \xrightarrow{\mu} B \xrightarrow{\lambda} C \to 0$$

the sequence

$$0 \to [X, A] \xrightarrow{\bar{\mu}} [X, B] \xrightarrow{\bar{\lambda}} [X, C] \xrightarrow{\theta} \mathrm{Ext}^1(X, A) \xrightarrow{\hat{\mu}} \mathrm{Ext}^1(X, B) \xrightarrow{\hat{\lambda}} \mathrm{Ext}^1(X, C)$$

is exact. Here we have denoted $[X, \mu]$ and $[X, \lambda]$ by $\bar{\mu}$ and $\bar{\lambda}$, respectively.

Proof. The exactness at places involving only the morphism functors is already known. There are six things to show, namely, image $\subset$ kernel and kernel $\subset$ image at each of the three remaining places in the sequence.

1. It follows from 2.1 that $\theta\bar{\lambda}(\beta) = 0$ for any $\beta \in [X, B]$.
2. An easy application of 2.1* shows that $\hat{\mu}\theta(\gamma) = 0$ for any $\gamma \in [X, C]$.
3. Since $\lambda\mu = 0$, we know $\hat{\lambda}\hat{\mu} = 0$ by a property of the additive functor $\mathrm{Ext}^1(X, \ )$.
4. Suppose that $\theta(\gamma) = 0$. Then by 2.1, $\gamma = \bar{\lambda}(\beta)$ for some $\beta \in [X, B]$.
5. Suppose that $\hat{\mu}(E) = 0$. Consider the following commutative diagram:

$$\begin{array}{ccccccccc}
 & 0 & \longrightarrow & A & \xrightarrow{\mu} & B & \xrightarrow{\lambda} & C & \longrightarrow & 0 \\
 & & & \| & & & & & & \\
E: & 0 & \longrightarrow & A & \longrightarrow & B' & \longrightarrow & X & \longrightarrow & 0 \\
 & & & \downarrow{\scriptstyle \mu} & & \downarrow{\scriptstyle \beta} & & \| & & \\
 & 0 & \longrightarrow & B & \underset{p}{\rightleftarrows} & B \oplus X & \longrightarrow & X & \longrightarrow & 0
\end{array}$$

Now $p\beta : B' \to B$ makes the northwest corner of the diagram commutative. Defining $\gamma : X \to C$ as the morphism making the northeast corner commutative, we have $E = \theta(\gamma)$.

6. Suppose that $\hat{\lambda}(E) = 0$. Then we have the following commutative diagram

$$\begin{array}{ccccccccc}
 & & & 0 & & & & & & \\
 & & & \downarrow & & & & & & \\
E': & 0 & \longrightarrow & A & \longrightarrow & K & \longrightarrow & X & \longrightarrow & 0 \\
 & & & \downarrow{\scriptstyle \mu} & & \downarrow & & \| & & \\
E: & 0 & \longrightarrow & B & \longrightarrow & B' & \longrightarrow & X & \longrightarrow & 0 \\
 & & & \downarrow{\scriptstyle \lambda} & & \downarrow{\scriptstyle \beta} & & \| & & \\
 & 0 & \longrightarrow & C & \underset{p}{\rightleftarrows} & C \oplus X & \longrightarrow & X & \longrightarrow & 0 \\
 & & & \downarrow & & & & & & \\
 & & & 0 & & & & & &
\end{array}$$

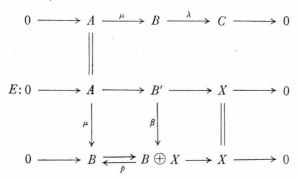

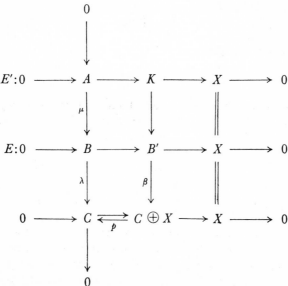

where $K \to B'$ is defined as the kernel $p\beta$, the morphism $A \to K$ is defined since $A \to B \to B' \to C \oplus X \to C = A \to B \to C = 0$, and $K \to X$ is just $K \to B' \to X$. We must show that E' is exact. In the first place $A \to K$ is a monomorphism since $A \to B$ and $B \to B'$ are monomorphisms. Also

$$A \to K \to X = A \to K \to B' \to X = A \to B \to B' \to X = 0.$$

Suppose that $Y \to K \to X = 0$. Then $Y \to K \to B' \to X = 0$ and so we obtain a morphism $Y \to B$ such that $Y \to B \to B' = Y \to K \to B'$. But then $Y \to B \to C = Y \to B \to B' \to C \oplus X \to C = Y \to K \to B' \to C \oplus X \to C = 0$, and so we have a morphism $Y \to A$ such that $Y \to A \to B = Y \to B$. It then follows from the fact that $K \to B'$ is a monomorphism that $Y \to K = Y \to A \to K$. Therefore $A \to K$ is the kernel of $K \to X$. It remains to be shown that $K \to X$ is an epimorphism. Observe first that β, being opposite an epimorphism in a pushout diagram, is an epimorphism. Also since $p\beta$ is an epimorphism, it is the cokernel of $K \to B'$. Now suppose that $K \to X \to Z = 0$. Then

$$K \to B' \to C \oplus X \to X \to Z = 0,$$

and so there is a morphism $C \to Z$ such that

$$B' \to C \oplus X \to C \to Z = B' \to C \oplus X \to X \to Z.$$

But since $B' \to C \oplus X$ is an epimorphism, we must have

$$C \oplus X \to X \to Z = C \oplus X \to C \to Z,$$

and so it follows that $X \to Z = 0$. Therefore E' is exact, and so we have $E = \hat{\mu}(E')$. ∎

3. Ext^n

Consider an exact sequence

$$\mathbf{E}: 0 \to A \to B_{n-1} \to B_{n-2} \to \dots \to B_1 \to B_0 \xrightarrow{\lambda} C \to 0.$$

We call n the **length** of **E**, and we call A and C the **left** and **right ends** respectively of **E**. A morphism $\mathbf{E} \to \mathbf{E}'$ of sequences of length n is a commutative diagram

$$\begin{array}{cccccccccccccccc}
\mathbf{E}: 0 & \to & A & \to & B_{n-1} & \to & B_{n-2} & \to & \dots & \to & B_1 & \to & B_0 & \to & C & \to 0 \\
 & & \downarrow{\scriptstyle\alpha} & & \downarrow & & \downarrow & & & & \downarrow & & \downarrow & & \downarrow{\scriptstyle\gamma} & \\
\mathbf{E}': 0 & \to & A' & \to & B'_{n-1} & \to & B'_{n-2} & \to & \dots & \to & B'_1 & \to & B'_0 & \to & C' & \to 0
\end{array}$$

If **E** and **E**$'$ have the same left end and the same right end and if α and γ are identity morphisms, then we shall say that the above morphism of sequences has **fixed ends**. Again we shall write $\mathbf{E} = \mathbf{E}'$ if there is a morphism from **E** to **E**$'$ with fixed ends such that the morphisms $B_i \to B'_i$ are all isomorphisms. However, it does not follow for $n > 1$ as it did for $n = 1$ that if α and γ are identities, then all the other vertical morphisms are isomorphisms.

Suppose that

$$\mathbf{F} : 0 \overset{\mu}{\to} C \to B'_{m-1} \to B'_{m-2} \to \ldots \to B'_1 \to B'_0 \to D \to 0$$

is an exact sequence of length m whose left end is the same as the right end of **E** above. Then we can "splice" the two exact sequences, obtaining an exact sequence

$$\mathbf{EF} : 0 \to A \to B_{n-1} \to \ldots \to B_1 \to B_0 \overset{\mu\lambda}{\to} B'_{m-1} \to \ldots \to B'_0 \to D \to 0$$

of length $m + n$.

On the other hand, given **E** we can define

$$K_i = \mathrm{Im}(B_i \to B_{i-1}) = \mathrm{Ker}(B_{i-1} \to B_{i-2}), \qquad i = 1, 2, \ldots, n-1,$$

and obtain the following exact sequences of length 1:

$$\begin{aligned} E_n &: 0 \to A \to B_{n-1} \to K_{n-1} \to 0 \\ E_{n-1} &: 0 \to K_{n-1} \to B_{n-2} \to K_{n-2} \to 0 \\ &\vdots \\ E_i &: 0 \to K_i \to B_{i-1} \to K_{i-1} \to 0 \\ &\vdots \\ E_1 &: 0 \to K_1 \to B_0 \to C \to 0. \end{aligned} \tag{1}$$

Then we have $\mathbf{E} = E_n E_{n-1} \ldots E_3 E_2 E_1$. If $\alpha : A \to A'$ we define

$$\alpha\mathbf{E} = (\alpha E_n) E_{n-1} \ldots E_2 E_1.$$

Dually, if $\gamma : C' \to C$ we define

$$\mathbf{E}\gamma = E_n E_{n-1} \ldots E_2 (E_1 \gamma).$$

Then, clearly, the relations

$$\begin{aligned} 1\mathbf{E} &= \mathbf{E} = \mathbf{E}1 \\ (\alpha'\alpha)\mathbf{E} &= \alpha'(\alpha\mathbf{E}) \\ \mathbf{E}(\gamma\gamma') &= (\mathbf{E}\gamma)\gamma' \\ (\alpha\mathbf{E})\gamma &= \alpha(\mathbf{E}\gamma) \end{aligned} \tag{2}$$

are true whenever either side makes sense.

Suppose that E and E' are exact sequences of length 1, and that β is a morphism such that $(E\beta)E'$ is defined. Then $E(\beta E')$ is defined, but unless β is an isomorphism this will not in general be the same as $(E\beta)E'$. What we have is a morphism with fixed ends

$$(E\beta)E' \to E(\beta E'). \tag{3}$$

We shall say that two exact sequences $\mathbf{E} = E_n E_{n-1} \ldots E_2 E_1$ and

$$\mathbf{E}' = E'_n E'_{n-1} \ldots E'_2 E'_1$$

are **equivalent** if we can obtain one from the other by a finite number of switches of the type (3). In this case we write $\mathbf{E} \sim \mathbf{E}'$. If $\mathbf{E} \sim \mathbf{E}'$, then clearly $\mathbf{EF} \sim \mathbf{E'F}$ and $\mathbf{GE} \sim \mathbf{GE}'$ for any $\mathbf{F}$ and $\mathbf{G}$ for which the splicing makes sense.

Proposition 3.1. *Suppose that we have a morphism of exact sequences with fixed ends*

$$\begin{array}{cccccccccccccc} \mathbf{E}: 0 & \to & A & \to & B_{n-1} & \to & B_{n-2} & \to \cdots \to & B_1 & \to & B_0 & \to & C & \to 0 \\ & & \| & & \downarrow & & \downarrow & & \downarrow & & \downarrow & & \| & \\ \mathbf{E}': 0 & \to & A & \to & B'_{n-1} & \to & B'_{n-2} & \to \cdots \to & B'_1 & \to & B'_0 & \to & C & \to 0 \end{array}$$

Then $\mathbf{E} \sim \mathbf{E}'$. *Conversely, suppose that* $\mathbf{E} \sim \mathbf{E}'$. *Then there is a chain of exact sequences*

$$\mathbf{E} = \mathbf{E}_0, \mathbf{E}_1, \mathbf{E}_2, \ldots, \mathbf{E}_{k-1}, \mathbf{E}_k = \mathbf{E}'$$

such that for each i, $0 \leqslant i \leqslant k-1$, *we have either a morphism* $\mathbf{E}_i \to \mathbf{E}_{i+1}$ *or a morphism* $\mathbf{E}_{i+1} \to \mathbf{E}_i$ *with fixed ends.*

Proof. We decompose $\mathbf{E}$ and $\mathbf{E}'$ into exact sequences of length one as in (1). Then the morphism $\mathbf{E} \to \mathbf{E}'$ induces the following commutative diagram for each i:

$$\begin{array}{ccccccccc} E_i: 0 & \longrightarrow & K_i & \longrightarrow & B_{i-1} & \longrightarrow & K_{i-1} & \longrightarrow & 0 \\ & & \downarrow \beta_i & & \downarrow & & \downarrow \beta_{i-1} & & \\ E'_i: 0 & \longrightarrow & K'_i & \longrightarrow & B'_{i-1} & \longrightarrow & K'_{i-1} & \longrightarrow & 0 \end{array}$$

Therefore we have

$$\begin{aligned} \beta_i E_i &= E'_i \beta_{i-1}, \qquad i = 2, 3, \ldots, n-1 \\ E_n &= E'_n \beta_{n-1} \\ \beta_1 E_1 &= E'_1. \end{aligned}$$

Thus we can write

$$\begin{aligned} E_n E_{n-1} \ldots E_2 E_1 &= (E'_n \beta_{n-1}) E_{n-1} E_{n-2} \ldots E_2 E_1 \\ &\sim E'_n (\beta_{n-1} E_{n-1}) E_{n-2} \ldots E_2 E_1 \\ &= E'_n (E'_{n-1} \beta_{n-2}) E_{n-2} \ldots E_2 E_1 \\ &\vdots \\ &= E'_n E'_{n-1} E'_{n-2} \ldots (E'_2 \beta_1) E_1 \\ &\sim E'_n E'_{n-1} E'_{n-2} \ldots E'_2 (\beta_1 E_1) \\ &= E'_n E'_{n-1} E'_{n-2} \ldots E'_2 E'_1. \end{aligned}$$

The converse is simpler. In the case where we make a single switch on sequences of length two, we have a morphism from one sequence to the other as indicated by (3). If the length of the sequences is greater than two, we can use the morphism (3) on the parts of the sequences where the switch takes place, and extend to the other positions by using identity morphisms. A finite number of such switches will thus give rise to a finite chain of morphisms, the direction of each morphism being indicated by (3). ▮

Define $\text{Pretext}^n(C, A)$ $(n \geqslant 2)$ as the class of all exact sequences of length n with left end A and right end C. Define $\text{Ext}^n(C, A)$ as the class of equivalence classes of $\text{Pretext}^n(C, A)$ modulo the equivalence relation $\sim$. We put an addition on $\text{Pretext}^n(C, A)$ by the rule

$$\mathbf{E} + \mathbf{E}' = \nabla(\mathbf{E} \oplus \mathbf{E}')\Delta.$$

We proceed to show that $+$ defines an abelian semigroup structure on $\text{Pretext}^n(C, A)$, and furthermore induces an abelian group structure on $\text{Ext}^n(C, A)$.

Lemma 3.2. *The following are true whenever the combinations make sense.*

(i) $(\alpha \oplus \alpha')(\mathbf{E} \oplus \mathbf{E}') = \alpha\mathbf{E} \oplus \alpha'\mathbf{E}'$ (i*) $(\mathbf{E} \oplus \mathbf{E}')(\gamma \oplus \gamma') = \mathbf{E}\gamma \oplus \mathbf{E}'\gamma'$

(ii) $(\mathbf{E} \oplus \mathbf{E}')(\mathbf{F} \oplus \mathbf{F}') = \mathbf{EF} \oplus \mathbf{E}'\mathbf{F}'$

(iii) $(\mathbf{E} + \mathbf{E}')\mathbf{F} \sim \mathbf{EF} + \mathbf{E}'\mathbf{F}$ (iii*) $\mathbf{E}(\mathbf{F} + \mathbf{F}') \sim \mathbf{EF} + \mathbf{EF}'$

(iv) $(\alpha + \alpha')\mathbf{E} \sim \alpha\mathbf{E} + \alpha'\mathbf{E}$ (iv*) $\mathbf{E}(\gamma + \gamma') \sim \mathbf{E}\gamma + \mathbf{E}\gamma'$

(v) $\alpha(\mathbf{E} + \mathbf{E}') = \alpha\mathbf{E} + \alpha\mathbf{E}'$ (v*) $(\mathbf{E} + \mathbf{E}')\gamma = \mathbf{E}\gamma + \mathbf{E}'\gamma$.

(vi) *Given a morphism* $\mathbf{E} \to \mathbf{E}'$ *with fixed ends, there exists morphisms* $\alpha\mathbf{E} \to \alpha\mathbf{E}'$ *an* $\mathbf{E}\gamma \to \mathbf{E}'\gamma$ *with fixed ends. Hence, if* $\mathbf{E} \sim \mathbf{E}'$, *then* $\alpha\mathbf{E} \sim \alpha\mathbf{E}'$ *and* $\mathbf{E}\gamma \sim \mathbf{E}'\gamma$.

Proof. (i) and (ii) are trivial.

(iii) Write
$$\begin{aligned} \mathbf{E} &= E_n \ldots E_1 \\ \mathbf{E}' &= E'_n \ldots E'_1 \\ \mathbf{F} &= F_m \ldots F_1. \end{aligned}$$

Then using (ii) we have

$$\begin{aligned} (\mathbf{E} + \mathbf{E}')\mathbf{F} &= (\nabla(\mathbf{E} \oplus \mathbf{E}')\Delta)\mathbf{F} \\ &= \nabla(E_n \oplus E'_n)\ldots((E_1 \oplus E'_1)\Delta)F_m \ldots F_1 \\ &\sim \nabla(E_n \oplus E'_n)\ldots(E_1 \oplus E'_1)(\Delta F_m)\ldots F_1 \\ &= \nabla(E_n \oplus E'_n)\ldots(E_1 \oplus E'_1)((F_m \oplus F_m)\Delta)\ldots F_1 \\ &\vdots \\ &= \nabla(E_n \oplus E'_n)\ldots(E_1 \oplus E'_1)(F_m \oplus F_m)\ldots(F_1 \oplus F_1)\Delta \\ &= \nabla(\mathbf{EF} \oplus \mathbf{E}'\mathbf{F})\Delta \\ &= \mathbf{EF} + \mathbf{E}'\mathbf{F}. \end{aligned}$$

(iv) Using (iii) and 1.4 we have

$$\begin{aligned}(\alpha+\alpha')\mathbf{E} &= (\alpha+\alpha')E_n\ldots E_1\\ &= (\alpha E_n+\alpha' E_n)E_{n-1}\ldots E_1\\ &\sim \alpha E_n\ldots E_1+\alpha' E_n\ldots E_1\\ &= \alpha\mathbf{E}+\alpha'\mathbf{E}.\end{aligned}$$

(v) Using (i) we have

$$\begin{aligned}\alpha(\mathbf{E}+\mathbf{E}') &= \alpha\nabla(\mathbf{E}\oplus\mathbf{E}')\Delta\\ &= \nabla(\alpha\oplus\alpha)(\mathbf{E}\oplus\mathbf{E}')\Delta\\ &= \nabla(\alpha\mathbf{E}\oplus\alpha\mathbf{E}')\Delta\\ &= \alpha\mathbf{E}+\alpha\mathbf{E}'.\end{aligned}$$

(vi) is an easy consequence of 1.1. ▮

Theorem 3.3. *The operation* $+$ *makes* $\mathrm{Pretext}^n(C, A)$ *an abelian semigroup. Furthermore* $+$ *induces an addition on* $\mathrm{Ext}^n(C, A)$ *yielding the structure of an abelian group.*

Proof. The proof of associativity of $+$ is the same as in the case of $\mathrm{Ext}^1(C, A)$. To prove commutativity we have

$$\begin{aligned}\mathbf{E}+\mathbf{E}' &= \nabla(\mathbf{E}\oplus\mathbf{E}')\Delta\\ &= \nabla\tau(E_n\oplus E_n')\ldots(E_1\oplus E_1')\Delta\\ &= \nabla(E_n'\oplus E_n)\tau)\ldots(E_1\oplus E_1')\Delta\\ &= \nabla(E_n'\oplus E_n)(\tau(E_{n-1}\oplus E_{n-1}'))\ldots(E_1\oplus E_1'))\ldots(E_1\oplus E_1')\Delta\\ &\ \ \vdots\\ &= \nabla(E_n'\oplus E_n)(E_{n-1}'\oplus E_{n-1})\ldots(E_1'\oplus E_1)\tau\Delta\\ &= \nabla(\mathbf{E}'\oplus\mathbf{E})\Delta\\ &= \mathbf{E}'+\mathbf{E}\end{aligned}$$

where we are justified in writing $=$ in place of $\sim$ at the switches since τ is an isomorphism.

It is straightforward to show that the sequence

$$\mathbf{E}_0: 0\to A = A\to 0\to 0\ldots\to 0\to C = C\to 0$$

behaves as a zero for $+$.

To show that $+$ induces an addition on $\mathrm{Ext}^n(C, A)$ we must verify that $\mathbf{E}+\mathbf{F}\sim\mathbf{E}'+\mathbf{F}$ whenever $\mathbf{E}\sim\mathbf{E}'$. In view of 3.1 it suffices to show that given a morphism $\mathbf{E}\to\mathbf{E}'$ with fixed ends, there exists a morphism $\mathbf{E}+\mathbf{F}\to\mathbf{E}'+\mathbf{F}$ with fixed ends. Now clearly there is a morphism $\mathbf{E}\oplus\mathbf{F}\to\mathbf{E}'\oplus\mathbf{F}$ with fixed ends. Hence taking α and γ to be ∇ and Δ respectively in 3.2, (vi), we obtain the required morphism $\mathbf{E}+\mathbf{F}\to\mathbf{E}'+\mathbf{F}$.

Finally we show that $\mathrm{Ext}^n(C, A)$ has additive inverses. We first form the commutative diagram

$$\begin{array}{ccccccccccccccc}
\mathbf{0E}: 0 & \to & A & \to & A \oplus K_{n-1} & \to & B_{n-2} & \to & \cdots & \to & B_1 & \to & B_0 & \to & C \to 0 \\
 & & \| & & \downarrow & & \downarrow & & & & \downarrow & & \downarrow & & \| \\
\mathbf{E}_0: 0 & \to & A & = & A & \to & 0 & \to & \cdots & \to & 0 & \to & C & = & C \to 0
\end{array}$$

which shows that $\mathbf{0E} \sim \mathbf{E}_0$. Then we have, using 3.2, (iv),

$$\mathbf{E}_0 \sim \mathbf{0E} = (1 + (-1))\mathbf{E} \sim 1\mathbf{E} + (-1)\mathbf{E} = \mathbf{E} + (-1)\mathbf{E},$$

so that the class of $(-1)\mathbf{E}$ is an additive inverse for the class of $\mathbf{E}$ in $\mathrm{Ext}^n(C, A)$. ∎

Again we shall write 0 in place of $\mathbf{E}_0$.

Given $\alpha : A \to A'$, we can define a function

$$\hat{\alpha} = \mathrm{Ext}^n(C, \alpha) : \mathrm{Ext}^n(C, A) \to \mathrm{Ext}^n(C, A')$$

by the relation $\hat{\alpha}([\mathbf{E}]) = [\alpha\mathbf{E}]$ where $[\mathbf{E}]$ represents the class of $\mathbf{E}$. By (vi) of 3.2 we see that $\hat{\alpha}$ is well defined, and by (v) of 3.2 we see that it is a morphism of groups. A dual discussion applies to the other variable. It then follows from the relations (2) that Ext^n is a group valued bifunctor, contravariant in the first variable and covariant in the second, and furthermore by 3.2, (iv) and (iv*), it is additive.

We define $\mathrm{Ext}^0(C, A) = [C, A]$. Then we have the pairing

$$\mathrm{Ext}^m(B, A) \times \mathrm{Ext}^n(C, B) \to \mathrm{Ext}^{m+n}(C, A)$$

defined for $m, n \geqslant 1$ by splicing sequences, and defined for m or $n = 0$ by the functorial character of Ext. From 3.2, (iii), we see that this pairing is bilinear. In particular, it follows from this that if $\mathbf{E} \sim 0$, then $\mathbf{EF} \sim 0$ and $\mathbf{GE} \sim 0$ for any $\mathbf{F}$ and $\mathbf{G}$ for which the splicing makes sense.

4. The Relation $\sim$

In 3.1 it was shown that $\mathbf{E} \sim \mathbf{E}'$ if and only if there is a chain of exact sequences $\mathbf{E} = \mathbf{E}_0, \mathbf{E}_1, \mathbf{E}_2, \ldots, \mathbf{E}_k = \mathbf{E}'$ such that for each i, $0 \leqslant i \leqslant k-1$, there is either a morphism $\mathbf{E}_i \to \mathbf{E}_{i+1}$ with fixed ends or a morphism $\mathbf{E}_{i+1} \to \mathbf{E}_i$ with fixed ends. In this section we shall show that we may always take $k \leqslant 3$. We shall adopt the following notation. Given a short exact sequence

$$E : 0 \to A \to B \to C \to 0,$$

we denote the morphism $A \to B$ by μ_E and the morphism $B \to C$ by λ_E.

The following lemma is due to Steven Schanuel.

Lemma 4.1. *Let* $\mathbf{E}^r$ and $\mathbf{F}^s$ *denote exact sequences of lengths* r *and* s, *respectively* $(r, s \geqslant 1)$, *such that the splicing* $\mathbf{E}^r\mathbf{F}^s$ *is defined. Then the following are equivalent.*

(a) $\mathbf{E}^r\mathbf{F}^s \sim 0$.
(b) *There is a sequence* $\mathbf{G}^r$ *and a morphism* φ *such that* $\mathbf{E}^r \sim \mathbf{G}^r\varphi$ *and* $\varphi\mathbf{F}^s \sim 0$.
(c) *There is a sequence* $\mathbf{H}^s$ *and a morphism* ψ *such that* $\mathbf{F}^s \sim \psi\mathbf{H}^s$ *and* $\mathbf{E}^r\psi \sim 0$.
Furthermore, in case $r = s = 1$, φ *may be taken as* μ_F *and* ψ *may be taken as* λ_E.

Proof. It follows immediately from the last remark of §3 that (b)$\Rightarrow$(a) and (c)$\Rightarrow$(a). We first prove (b)$\Rightarrow$(c) in the case $r = s = 1$. Let $E \sim G\varphi$ where $\varphi F \sim 0$. Observe that $\sim$ means equality in this case since we are working with sequences of length one. By 2.1* we can write $\varphi = \rho\mu_F$ for some morphism ρ, and then we have $E = G\varphi = G\rho\mu_F$. Since $\mu_F F = 0$, this shows that we may assume $\varphi = \mu_F$. The pullback diagram (I, 16.3)

$$
\begin{array}{ccccccccc}
 & & & & H\colon 0 & & F\colon 0 & & \\
 & & & & \downarrow & & \downarrow & & \\
E: 0 & \longrightarrow & A & \longrightarrow & B_1 & \xrightarrow{\lambda_E} & K_1 & \longrightarrow & 0 \\
 & & \| & & \downarrow & & \downarrow{\scriptstyle \mu_F} & & \\
G: 0 & \longrightarrow & A & \longrightarrow & M & \longrightarrow & B_0 & \longrightarrow & 0 \\
 & & & & \downarrow & & \downarrow & & \\
 & & & & C & = & C & & \\
 & & & & \downarrow & & \downarrow & & \\
 & & & & 0 & & 0 & &
\end{array}
$$

then shows that $F = \lambda_E H$ as required. This proves (b)$\Rightarrow$(c), and by duality, (c)$\Rightarrow$(b).

Next we show that (a)$\Rightarrow$(b) and (c), still in the case $r = s = 1$. We do it by induction on the minimum number of switches necessary to change EF into 0. If no switches are necessary (that is, if $EF = 0$) then this is trivial. Otherwise we may have $E = E'\eta$ where the number of switches to change $E'(\eta F)$ into zero is one less than that required for EF, or we may have $F = \eta F'$ where the number of switches necessary to change $(E\eta)F'$ into zero is one less than that required for EF. In the former case we have by induction $E' = G\varphi'$ where $\varphi'(\eta F) = 0$. Hence $E = E'\eta = G\varphi'\eta$, and $\varphi'\eta F = 0$, so that we may take $\varphi = \varphi'\eta$ to see that (b) holds. In the latter case we see by duality that (c) holds.

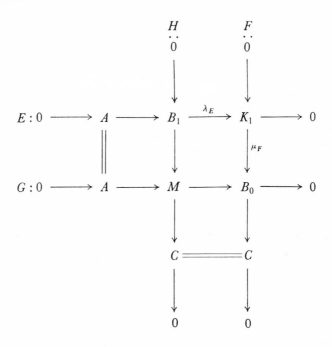

Since in any case (b) and (c) are equivalent, this shows that (a) implies (b) and (c).

We proceed now by induction on $r+s$. We assume (a), (b), (c) equivalent when $r+s<n$ ($n>2$), and take $r+s=n$. We first show that (b)$\Rightarrow$(c). We have $\mathbf{E}^r \sim \mathbf{G}^r\varphi$ where $\varphi\mathbf{F}^s \sim 0$. If $s>1$, write $\mathbf{F}^s = F\mathbf{F}^{s-1}$. Then $\varphi F\mathbf{F}^{s-1} \sim 0$, so by induction we can write

$$\mathbf{F}^{s-1} \sim \eta\mathbf{H}^{s-1}, \qquad \varphi F\eta \sim 0.$$

Hence $\mathbf{E}^r F\eta \sim \mathbf{G}^r\varphi F\eta \sim 0$, so again by induction we can find a morphism ψ such that $F\eta = \psi H$, $\mathbf{E}^r\psi \sim 0$. Then we have

$$\mathbf{F}^s = F\mathbf{F}^{s-1} \sim F\eta\mathbf{H}^{s-1} = \psi H\mathbf{H}^{s-1}$$

and therefore we can take $\mathbf{H}^s = H\mathbf{H}^{s-1}$. If $s=1$, then $r>1$, so we can write $\mathbf{G}^r\varphi = \mathbf{G}^{r-1}G\varphi$. From the case $r=s=1$ we then have a morphism ψ such that $F=\psi H$ and $G\varphi\psi=0$. Then $\mathbf{E}^r\psi = \mathbf{G}^{r-1}G\varphi\psi \sim 0$. This shows (b)$\Rightarrow$(c) and dually (c)$\Rightarrow$(b).

We now have only to show that (a)$\Rightarrow$(b) and (c). We do it by induction on the number of switches required to change $\mathbf{E}^r\mathbf{F}^s$ into 0. Again this is trivial if the number is zero. Also it is trivial if the switch made to reduce $\mathbf{E}^r\mathbf{F}^s$ so as to meet the inductive hypothesis can be made at a position within $\mathbf{E}^r$ or $\mathbf{F}^s$. Therefore assume that $\mathbf{E}^r = \mathbf{E}^{r'}\eta$ where the number of switches required to change $\mathbf{E}^{r'}(\eta\mathbf{F}^s)$ into 0 is one less than for $\mathbf{E}^r\mathbf{F}^s$. Then by induction we can write $\mathbf{E}^{r'} \sim \mathbf{G}^r\varphi'$ where $\varphi'\eta\mathbf{F}^s \sim 0$. Then $\mathbf{E}^r = \mathbf{E}^{r'}\eta \sim \mathbf{G}^r\varphi'\eta$, so that we may take $\varphi = \varphi'\eta$. Similarly, if we assume that $\mathbf{F}^s = \eta\mathbf{F}^{s'}$ where the number of switches required for $(\mathbf{E}^r\eta)\mathbf{F}^{s'}$ is one less, then we can find ψ. Hence in any case one of (b) or (c) is true, and so both of them are true. ∎

Theorem 4.2. *If* $\mathbf{E} \sim 0$, *then there is a sequence* $\mathbf{F}$ *and morphisms* $0 \to \mathbf{F} \leftarrow \mathbf{E}$ *with fixed ends, and a sequence* $\mathbf{G}$ *and morphisms* $0 \leftarrow \mathbf{G} \to \mathbf{E}$ *with fixed ends. If* $\mathbf{E} \sim \mathbf{E}'$, *then there is a chain of morphisms*

$$\mathbf{E} \to \mathbf{E}_1 \leftarrow \mathbf{E}_2 \to \mathbf{E}'$$

with fixed ends.

Proof. Suppose $\mathbf{E} \sim 0$. Write $\mathbf{E} = E_nE_{n-1}\ldots E_1$, and $\mathbf{E}^i = E_iE_{i-1}\ldots E_1$. By 4.1 we can write $E_n = E_n'\varphi_n$, $\varphi_n\mathbf{E}^{n-1} \sim 0$, where we have equality in the former relation since the sequences involved have length one. Then we can write

$$\varphi_nE_{n-1} = E_{n-1}'\varphi_{n-1}$$

where $\varphi_{n-1}\mathbf{E}^{n-2} \sim 0$. Continuing this process we obtain finally $\varphi_3E_2 = E_2'\varphi_2$ where $\varphi_2E_1 = 0$. Denoting $\varphi_2E_1 = E_1'$, we let $\mathbf{F} = E_n'E_{n-1}'\ldots E_2'E_1'$. The morphisms φ_i then define a morphism $\mathbf{E} \to \mathbf{F}$ with fixed ends. Since E_1' is a split sequence, it is easy to define a morphism $0 \to \mathbf{F}$. The sequence $\mathbf{G}$ and morphisms $0 \leftarrow \mathbf{G} \to \mathbf{E}$ are obtained by duality.

Now if $\mathbf{E} \sim \mathbf{E}'$, we have $\mathbf{E} + (-1)\mathbf{E}' \sim 0$. Hence by the above we can find

$$0 \leftarrow \mathbf{G} \rightarrow \mathbf{E} + (-1)\mathbf{E}'$$

and similarly

$$0 \rightarrow \mathbf{F} \leftarrow (-1)\mathbf{E}' + \mathbf{E}'$$

with fixed ends. We can then write

$$0 \oplus \mathbf{E}' \leftarrow \mathbf{G} \oplus \mathbf{E}' \rightarrow (\mathbf{E} + (-1)\mathbf{E}') \oplus \mathbf{E}' \tag{1}$$

$$\mathbf{E} \oplus 0 \rightarrow \mathbf{E} \oplus \mathbf{F} \leftarrow \mathbf{E} \oplus ((-1)\mathbf{E}' + \mathbf{E}'). \tag{2}$$

Using 3.2, (vi), we can apply ∇ on the left and Δ on the right throughout (1) and (2) to obtain

$$0 + \mathbf{E}' \leftarrow \mathbf{G} + \mathbf{E}' \rightarrow (\mathbf{E} + (-1)\mathbf{E}') + \mathbf{E}' \tag{3}$$

$$\mathbf{E} + 0 \rightarrow \mathbf{E} + \mathbf{F} \leftarrow \mathbf{E} + ((-1)\mathbf{E}' + \mathbf{E}'). \tag{4}$$

By 3.3 we have $0 + \mathbf{E}' = \mathbf{E}'$, $\mathbf{E} + 0 = \mathbf{E}$, and

$$(\mathbf{E} + (-1)\mathbf{E}') + \mathbf{E}' = \mathbf{E} + ((-1)\mathbf{E}' + \mathbf{E}').$$

Hence the theorem follows from (3) and (4) by taking $\mathbf{E}_1 = \mathbf{E} + \mathbf{F}$ and $\mathbf{E}_2 = \mathbf{G} + \mathbf{E}'$. ▌

5. The Exact Sequence

Given an exact sequence

$$E: 0 \rightarrow A \xrightarrow{\rho} B \xrightarrow{\epsilon} C \rightarrow 0 \tag{1}$$

and an object X, we can define a function

$$\theta = \theta(n, E, X) : \mathrm{Ext}^n(X, C) \rightarrow \mathrm{Ext}^{n+1}(X, A) \qquad (n \geqslant 1)$$

by the relation $\theta([\mathbf{E}]) = [E\mathbf{E}]$. It follows from (iii*) of 3.2 that θ is a group morphism, called the covariant connecting morphism of degree n at X with respect to the sequence E. A morphism $X \rightarrow Y$ induces a commutative diagram

$$\begin{array}{ccc} \mathrm{Ext}^n(Y, C) & \rightarrow & \mathrm{Ext}^{n+1}(Y, A) \\ \downarrow & & \downarrow \\ \mathrm{Ext}^n(X, C) & \rightarrow & \mathrm{Ext}^{n+1}(X, A) \end{array} \tag{2}$$

and the diagram (2) of §2 induces a commutative diagram

$$\begin{array}{ccc} \mathrm{Ext}^n(X, C) & \to & \mathrm{Ext}^{n+1}(X, A) \\ \downarrow & & \downarrow \\ \mathrm{Ext}^n(X, C') & \to & \mathrm{Ext}^{n+1}(X, A') \end{array} \tag{3}$$

Dually, we have the contravariant connecting morphism

$$\theta : \mathrm{Ext}^n(A, X) \to \mathrm{Ext}^{n+1}(C, X)$$

defined by $\theta([\mathbf{E}]) = [\mathbf{E}E]$.

Theorem 5.1 (Schanuel). *Relative to the exact sequence* (1), *the sequence of groups*

$$\mathrm{Ext}^{n-1}(X, C) \xrightarrow{\theta} \mathrm{Ext}^n(X, A) \xrightarrow{\hat{\rho}} \mathrm{Ext}^n(X, B) \xrightarrow{\hat{\epsilon}} \mathrm{Ext}^n(X, C) \xrightarrow{\theta} \mathrm{Ext}^{n+1}(X, A)$$

is exact for all $n \geqslant 1$.

Proof. Using the relations $\rho E = 0$, $\epsilon\rho = 0$, and $E\epsilon = 0$, one sees without difficulty that the sequence is of order two. Therefore to show exactness we must prove three things ($n \geqslant 1$):

I^n: $\rho\mathbf{E}^n \sim 0 \Rightarrow \mathbf{E}^n \sim E\mathbf{F}^{n-1}$ for some $\mathbf{F}^{n-1} \in \mathrm{Pretext}^{n-1}(X, C)$

II^n: $\epsilon\mathbf{E}^n \sim 0 \Rightarrow \mathbf{E}^n \sim \rho\mathbf{F}^n$ for some $\mathbf{F}^n \in \mathrm{Pretext}^n(X, A)$

III^n: $E\mathbf{E}^n \sim 0 \Rightarrow \mathbf{E}^n \sim \epsilon\mathbf{F}^n$ for some $\mathbf{F}^n \in \mathrm{Pretext}^n(X, B)$.

First we prove III^n ($n \geqslant 1$). If $E\mathbf{E}^n \sim 0$, then by 4.1 we have $\mathbf{E}^n \sim \psi\mathbf{F}^n$ where $E\psi = 0$. But then by 2.1 we can write $\psi = \epsilon\psi'$, and so we have $\mathbf{E}^n \sim \epsilon\psi'\mathbf{F}^n$. This proves III.

Observe that I^1 and II^1 have already been proved in 2.2. To prove $\mathrm{I}^n (n > 1)$ suppose that $\rho\mathbf{E}^n \sim 0$ and write $\mathbf{E}^n = F\mathbf{E}^{n-1}$. Then $\rho F\mathbf{E}^{n-1} \sim 0$, so by III^{n-1} applied to the sequence ρF we have $\mathbf{E}^{n-1} \sim \lambda_{\rho F}\mathbf{F}^{n-1}$. Hence we have $\mathbf{E}^n \sim F\lambda_{\rho F}\mathbf{F}^{n-1}$. Applying I^1 to the relation $\rho F\lambda_{\rho F} = 0$ we can write $F\lambda_{\rho F} = E\varphi$ for some φ. Therefore $\mathbf{E}^n \sim E\varphi\mathbf{F}^{n-1}$ and so this proves I^n.

Finally, to prove $\mathrm{II}^n (n > 1)$ suppose that $\epsilon\mathbf{E}^n \sim 0$, and again write $\mathbf{E}^n = F\mathbf{E}^{n-1}$. Then $\epsilon F\mathbf{E}^{n-1} \sim 0$, and so by III^{n-1} we have $\mathbf{E}^{n-1} \sim \lambda_{\epsilon F}\mathbf{F}^{n-1}$. Therefore $\mathbf{E}^n \sim F\lambda_{\epsilon F}\mathbf{F}^{n-1}$. Applying II^1 to the relation $\epsilon F\lambda_{\epsilon F} = 0$, we can write $F\lambda_{\epsilon F} = \rho G$ for some short exact sequence G. Hence $\mathbf{E}^n \sim \rho G\mathbf{F}^{n-1}$, and so this proves II^n. ∎

6. Global Dimension

Following Cartan and Eilenberg [6] we define the **homological dimension** of a nonzero object A (therein called the projective dimension of A)

as the least integer n such that the one variable functor $\text{Ext}^n(A, \ )$ is not zero (notation h.d. A). If no such integer exists we define h.d. $A = \infty$. If $A = 0$ we define h.d. $A = -1$. Dually the **cohomological dimension** of A is the least n such that $\text{Ext}^n(\ , A)$ is not zero. The duality $\text{Ext}^n(C, A) = \text{Ext}^n(A^*, C^*)$ shows that the cohomological dimension of A^* is the same as the homological dimension of A.

The **global dimension** of a category $\mathscr{A}$ (gl. dim. $\mathscr{A}$) is the least integer n (or infinity) such that the two variable functor Ext^n is not zero. Thus we have

$$\text{gl. dim. } \mathscr{A} = \sup_{A \in \mathscr{A}} (\text{h.d. } A) = \sup_{A \in \mathscr{A}} (\text{h.d. } A^*)$$

Clearly gl. dim. $\mathscr{A}$ = gl. dim. $\mathscr{A}^*$. The **left global dimension** of a ring $\mathbf{R}$ (l. gl. dim. $\mathbf{R}$) is defined as gl. dim. ${}^{\mathbf{R}}\mathscr{G}$. Similarly r. gl. dim. $\mathbf{R}$ = gl. dim. $\mathscr{G}^{\mathbf{R}}$.

Proposition 6.1. *Consider an exact sequence*

$$0 \to A \to B \to C \to 0.$$

1. *If* h.d. $B \leqslant$ h.d. A, *then* h.d. $C \leqslant 1 +$ h.d. A.
2. *If* h.d. $B <$ h.d. A, *then* h.d. $C = 1 +$ h.d. A.

Proof. The proof follows by examining the exact sequence of 5.1*. If either of the above claims were not true, then we would have a nonzero term flanked by two zero terms in an exact sequence which is impossible. ▌

Lemma 6.2. *If P is a nonzero projective object, then* h.d. $P = 0$.

Proof. By II, 14.2, every short exact sequence with right end P splits. Consequently, every long exact sequence with right end P is equivalent to 0 or, in other words, $\text{Ext}^k(P, \ ) = 0$ for $k > 0$. ▌

Lemma 6.3. *Given an exact sequence*

$$0 \to P_n \to P_{n-1} \to \ldots \to P_1 \to P_0 \to A \to 0 \tag{1}$$

with $n > 0$ and P_k projectuve for $0 \leqslant k \leqslant n-1$, we have for all X

$$\text{Ext}^p(P_n, X) \approx \text{Ext}^{n+p}(A, X) \tag{2}$$

for $p > 0$, and an exact sequence

$$[P_{n-1}, X] \to [P_n, X] \to \text{Ext}^n(A, X) \to 0. \tag{3}$$

Furthermore, the morphisms of (2) *and* (3) *are natural in X.*

Proof. Let $K_i = \text{Ker}(P_{i-1} \to P_{i-2})$ for $i = 1, 2, \ldots, n-1$. Then using 6.2, a part of the exact sequence of Ext relative to the short exact sequence

$$0 \to P_n \to P_{n-1} \to K_{n-1} \to 0 \tag{4}$$

yields $\text{Ext}^p(P_n, X) \approx \text{Ext}^{p+1}(K_{n-1}, X)$. The same argument relative to the exact sequence

$$0 \to K_{n-1} \to P_{n-2} \to K_{n-2} \to 0$$

gives $\text{Ext}^{p+1}(K_{n-1}, X) \approx \text{Ext}^{p+2}(K_{n-2}, X)$. Continuing in this way we get a chain of isomorphisms whose composition gives us (2). Naturality in X follows from n applications of the diagram (2*) of §5. Now using (4) and 2.2* we have an exact sequence

$$[P_{n-1}, X] \to [P_n, X] \to \text{Ext}^1(K_{n-1}, X) \to 0. \tag{5}$$

Applying (2) with n, P_n, and p replaced by $n-1$, K_{n-1}, and 1, respectively, we obtain $\text{Ext}^1(K_{n-1}, X) \approx \text{Ext}^n(A, X)$. Hence the exact sequence (5) gives us the desired sequence (3). Naturality of (3) follows from the naturality of (2) and the commutative diagram (1*) of §2. ▌

Proposition 6.4 [6, p. 110]. *The following statements are equivalent in a category with projectives* $(0 \leqslant n < \infty)$:

(a) h.d. $A \leqslant n$.

(b) $\text{Ext}^{n+1}(A, \ ) = 0$.

(c) $\text{Ext}^n(A, \ )$ *is cokernel preserving.*

(d) *Given an exact sequence* (1) *with* P_k *projective for* $0 \leqslant k \leqslant n-1$, *the object* P_n *is projective.*

(e) *There exists an exact sequence* (1) *with* P_k *projective for* $0 \leqslant k \leqslant n$.

Proof. (a) ⇒ (b) is trivial.

(b) ⇒ (c) follows immediately from 5.1.

(c) ⇒ (d) is trivial if $n = 0$. If $n > 0$, consider an epimorphism $X \to X''$.

Using 6.3. we obtain an exact, commutative diagram

$$\begin{array}{ccccccc}
[P_{n-1}, X] & \longrightarrow & [P_n, X] & \longrightarrow & \text{Ext}^n(A, X) & \longrightarrow & 0 \\
\downarrow & & \downarrow & & \downarrow & & \\
[P_{n-1}, X''] & \longrightarrow & [P_n, X''] & \longrightarrow & \text{Ext}^n(A, X'') & \longrightarrow & 0
\end{array}$$

Since P_{n-1} is projective and $\text{Ext}^n(A, \ )$ is cokernel preserving we see that the vertical morphisms on the left and right are epimorphisms. Hence by the 5-lemma, $[P_n X] \to [P_n, X'']$ is also an epimorphism. This shows that P_n is projective.

(d) ⇒ (e) is trivial.

(e) ⇒ (a) By 6.2 and 6.3 we have

$$\text{Ext}^{n+p}(A, X) \approx \text{Ext}^p(P_n, X) = 0$$

for $p > 0$. This shows that h.d. $A \leqslant n$. ▌

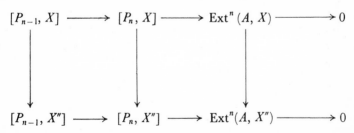

We shall return to questions of global dimension in Chapter IX, where we shall prove in particular a generalization of the Hilbert syzygy theorem for abelian categories.

7. Appendix: Alternative Description of Ext

Throughout this appendix, we shall be dealing with an abelian category with projectives.

As in [6, Chapters V, VI], we can define the functor $\overline{\text{Ext}}^n(C, A)$ as the nth right derived functor of the functor H_A. Explicitly, we take a projective resolution X of C

$$\cdots \longrightarrow X_{n+1} \xrightarrow{d_{n+1}} X_n \xrightarrow{d_n} X_{n-1} \longrightarrow \cdots \longrightarrow X_2 \xrightarrow{d_2} X_1 \xrightarrow{d_1} X_0 \xrightarrow{\epsilon} C \longrightarrow 0.$$

Then $\overline{\text{Ext}}^n(C, A)$ is defined as the nth homology group of the complex $[X, A]$; in other words

$$\overline{\text{Ext}}^n(C, A) = \text{Ker}[d_{n+1}, A]/\text{Im}[d_n, A].$$

Equivalently, if we let $K_n \to X_{n-1}$ be the kernel of d_{n-1} (or the image of d_n), then we have

$$\overline{\text{Ext}}^n(C, A) = [K_n, A]/\text{Im}([X_{n-1}, A] \to [K_n, A]).$$

Thus $\overline{\text{Ext}}^n(C, A)$ is the group of morphisms $K_n \to A$ reduced modulo the subgroup consisting of all those morphisms which can be extended to X_{n-1}. A morphism $A \to A'$ induces a morphism of complexes $[X, A] \to [X, A']$, and hence gives rise to a morphism of the homology groups

$$\overline{\text{Ext}}^n(C, A) \to \overline{\text{Ext}}^n(C, A').$$

On the other hand, suppose that we have a morphism $\varphi : C' \to C$, and let X' and X be projective resolutions for C' and C, respectively. Using projectivity of X' and exactness of X, we can construct a morphism $\Phi : X' \to X$ over φ; that is, a commutative diagram

$$\begin{array}{ccccccccccccc}
\cdots \longrightarrow & X'_n & \longrightarrow & X'_{n-1} & \longrightarrow \cdots \longrightarrow & X'_2 & \longrightarrow & X'_1 & \longrightarrow & X'_0 & \longrightarrow & C' & \longrightarrow 0 \\
& \downarrow{\scriptstyle \Phi_n} & & \downarrow{\scriptstyle \Phi_{n-1}} & & \downarrow{\scriptstyle \Phi_2} & & \downarrow{\scriptstyle \Phi_1} & & \downarrow{\scriptstyle \Phi_0} & & \downarrow{\scriptstyle \varphi} & \\
\cdots \longrightarrow & X_n & \longrightarrow & X_{n-1} & \longrightarrow \cdots \longrightarrow & X_2 & \longrightarrow & X_1 & \longrightarrow & X_0 & \longrightarrow & C & \longrightarrow 0
\end{array}$$

This gives rise to a morphism $[X, A] \to [X', A]$ of complexes, and hence a morphism of the homology groups

$$\overline{\text{Ext}}^n[C, A] \to \overline{\text{Ext}}^n[C', A]$$

which can be shown to be independent of the choice of Φ. This independence incidentally serves to show the independence of $\overline{\text{Ext}}^n[C, A]$ from the choice of the resolution X. In this way $\overline{\text{Ext}}^n$ becomes a bifunctor into $\mathcal{G}$, contravariant in the first variable and covariant in the second.

Furthermore, we can define connecting morphisms as follows. Given an exact sequence

$$0 \to A' \to A \to A'' \to 0,$$

then using the fact that X is projective we get an exact sequence of complexes

$$0 \to [X, A'] \to [X, A] \to [X, A''] \to 0.$$

Hence we have the usual connecting morphism between the homology groups

$$\bar{\theta} : \overline{\mathrm{Ext}}^n(C, A'') \to \overline{\mathrm{Ext}}^{n+1}(C, A').$$

Explicitly, if $f : K_n \to A''$ represents an element of $\overline{\mathrm{Ext}}^n[C, A'']$, then using projectivity of X_n, we may find a morphism $X_n \to A$ such that the diagram

$$\begin{array}{ccccccccc} 0 & \longrightarrow & K_{n+1} & \longrightarrow & X_n & \longrightarrow & K_n & \longrightarrow & 0 \\ & & & & \big\downarrow & & \big\downarrow f & & \\ 0 & \longrightarrow & A' & \longrightarrow & A & \longrightarrow & A'' & \longrightarrow & 0 \end{array} \qquad (1)$$

is commutative. Then we may find a morphism $g : K_{n+1} \to A'$ such that (1) remains commutative, and by definition g represents the image under $\bar{\theta}$ of the equivalence class of f.

The connecting morphism with respect to the first variable is more complicated. Given an exact sequence

$$0 \to C' \overset{\mu}{\to} C \overset{\lambda}{\to} C'' \to 0$$

and projective resolutions X' and X'' of C' and C'', respectively, we consider the exact commutative diagram with split columns

$$\begin{array}{ccccccccccc} 0 & & 0 & & & & 0 & & 0 & & 0 & & \\ \downarrow & & \downarrow & & & & \downarrow & & \downarrow & & \downarrow & & \\ X'_n & \xrightarrow{d'_n} & X'_{n-1} & \longrightarrow & \cdots & \to & X'_1 & \longrightarrow & X'_0 & \xrightarrow{\epsilon'} & C' & \longrightarrow & 0 \\ \downarrow & & \downarrow & & & & \downarrow & & \downarrow & & \downarrow & & \\ X'_n \oplus X''_n & \xrightarrow{d_n} & X'_{n-1} \oplus X''_{n-1} & \to & \cdots & \to & X'_1 \oplus X''_1 & \to & X'_0 \oplus X''_0 & \xrightarrow{\epsilon} & C & \longrightarrow & 0 \\ \downarrow & & \downarrow & & & & \downarrow & & \downarrow & & \downarrow & & \\ X''_n & \xrightarrow{d''_n} & X''_{n-1} & \longrightarrow & \cdots & \to & X''_1 & \longrightarrow & X''_0 & \xrightarrow{\epsilon''} & C'' & \longrightarrow & 0 \\ \downarrow & & \downarrow & & & & \downarrow & & \downarrow & & \downarrow & & \\ 0 & & 0 & & & & 0 & & 0 & & 0 & & \end{array} \qquad (2)$$

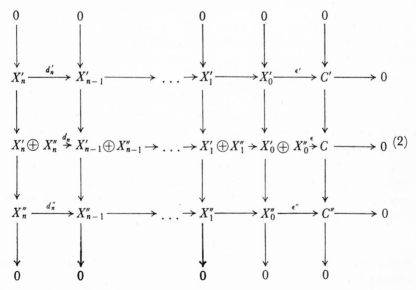

which is constructed by iterating the procedure given in IV, 5.2 (diagram (4)). In order to have commutativity and order two in the middle row we see that ϵ must be defined by a matrix $(\mu\epsilon', \sigma)$ and d_n by a matrix $\begin{pmatrix} d_n' & \Theta_n \\ 0 & d_n'' \end{pmatrix}$ where $\Theta_n : X_n'' \to X_{n-1}'$ and $\sigma : X_0'' \to C$ satisfy the relations

$$\begin{aligned} \epsilon'' &= \lambda\sigma \\ \mu\epsilon'\Theta_1 + \sigma d_1'' &= 0 \\ d_{n-1}'\Theta_n + \Theta_{n-1}d_n'' &= 0. \end{aligned} \tag{3}$$

Using the fact that the vertical sequences split, we get an exact sequence of complexes

$$0 \to [X'', A] \to [X' \oplus X'', A] \to [X', A] \to 0,$$

and consequently we have a connecting morphism

$$\bar{\theta} : \overline{\mathrm{Ext}}^n(C', A) \to \overline{\mathrm{Ext}}^{n+1}(C'', A).$$

Explicitly, if $f : X_n' \to A$ represents an element of $\overline{\mathrm{Ext}}^n(C, A)$, then

$$f\Theta_{n+1} : X_{n+1}'' \to A$$

represents the image under $\bar{\theta}$ of the equivalence class of f.

Our purpose now is to show a natural equivalence of the bifunctors $\overline{\mathrm{Ext}}^n$ and Ext^n, and furthermore to show that this equivalence is compatible (up to a sign) with the connecting morphisms.

Let X be a projective resolution for C, and let $\mathbf{E}$ denote the exact sequence

$$0 \to K_n \to X_{n-1} \to X_{n-2} \to \ldots \to X_1 \to X_0 \to C \to 0.$$

For $n \geqslant 1$ we define a morphism $\bar{\eta} : [K_n, A] \to \mathrm{Ext}^n(C, A)$ by the relation $\bar{\eta}(f) = f\mathbf{E}$. By (iv) of 3.2 we see that $\bar{\eta}$ is a group morphism. Furthermore, if $f : K_n \to A$ can be extended to X_{n-1}, then $f\mathbf{E} \sim 0$. Hence $\bar{\eta}$ induces a group morphism

$$\eta : \overline{\mathrm{Ext}}^n(C, A) \to \mathrm{Ext}^n(C, A).$$

On the other hand, given a sequence $\mathbf{F} \in \mathrm{Pretext}^n(C, A)$, using exactness of $\mathbf{F}$ and projectivity of $\mathbf{E}$ we can define a morphism $\Phi : \mathbf{E} \to \mathbf{F}$ with fixed right end. The morphism $\Phi_n : K_n \to A$ of left ends represents an element of $\overline{\mathrm{Ext}}^n(C, A)$ which can be shown to be independent of the choice of Φ. Hence we have defined a function $\bar{\eta}' : \mathrm{Pretext}^n(C, A) \to \overline{\mathrm{Ext}}^n(C, A)$. Furthermore if $\mathbf{F}'$ is another member of $\mathrm{Pretext}^n(C, A)$ and $\mathbf{F} \to \mathbf{F}'$ is a morphism with fixed ends, then clearly $\bar{\eta}'(\mathbf{F}) = \bar{\eta}'(\mathbf{F}')$. Hence $\bar{\eta}'$ induces a function

$$\eta' : \mathrm{Ext}^n(C, A) \to \overline{\mathrm{Ext}}^n(C, A),$$

and it is easy to show that $\eta'\eta$ and $\eta\eta'$ are identities. Therefore η is a group isomorphism.

We now show naturality of η. Let $f: K_n \to A$ represent an element of $\overline{\text{Ext}}^n(C, A)$ and consider a morphism $\alpha: A \to A'$. Then commutativity of the square

$$\begin{array}{ccc}
\overline{\text{Ext}}^n(C, A) & \xrightarrow{\eta} & \text{Ext}^n(C, A) \\
\big\downarrow & & \big\downarrow \\
\overline{\text{Ext}}^n(C, A') & \xrightarrow{\eta} & \text{Ext}^n(C, A')
\end{array}$$

follows from the relation $\alpha(f\mathbf{E}) = (\alpha f)\mathbf{E}$. On the other hand, if we have a morphism $\gamma: C' \to C$, we construct a commutative diagram

$$\begin{array}{ccccccccccccccc}
\mathbf{E}': 0 & \longrightarrow & K'_n & \longrightarrow & X'_{n-1} & \to \cdots \to & X'_1 & \longrightarrow & X'_0 & \longrightarrow & C' & \longrightarrow & 0 \\
 & & \Big\downarrow{\scriptstyle\beta} & & \Big\downarrow & & \Big\downarrow & & \Big\downarrow & & \Big\downarrow{\scriptstyle\gamma} & & \\
\mathbf{E}: 0 & \longrightarrow & K_n & \longrightarrow & X_{n-1} & \to \cdots \to & X_1 & \longrightarrow & X_0 & \longrightarrow & C & \longrightarrow & 0
\end{array} \tag{4}$$

where $\mathbf{E}$ and $\mathbf{E}'$ are exact, and the X's are all projectives. Again let $f: K_n \to A$ represent an element of $\overline{\text{Ext}}^n(C, A)$. Then a chase of the class of f around the diagram

$$\begin{array}{ccc}
\overline{\text{Ext}}^n(C, A) & \longrightarrow & \text{Ext}^n(C, A) \\
\big\downarrow & & \big\downarrow \\
\overline{\text{Ext}}^n(C', A) & \longrightarrow & \text{Ext}^n(C', A)
\end{array} \tag{5}$$

yields the class of $(f\mathbf{E})\gamma$ clockwise, and the class of $(f\beta)\mathbf{E}'$ counterclockwise. But from the morphism (4) of sequences we know that $\beta\mathbf{E}' = \mathbf{E}\gamma$, and so $f\mathbf{E}\gamma = f\beta\mathbf{E}'$. This proves commutativity of (5).

We now examine the behavior of η with respect to the connecting morphisms. Given an exact sequence

$$E: 0 \to A' \to A \to A'' \to 0,$$

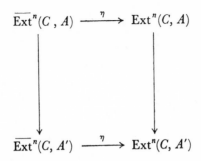

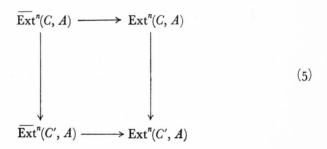

we consider the commutative diagram

$$
\begin{array}{ccccccccccccc}
 & & & & 0 & & & & 0 & & & & \\
 & & & & & \searrow & & \nearrow & & & & & \\
 & & & & & & K_n & & & & & & \\
 & & & & & \nearrow & \Big\downarrow{\scriptstyle f} & \searrow & & & & & \\
0 & \longrightarrow & K_{n+1} & \rightarrow & X_n & & & & X_{n-1} \rightarrow X_{n-1} \rightarrow \dots \rightarrow X_0 \rightarrow C \rightarrow 0 \\
 & & {\scriptstyle g}\Big\downarrow & & \Big\downarrow & & \Big\downarrow & & & & & & \\
0 & \longrightarrow & A' & \longrightarrow & A & \longrightarrow & A'' & \longrightarrow & 0 & & & &
\end{array}
$$

where the morphism f represents any element of $\mathrm{Ext}^n(C, A)$. We denote the short sequence

$$0 \to K_{n+1} \to X_n \to K_n \to 0$$

by F, and the long sequence

$$0 \to K_n \to X_{n-1} \to X_{n-2} \to \dots \to X_0 \to C \to 0$$

by **E**. Chasing the class of f around the diagram

$$
\begin{array}{ccc}
\overline{\mathrm{Ext}}^n(C, A'') & \xrightarrow{\ \eta\ } & \mathrm{Ext}^n(C, A'') \\
{\scriptstyle \bar\theta}\Big\downarrow & & \Big\downarrow{\scriptstyle \theta} \\
\overline{\mathrm{Ext}}^{n+1}(C, A') & \xrightarrow{\ \eta\ } & \mathrm{Ext}^{n+1}(C, A')
\end{array}
\qquad (6)
$$

yields the class of $E(f\mathbf{E})$ clockwise and the class of $g(F\mathbf{E})$ counterclockwise. Since $Ef = gF$, these classes are the same, and so (6) is commutative.

Finally, consider an exact sequence

$$E : 0 \to C' \to C \to C'' \to 0.$$

We refer to the diagram (2). Denote by $\mathbf{E}'$ and $\mathbf{E}''$, respectively, the exact sequences

$$0 \to K'_n \to X'_{n-1} \to X'_{n-2} \to \dots \to X'_1 \to X'_0 \to C' \to 0$$

$$0 \to K''_{n+1} \to X''_n \to X''_{n-1} \to X''_{n-2} \to \dots \to X''_1 \to X''_0 \to C'' \to 0.$$

Let $\alpha : K''_{n+1} \to K'_n$ be the morphism induced by $\Theta_{n+1} : X''_{n+1} \to X'_n$. Let $f : K'_n \to A$ represent an element of $\mathrm{Ext}^n(C', A)$, and let us chase the class of f around the diagram

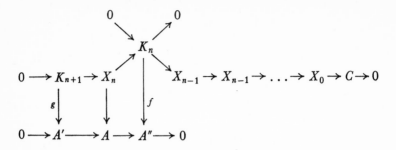

$$\begin{array}{ccc}
\overline{\mathrm{Ext}}^n(C', A) & \xrightarrow{\eta} & \mathrm{Ext}^n(C', A) \\
\Big\downarrow {\scriptstyle (-1)^{n+1}\theta} & & \Big\downarrow {\scriptstyle \theta} \\
\overline{\mathrm{Ext}}^{n+1}(C'', A) & \xrightarrow{\eta} & \mathrm{Ext}^{n+1}(C'', A)
\end{array} \tag{7}$$

Clockwise we obtain the class of $(f\mathbf{E}')E$. Counterclockwise we obtain the class of $((-1)^{n+1}f\alpha)\mathbf{E}''$. But using (3) we have a commutative diagram

$$\begin{array}{lccccccccccccc}
\mathbf{E}'E: 0 & \longrightarrow & K'_n & \longrightarrow & X'_{n+1} \rightarrowtail \cdots \rightarrowtail X'_1 & \longrightarrow & X'_0 & \longrightarrow & C & \longrightarrow & C'' & \longrightarrow & 0 \\
 & & \Big\uparrow {\scriptstyle (-1)^{n+1}\alpha} & & \Big\uparrow {\scriptstyle (-1)^n\Theta_n} \quad \Big\uparrow {\scriptstyle \Theta_2} & & \Big\uparrow {\scriptstyle -\Theta_1} & & \Big\uparrow {\scriptstyle \sigma} & & \Big\| & & \\
\mathbf{E}'': 0 & \longrightarrow & K''_{n+1} & \longrightarrow & X''_n \rightarrow \cdots \rightarrow X''_2 & \longrightarrow & X''_1 & \longrightarrow & X''_0 & \xrightarrow{\epsilon''} & C'' & \longrightarrow & 0
\end{array}$$

This shows that $(-1)^{n+1}\alpha\mathbf{E}'' \sim \mathbf{E}'E$, and so we have proved commutativity of (7).

If, instead of having projective resolutions, the category has injective resolutions, then the above dualizes to show that $\mathrm{Ext}^n(C, A)$ can be regarded as the nth homology group of the complex $[C, Y]$ where Y represents an injective resolution for A. In this case the discrepancy in the sign of the connecting morphism comes in the second variable.

Finally, it should be remarked that the natural equivalence η was defined only for values of n greater than zero. However, if $n = 0$, we still have a natural equivalence

$$\overline{\mathrm{Ext}}^0(C, A) \approx \mathrm{Ext}^0(C, A) = [C, A]$$

and naturality and commutativity with the connecting morphisms can still be established (exercise 3).

Exercises

1. If $\mathscr{A}$ has a generator, then $\mathrm{Ext}^1(C, A)$ is a set for all $A, C \in \mathscr{A}$.

2. Demonstrate how badly we are abusing the foundations by showing that in a nontrivial cocomplete abelian category each equivalence class in $\mathrm{Ext}^n(C, A)$ is not a set $(n > 1)$.

3. If X is a projective resolution for C, then the 0th homology group of the complex $[X, C]$ is

$$\overline{\mathrm{Ext}}^0(C, A) = \mathrm{Ker}([X_0, A] \rightarrow [X_1, A]) \approx [C, A].$$

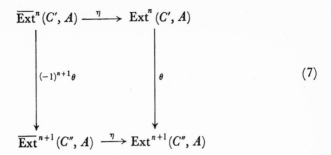

Show that this isomorphism is natural in C and A, that it commutes with the covariant connecting morphisms, and that it anticommutes with the contravariant connecting morphisms.

4. Let $\mathscr{A}$ be an abelian category and $\mathbf{R}$ a commutative ring. Considering extensions in the category ${}^{\mathbf{R}}\mathscr{A}$, the group $\mathrm{Ext}^n(C, A)$ becomes an $\mathbf{R}$-module either through operation of $\mathbf{R}$ on C or on A. Show that these two $\mathbf{R}$-module structures are the same.

5. Use 6.3 to show that if $\mathbf{E}$ and $\mathbf{E}'$ are equivalent sequences of length n from A to C in a category $\mathscr{A}$ with projectives, then there is an exact sequence

$$\mathbf{F}: 0 \to A \to B \to P_{n-2} \to \ldots \to P_2 \to P_1 \to P_0 \to C \to 0$$

with P_k projective for $0 \leqslant k \leqslant n-2$, together with morphisms

$$\mathbf{E}' \leftarrow \mathbf{F} \to \mathbf{E}$$

with fixed ends. Dually, if $\mathscr{A}$ has injectives, then there is a sequence $\mathbf{G}$ and morphisms

$$\mathbf{E}' \to \mathbf{G} \leftarrow \mathbf{E}$$

with fixed ends (cf. 4.2).

6. Let $\mathscr{E}$ be an h.f. class of epimorphisms in an abelian category (see V, exercise 5) and let $\mathscr{C}$ be the class of all short exact sequences E such that $\lambda_E \in \mathscr{E}$ (hence $\mu_E \in \mathscr{M}(\mathscr{E})$). If $E, E' \in \mathscr{C}$, then $E \oplus E' \in \mathscr{C}$. If $E \in \mathscr{C}$ and $E\gamma$ is defined, then $E\gamma \in \mathscr{C}$. (Consider the pullback diagram

$$\begin{array}{ccccccccc} E\gamma: 0 & \longrightarrow & A & \longrightarrow & \bar{B} & \longrightarrow & C' & \longrightarrow & 0 \\ & & \| & & \downarrow & & \downarrow{\scriptstyle\gamma} & & \\ E: 0 & \longrightarrow & A & \longrightarrow & B & \longrightarrow & C & \longrightarrow & 0 \end{array}$$

and show that the composition $A \to B \to B \times C'$ is in $\mathscr{M}(\mathscr{E})$). Dually, if αE is defined, then $\alpha E \in \mathscr{C}$. Hence if $E, E' \in \mathrm{Ext}^1(C, A) \cap \mathscr{C}$, then $E + E' \in \mathscr{C}$. Thus, defining $\mathscr{E}$-$\mathrm{Ext}^1(C, A)$ as the subgroup $\mathrm{Ext}^1(C, A) \cap \mathscr{C}$ of $\mathrm{Ext}^1(C, A)$ we obtained a group valued bifunctor. Furthermore, relative to an exact sequence $0 \to A \to B \to C \to 0$ in $\mathscr{C}$ we have connecting morphisms

$$[X, C] \to \mathscr{E}\text{-}\mathrm{Ext}^1(X, A)$$
$$[A, X] \to \mathscr{E}\text{-}\mathrm{Ext}^1(C, X)$$

and the proof of 2.2 is valid.

More generally, define $\mathbf{E} = E_n E_{n-1} \ldots E_2 E_1$ to be $\mathscr{E}$-exact if $E_i \in \mathscr{C}$ for $1 \leqslant i \leqslant n$. Then define $\mathscr{E}$-$\mathrm{Ext}^n(C, A)$ as the class of $\mathscr{E}$-exact sequences from A to C of length n, modulo the following equivalence relation. Write $\mathbf{E} \sim \mathbf{E}'$ if there is a chain of $\mathscr{E}$-exact sequences

$$\mathbf{E} = \mathbf{E}_0, \mathbf{E}_1, \ldots, \mathbf{E}_k = \mathbf{E}'$$

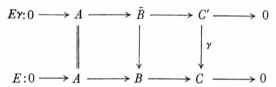

such that for each i we have either a morphism $\mathbf{E}_i \to \mathbf{E}_{i+1}$ with fixed ends or a morphism $\mathbf{E}_{i+1} \to \mathbf{E}_i$ with fixed ends. Then again $\mathscr{E}$-Ext$^n(C, A)$ is a group valued bifunctor, and we have connecting morphisms for short exact sequences in $\mathscr{C}$ relative to which 5.1 is valid. If $\mathscr{E}$ is a projective class, then $\mathscr{E}$-Ext$^n(C, A)$ can be defined alternatively as the nth homology group of the complex $[X, A]$ where X represents an $\mathscr{E}$-projective resolution for C.

This generalization is due to D. Buchsbaum [4].

7. Consider an exact commutative diagram

$$\begin{array}{ccccccccc}
 & & E' & & & & E'' & & \\
 & & \vdots & & & & \vdots & & \\
 & & 0 & & 0 & & 0 & & \\
 & & \downarrow & & \downarrow & & \downarrow & & \\
F:0 & \longrightarrow & A' & \longrightarrow & A & \longrightarrow & A'' & \longrightarrow & 0 \\
 & & \downarrow & & \downarrow & & \downarrow & & \\
0 & \longrightarrow & B' & \longrightarrow & B & \longrightarrow & B'' & \longrightarrow & 0 \\
 & & \downarrow & & \downarrow & & \downarrow & & \\
G:0 & \longrightarrow & C' & \longrightarrow & C & \longrightarrow & C'' & \longrightarrow & 0 \\
 & & \downarrow & & \downarrow & & \downarrow & & \\
 & & 0 & & 0 & & 0 & &
\end{array}$$

Show that the twofold sequences FE'' and $(-1)E'G$ are equivalent. (Construct an exact sequence

$$\mathbf{E} : 0 \to A' \to A \oplus B' \to B \to C'' \to 0$$

together with a morphism $\mathbf{E} \to FE''$ with fixed ends and a morphism $\mathbf{E} \to E'G$ with -1 at the left end and fixed right end.)

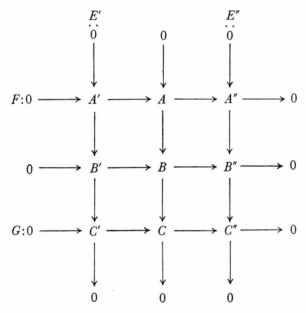

[CHAPTER VIII]

Satellites

Introduction

Satellites were first defined in Cartan–Eilenberg [6] (therein called left satellites) for functors between categories of modules. The definition applied to any additive functor $T : \mathscr{A} \to \mathscr{B}$ where $\mathscr{A}$ and $\mathscr{B}$ are abelian categories and $\mathscr{A}$ has projectives. A definition was also given in terms of universal mapping properties [6, p. 51, exercise 1].

In [5] Buchsbaum constructed satellites for a functor $T : \mathscr{A} \to \mathscr{B}$ in the case where $\mathscr{A}$ is small and $\mathscr{B}$ is cocomplete. He also proved that when $\mathscr{B}$ is a category of modules the connected sequence of cosatellite functors of a half-exact functor T is exact. Most of the material of [5] is reproduced in §2 and §3 of this chapter. We have proved the exactness of the cosatellite sequence for a half-exact functor $T : \mathscr{A} \to \mathscr{B}$ under the assumption that $\mathscr{B}$ is C_3. In particular, this applies to group valued functors. However, the proof does not dualize to the case of the satellite sequence of a half-exact group valued functor. Exactness of the sequence in this case is an open question.

In §4 we show that the nth satellite evaluated at A of a functor $T : \mathscr{A} \to \mathscr{B}$ is given by the group of natural transformations from the functor $\mathrm{Ext}^n(A, \ )$ to T^n. This generalizes the natural equivalence of Yoneda

$$[\mathrm{Ext}^n_{\mathbf{R}}(A, \ ), B \otimes_{\mathbf{R}} \ ] \approx \mathrm{Tor}^{\mathbf{R}}_n(B, A)$$

where $A \in {}^{\mathbf{R}}\mathscr{G}$ and $B \in \mathscr{G}^{\mathbf{R}}$. Section 5 contains a further application of the projective class theory of V, §7. In the last section (§6) we extend the theory of satellites to functors of several variables.

1. Connected Sequences of Functors

All categories in this chapter will be abelian, and all functors will be additive.

A **connected sequence** of covariant functors from $\mathscr{A}$ to $\mathscr{B}$ is a family $T^n : \mathscr{A} \to \mathscr{B}$, where n runs through all the integers, together with **connecting morphisms**

$$\delta^n_E : T^n(A'') \to T^{n+1}(A')$$

defined for each short exact sequence in $\mathscr{A}$

$$E: 0 \to A' \to A \to A'' \to 0 \tag{1}$$

and each integer n. Furthermore, the following conditions must hold:

1. The sequence of morphisms

$$\ldots \to T^{n-1}(A'') \to T^n(A') \to T^n(A) \to T^n(A'') \to T^{n+1}(A') \to \ldots \tag{2}$$

is of order two.

2. Relative to a morphism of short exact sequences

$$\begin{array}{ccccccccc} E:0 & \longrightarrow & A' & \longrightarrow & A & \longrightarrow & A'' & \longrightarrow & 0 \\ & & \downarrow{\scriptstyle \alpha} & & \downarrow & & \downarrow{\scriptstyle \gamma} & & \\ F:0 & \longrightarrow & B' & \longrightarrow & B & \longrightarrow & B'' & \longrightarrow & 0 \end{array}$$

the diagram

$$\begin{array}{ccc} T^n(A'') & \xrightarrow{\delta_E^n} & T^{n+1}(A') \\ \downarrow{\scriptstyle T^n(\gamma)} & & \downarrow{\scriptstyle T^{n+1}(\alpha)} \\ T^n(B'') & \xrightarrow{\delta_F^n} & T^{n+1}(B') \end{array} \tag{3}$$

is commutative.

A sequence of contravariant functors T^n is called a connected sequence if the sequence of covariant functors T_*^n is a connected sequence.

It will be convenient to denote T^{-n} by T_n. We then say that the connected sequence T^n is a **positive** connected sequence if $T^n = 0$ for $n < 0$, and a **negative** connected sequence if $T_n = 0$ for all $n < 0$. Clearly the theory of negative connected sequences can be obtained from the theory of positive connected sequences by applying duality to both domain and codomain.

A connected sequence of functors T^n will be called **exact** if, relative to any short exact sequence E in the domain, the sequence (2) is exact.

Let $\{T^n\}$ and $\{U^n\}$ be connected sequences of functors with the same domain and codomain. A **morphism** $\{T^n\} \to \{U^n\}$ is a family $\varphi^n : T^n \to U^n$ of natural transformations which commute with the connecting morphisms; that is, for each exact sequence (1) and each integer n, the diagram

$$\begin{array}{ccc} T^n(A'') & \longrightarrow & T^{n+1}(A') \\ \downarrow{\scriptstyle \varphi_{A''}^n} & & \downarrow{\scriptstyle \varphi_{A'}^{n+1}} \\ U^n(A'') & \longrightarrow & U^{n+1}(A') \end{array} \tag{4}$$

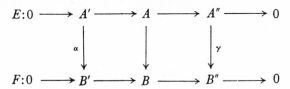

is commutative. If each φ^n is a natural equivalence, then $\{\varphi^n\}$ is called an **isomorphism**.

Let $\{T^n\}$ be a connected sequence of functors from $\mathscr{A}$ to $\mathscr{B}$, and let $\mathbf{E} = E_p\ldots E_3E_2E_1$ be an exact sequence of length p from A to C in $\mathscr{A}$. Then we can define the **iterated connecting morphism**

$$\delta^n_{\mathbf{E}} : T^n(C) \to T^{n+p}(A)$$

as the composition $\delta^{n+p-1}_{E_p}\ldots\delta^{n+2}_{E_3}\delta^{n+1}_{E_2}\delta^n_{E_1}$. If $\mathbf{E}\to\mathbf{E}'$ is a morphism of exact sequences, then it follows from p applications of the commutative diagram (3) that the diagram

$$\begin{array}{ccc} T^n(C) & \longrightarrow & T^{n+p}(A) \\ \Big\downarrow & & \Big\downarrow \\ T^n(C') & \longrightarrow & T^{n+p}(A') \end{array} \qquad (5)$$

is commutative. Likewise, if $\{\varphi^n\} : \{T^n\}\to\{U^n\}$ is a morphism of connected sequences of functors, then p applications of (4) shows that

$$\begin{array}{ccc} T^n(C) & \longrightarrow & T^{n+p}(A) \\ \Big\downarrow{\scriptstyle \varphi^n_C} & & \Big\downarrow{\scriptstyle \varphi^{n+p}_A} \\ U^n(C) & \longrightarrow & U^{n+p}(A) \end{array} \qquad (6)$$

is commutative. Observe from (5) that equivalent exact sequences induce the same iterated connecting morphism.

Consider a pair of covariant functors $T, T^1 : \mathscr{A}\to\mathscr{B}$ and morphisms $\delta_E : T(A'')\to T^1(A')$ defined for all exact sequences $E : 0\to A'\to A\to A''\to 0$ in $\mathscr{A}$. We call (T, T^1) a **connected pair** of functors if the associated sequence $T, T^1, 0, 0,\ldots$ is a positive connected sequence. Likewise, we shall say that a pair of natural transformations (φ, φ^1) is a **morphism** of connected pairs (T, T^1) and (U, U^1) if the family $\varphi, \varphi^1, 0, 0,\ldots$ is a morphism of the associated positive connected sequences. We then say that φ^1 **extends** φ. If (T, T^1) has the property that for every connected pair (U, U^1) and every natural transformation $\varphi : T\to U$ there is a unique extension φ^1 of φ, then we call T^1 the **first cosatellite** of T, and we denote it by S^1T. We define the **nth cosatellite** of T inductively as $S^nT = S^1(S^{n-1}T)$. If S^nT is defined for all $n > 0$, then setting $S^0T = T$ we obtain a positive connected sequence of functors $\{S^nT\}$ with the property that given any positive connected sequence $\{U^n\}$ and any natural transformation $\varphi^0 : T \to U^0$, there is a unique morphism $\{\varphi^n\}$ from $\{S^n T\}$ to $\{U^n\}$ which extends φ^0.

If T is contravariant, then we say that T^n is the nth cosatellite of T if T^n_* is the nth cosatellite of the covariant functor T_*.

Dually, we say that a negative connected sequence $\ldots T_2,\ T_1,\ T_0 = T$ is the sequence of **satellites** of T_0 if $T^*_* = T_{0*}^*,\ T_{1*}^*,\ T_{2*}^* \ldots$ is the sequence of cosatellites of T^*_*. In this case we denote T_n by $S_n T$ $(n > 0)$.

If $\varphi = \varphi^0 : T \to U$ is any natural transformation, then by definition of cosatellite, φ admits a unique extension $\{\varphi^n\} : (S^n T\} \to \{S^n U\}$. The natural transformation φ^n is then denoted by $S^n(\varphi)$. Clearly, we have

$$\begin{aligned} S^n(\psi\varphi) &= S^n(\psi)S^n(\varphi) \\ S^n(\psi + \varphi) &= S^n(\psi) + S^n(\varphi) \\ S^n(1_T) &= 1_{S^n T} \end{aligned}$$

whenever the combinations make sense. A dual definition applies to $S_n(\varphi)$.

If T is a covariant epifunctor, then it follows easily from the definition of cosatellite that $S^n T = 0$ for all $n > 0$.

2. Existence of Satellites

Lemma 2.1. *Let $T : \mathscr{A} \to \mathscr{B}$ be a covariant functor, and let*

$$\begin{array}{ccccccccc} E:0 & \longrightarrow & A & \xrightarrow{\mu} & B & \xrightarrow{\lambda} & C & \longrightarrow & 0 \\ & & \downarrow{\scriptstyle \alpha} & & \downarrow{\scriptstyle f} & & \downarrow{\scriptstyle g} & & \\ E':0 & \longrightarrow & A' & \xrightarrow{\mu'} & B' & \xrightarrow{\lambda'} & C' & \longrightarrow & 0 \end{array}$$

be a morphism of short exact sequences. Then the morphism h_α induced by the commutative diagram with exact rows

$$\begin{array}{ccccccc} T(B) & \xrightarrow{T(\lambda)} & T(C) & \xrightarrow{p_E} & F_E & \longrightarrow & 0 \\ \downarrow{\scriptstyle T(f)} & & \downarrow{\scriptstyle T(g)} & & \downarrow{\scriptstyle h_\alpha} & & \\ T(B') & \xrightarrow{T(\lambda')} & T(C') & \xrightarrow{p_{E'}} & F_{E'} & \longrightarrow & 0 \end{array}$$

is independent of f and g.

Proof. Let f' and g' be another pair which, together with α, define a morphism $E \to E'$. Then $(f - f')\mu = 0$, and so we have a morphism $\beta : C \to B'$ such that $\beta\lambda = f - f'$. Then we have

$$\lambda'\beta\lambda = \lambda'(f - f') = (g - g')\lambda,$$

and so $\lambda'\beta = g - g'$ since λ is an epimorphism. Hence

$$\begin{aligned}(h_\alpha - h'_\alpha)p_E &= p_{E'}(T(g) - T(g')) = p_{E'}T(g-g') \\ &= p_{E'}T(\lambda'\beta) = p_{E'}T(\lambda')T(\beta) = 0.\end{aligned}$$

Therefore, since p_E is an epimorphism we have $h_\alpha = h'_\alpha$. ▮

For an object A in a category $\mathscr{A}$ let $\mathscr{C}_A$ denote the class of all exact sequences of the form

$$E : 0 \to A \to B \to C \to 0.$$

If $E, E' \in \mathscr{C}_A$, define $E \leqslant E'$ if there is a morphism $(1_A, ,)$ from E to E'. Then under this ordering $\mathscr{C}_A$ becomes a directed class, for if E_1 and E_2 are any two members of $\mathscr{C}_A$, then $\nabla(E_1 \oplus E_2)$ follows both of them. If $E \leqslant E'$ and $T : \mathscr{A} \to \mathscr{B}$ is any functor, then 2.1 provides us with a unique morphism

$$\pi_E^{E'} : F_E \to F_{E'},$$

and in this way we obtain a direct system in $\mathscr{B}$ over the directed class $\mathscr{C}_A$. Now we can define direct limits over directed classes in precisely the same way that we define direct limits over directed sets. However, cocompleteness of $\mathscr{B}$ will be no guarantee that such direct limits exist, since cocompleteness applies only to diagrams over sets.

Theorem 2.2. *Consider a covariant functor $T : \mathscr{A} \to \mathscr{B}$, and suppose that for each $A \in \mathscr{A}$ the direct system $\{F_E, \pi\}_{E \in \mathscr{C}_A}$ over the directed class $\mathscr{C}_A$ has a direct limit in $\mathscr{B}$. Then the first cosatellite of T is given by the direct limit $\{\pi_E : F_E \to S^1T(A)\}_{E \in \mathscr{C}_A}$.*

Proof. First we show that S^1T is a functor. Relative to a morphism $\alpha : A \to A_1$ in $\mathscr{A}$ and a sequence $E \in \mathscr{C}_A$, we let E_1 be any sequence in $\mathscr{C}_{A_1}$ such that there is a morphism $(\alpha, ,)$ from E to E_1. Such exists, since we can always take $E_1 = \alpha E$. Then we have a morphism $\alpha_E : F_E \to S^1T(A_1)$. Using 2.1 and the fact that $\mathscr{C}_{A_1}$ is directed, it is easy to see that α_E is independent of the choice of E_1, and furthermore that $\{\alpha_E\}_{E \in \mathscr{C}_A}$ is a cocompatible system. There results a morphism

$$S^1T(\alpha) : S^1T(A) \to S^1T(A_1).$$

It is then a straightforward matter to check the additive functorial properties

$$\begin{aligned}S^1T(1_A) = 1_{S^1T(A)}, \qquad S^1T(\beta)S^1T(\alpha) &= S^1T(\beta\alpha), \\ S^1T(\alpha+\beta) &= S^1T(\alpha) + S^1T(\beta).\end{aligned}$$

Given an exact sequence

$$E : 0 \to A' \to A \to A'' \to 0 \tag{1}$$

in $\mathscr{A}$, we have a connecting morphism $\delta_E : T(A'') \to S^1T(A')$ given by the composition $T(A'') \to F_E \to S^1T(A')$. For a diagram

$$\begin{array}{ccccccccc} 0 & \longrightarrow & A' & \longrightarrow & A & \longrightarrow & A'' & \longrightarrow & 0 \\ & & \downarrow & & \downarrow & & \downarrow & & \\ 0 & \longrightarrow & B' & \longrightarrow & B & \longrightarrow & B'' & \longrightarrow & 0 \end{array}$$

it follows by definition of $S^1T(A') \to S^1T(B')$ that the diagram

$$\begin{array}{ccc} T(A'') & \longrightarrow & S^1T(A') \\ \downarrow & & \downarrow \\ T(B'') & \longrightarrow & S^1T(B') \end{array}$$

is commutative.

Relative to the sequence (1), we show that the sequence in $\mathscr{B}$

$$T(A') \to \underset{\mathrm{I}}{T(A)} \to \underset{\mathrm{II}}{T(A'')} \to \underset{\mathrm{III}}{S^1T(A')} \to \underset{\mathrm{IV}}{S^1T(A)} \to S^1T(A'')$$

is of order two. At positions I and IV this is just a property of additive functors. At position II this is trivial by definition of the connecting morphism. At position III we construct the commutative diagram

$$\begin{array}{rcccccccc} E: 0 & \longrightarrow & A' & \longrightarrow & A & \longrightarrow & A'' & \longrightarrow & 0 \\ & & \downarrow & & \downarrow & & \| & & \\ E': 0 & \longrightarrow & A & \longrightarrow & A \oplus A'' & \longrightarrow & A'' & \longrightarrow & 0 \end{array}$$

The composition in question is just $T(A'') \to F_E \to F_{E'} \to S^1T(A)$, which is zero since E' splits and so $F_{E'} = 0$.

Let (U^0, U^1) be a connected pair of functors and let $\varphi^0 : T \to U^0$ be any natural transformation. For $A \in \mathscr{A}$ and an exact sequence

$$E: 0 \to A \to B \to C \to 0 \tag{2}$$

we have a unique morphism $\varphi_E^1 : F_E \to U^1(A)$ yielding a commutative diagram

$$\begin{array}{ccccccc} T(B) & \longrightarrow & T(C) & \longrightarrow & F_E & \longrightarrow & 0 \\ \downarrow{\scriptstyle \varphi_B^0} & & \downarrow{\scriptstyle \varphi_C^0} & & \downarrow & & \\ U^0(B) & \longrightarrow & U^0(C) & \longrightarrow & U^1(A) & & \end{array} \tag{3_E}$$

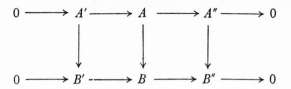

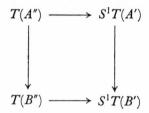

Using uniqueness of φ_E^1 we see that $\{\varphi_1^E\}$ is a cocompatible family, and so we get a direct limit morphism

$$\varphi_A^1 : S^1T(A) \to U^1(A).$$

Given $\alpha : A \to A_1$ and $(\alpha, ,) : E \to E_1$ we obtain a morphism from (3_E) to (3_{E_1}). Using §1, (3), we see that every face of the resulting cube is commutative save possibly the face

$$\begin{array}{ccc} F_E & \longrightarrow & F_{E_1} \\ \downarrow & & \downarrow \\ U^1(A) & \longrightarrow & U^1(A_1) \end{array} \tag{4}$$

By II, 1.1, we then see that (4) is commutative. Commutativity of the square

$$\begin{array}{ccc} S^1T(A) & \longrightarrow & S^1T(A_1) \\ \downarrow & & \downarrow \\ U^1(A) & \longrightarrow & U^1(A_1) \end{array}$$

then follows since it is commutative when composed with π_E for every $E \in \mathscr{C}_A$. Therefore φ^1 is a natural transformation, and by construction φ^1 and φ^0 commute with the connecting morphisms. To show uniqueness of φ^1, suppose that $\psi : S^1T \to U^1$ is another natural transformation which together with φ^0 commutes with the connecting morphisms. Relative to an exact sequence (2) we have the diagram

$$\begin{array}{ccccc} T(C) & \longrightarrow & F_E & \longrightarrow & S^1T(A) \\ \downarrow & & \downarrow{\scriptstyle \varphi_E^1} & \swarrow{\scriptstyle \psi_A} & \\ U^0(C) & \longrightarrow & U^1(A) & & \end{array}$$

where the square on the left is commutative and the outer border of the diagram is commutative. It then follows from the fact that $T(C) \to F_E$ is an epimorphism that the triangle on the right is commutative. Since this is true for all $E \in \mathscr{C}_A$, this shows that $\varphi_A^1 = \psi_A$. ∎

We now list a number of cases to which 2.2 applies.

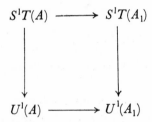

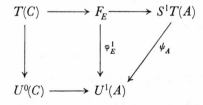

Case 1. $\mathscr{A}$ is a small category and $\mathscr{B}$ is cocomplete. In this case $\mathscr{C}_A$ is a set for all A, and so cocompleteness of $\mathscr{B}$ insures the existence of the direct limits.

Case 2. $\mathscr{A}$ has injectives. In this case any sequence $E: 0 \to A \to Q \to M \to 0$ with Q injective follows every member of $\mathscr{C}_A$, and so it is clear that the direct limit $S^1T(A)$ is just F_E.

Case 3. Let (T, T^1) be a connected pair of functors from $\mathscr{A}$ to $\mathscr{B}$, and suppose that for each $A \in \mathscr{A}$ there is a cofinal subclass of $\mathscr{C}_A$ consisting of sequences $0 \to A \to B \to C \to 0$ for which $T(B) \to T(C) \to T^1(A) \to 0$ is exact. Then since $F_E = T^1(A)$ on a cofinal subclass, the direct limit $S^1T(A)$ is just $T^1(A)$.

Case 4. Let (T, T^1) be a connected pair of functors from $\mathscr{A}$ to $\mathscr{B}$ where $\mathscr{B}$ is locally small and C_3. Suppose that for each exact sequence in $\mathscr{A}$

$$E: 0 \to A \overset{\mu_E}{\to} B \to C \to 0$$

the sequence

$$T(B) \to T(C) \to T^1(A) \to T^1(B) \tag{5_E}$$

is exact, and that for each $A \in \mathscr{A}$ we have

$$T^1(A) = \bigcup_{E \in \mathscr{C}_A} \operatorname{Ker} T^1(\mu_E) \tag{6}$$

where the right side of (6) is defined since $\mathscr{B}$ is locally small. From (5_E) we see that $F_E = \operatorname{Ker} T^1(\mu_E)$. If $E \leqslant E'$ in $\mathscr{C}_A$, then by definition of connected pair we have a morphism from (5_E) to $(5_{E'})$. It follows that the induced morphism $\pi_E^{E'}$ is just the inclusion $\operatorname{Ker} T^1(\mu_E) \subset \operatorname{Ker} T^1(\mu_{E'})$. Then by Eq. (6) and C_3 we have

$$S^1T(A) = \varinjlim F_E = T^1(A).$$

Corollary 2.3. *The positive connected sequence of one variable covariant functors*

$$H^C, \operatorname{Ext}^1(C, \ ), \quad \operatorname{Ext}^2(C, \ ), \ldots$$

is the cosatellite sequence of H^C.

Proof. The sequence is exact by VII, 5.1. Since for each

$$\mathbf{E} = E_n E_{n-1} \ldots E_2 E_1 \in \operatorname{Ext}^n(C, A)$$

we have $\operatorname{Ext}^n(C, \mu_{E_n})(\mathbf{E}) = 0$, our result follows from case 4 above. ▌

Corollary 2.3*. *The positive connected sequence of one variable contravariant functors*

$$H_A, \quad \operatorname{Ext}^1(\ , A), \quad \operatorname{Ext}^2(\ , A) \ldots$$

is the cosatellite sequence of H_A. ▌

3. The Exact Sequence

Given a morphism $\alpha : A \to A'$ and exact sequences

$$E : 0 \to A \to Q \to M \to 0$$

$$E' : 0 \to A' \to Q' \to M' \to 0$$

such that there is a morphism $(\alpha, ,) : E \to E'$, let $h_{\alpha,E,E'} : F_E \to F_{E'}$ denote the induced morphism of 2.1. Denoting the natural morphism $F_E \to S^1T(A)$ by π_E, we have

Lemma 3.1. *If $T : \mathscr{A} \to \mathscr{B}$ is a covariant functor where $\mathscr{B}$ is a C_3 category and $\mathscr{A}$ is small, then*

$$\operatorname{Ker}(S^1T(\alpha)) = \bigcup_{(\alpha, ,): E \to E'} \pi_E(\operatorname{Ker}(h_{\alpha,E,E'})).$$

Proof. First we have $S^1T(A) = \bigcup_{E \in \mathscr{C}_A} I_E$ where I_E is the image of π_E (II, 2.8). Denote $K = \operatorname{Ker}(S^1T(\alpha))$. Then by C_3 we have

$$K = \bigcup_{E \in \mathscr{C}_A} (I_E \cap K).$$

By I, 13.2, the kernel of the composition $F_E \to S^1T(A) \to S^1T(A')$ is $\pi_E^{-1}(K)$. It therefore follows from III, 1.8, that

$$\bigcup_{(\alpha, ,): E \to E'} \operatorname{Ker}(h_{\alpha,E,E'}) = \pi_E^{-1}(K).$$

Using the relation $I_E \cap K = \pi_E(\pi_E^{-1}(K))$ (I, 16.4) and the distributivity rule for images (I, 11.2), we can then write

$$K = \bigcup_{E \in \mathscr{C}_A} (I_E \cap K) = \bigcup_{E \in \mathscr{C}_A} \pi_E(\pi_E^{-1}(K))$$
$$= \bigcup_{E \in \mathscr{C}_A} \pi_E\Big(\bigcup_{(\alpha, ,): E \to E'} \operatorname{Ker}(h_{\alpha,E,E'})\Big)$$
$$= \bigcup_{(\alpha, ,): E \to E'} \pi_E(\operatorname{Ker}(h_{\alpha,E,E'})). \quad \blacksquare$$

Recall that a functor $T : \mathscr{A} \to \mathscr{B}$ is called half-exact if for any short exact sequence

$$0 \to A' \to A \to A'' \to 0 \tag{1}$$

in $\mathscr{A}$, the sequence $T(A') \to T(A) \to T(A'')$ is exact in $\mathscr{B}$.

Theorem 3.2. *Let $T : \mathscr{A} \to \mathscr{B}$ be a half-exact functor where $\mathscr{A}$ is small and $\mathscr{B}$ is C_3. Then relative to the exact sequence* (1), *the sequence*

$$T(A') \to \overset{\mathrm{I}}{T(A)} \to \overset{\mathrm{II}}{T(A'')} \to \overset{\mathrm{III}}{S^1T(A')} \to \overset{\mathrm{IV}}{S^1T(A)} \to S^1T(A'') \to S^2T(A') \to \ldots$$

is exact.

Proof. We have exactness at position I in the sequence by assumption on T. To show exactness at positions II, III, and IV it suffices to show that kernel $\subset$ image since the reverse inclusions were proved in 2.2. In particular, this will prove that S^1T is half-exact, and so exactness of the rest of the sequence will follow by induction.

We first show that kernel $\subset$ image at position IV. Taking into account 3.1, it suffices to show the following: given a morphism of sequences

$$\begin{array}{rcccccccc}
E:0 & \longrightarrow & A & \xrightarrow{\alpha} & Q & \longrightarrow & M & \longrightarrow & 0 \\
 & & \downarrow{\scriptstyle\lambda} & & \downarrow & & \downarrow & & \\
E'':0 & \longrightarrow & A'' & \xrightarrow{\alpha''} & Q'' & \longrightarrow & M'' & \longrightarrow & 0
\end{array} \tag{2}$$

there are morphisms $(\mu, ,) : E' \to E_1$ and $(\lambda, ,) : E_1 \to E''$ such that $\operatorname{Ker}(h_{\lambda,E_1,E''}) = \operatorname{Im}(h_{\mu,E',E_1})$ and $E_1 \geqslant E$ in $\mathscr{C}_A$. Given (2), construct the diagram

$$\begin{array}{rcccccccc}
 & & 0 & & 0 & & 0 & & \\
 & & \downarrow & & \downarrow & & \downarrow & & \\
E':0 & \longrightarrow & A' & \longrightarrow & Q & \longrightarrow & M' & \longrightarrow & 0 \\
 & & \downarrow{\scriptstyle\mu} & & \downarrow & & \downarrow & & \\
E_1:0 & \longrightarrow & A & \longrightarrow & Q \oplus Q'' & \longrightarrow & N & \longrightarrow & 0 \\
 & & \downarrow{\scriptstyle\lambda} & & \downarrow & & \downarrow & & \\
E'':0 & \longrightarrow & A'' & \longrightarrow & Q'' & \longrightarrow & M'' & \longrightarrow & 0 \\
 & & \downarrow & & \downarrow & & \downarrow & & \\
 & & 0 & & 0 & & 0 & &
\end{array} \tag{3}$$

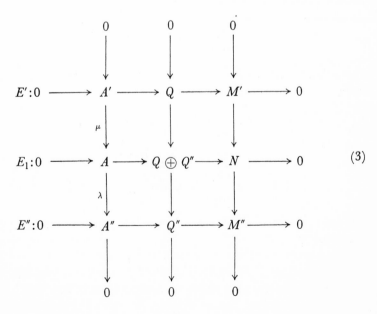

where the coordinates of $A \to Q \oplus Q''$ are α and $\alpha''\lambda$, the middle column is a split exact sequence, and the rest of the diagram is defined so as to have exactness of the rows and columns (I, 16.1*). Then $E_1 \geqslant E$. If we apply T to (3), the middle column is still a split exact sequence, and the sequence $T(M') \to T(N) \to T(M'')$ is exact by half-exactness of T. An easy diagram chase then shows that $F_{E'} \to F_{E_1} \to F_{E''}$ is exact as required.

Next we show kernel $\subset$ image at position III. Again, in view of 3.1 it suffices to show the following: given a morphism of sequences

$$\begin{array}{rcccccccc}
E':0 & \longrightarrow & A' & \longrightarrow & Q' & \longrightarrow & M' & \longrightarrow & 0 \\
 & & \downarrow{\scriptstyle \mu} & & \downarrow & & \downarrow & & \\
E:0 & \longrightarrow & A & \xrightarrow{\alpha} & Q & \longrightarrow & M & \longrightarrow & 0
\end{array} \tag{4}$$

there are morphisms of sequences $(1_{A'}, \ , \ ) : \bar{E} \to E_1$ and $(\mu, \ , \ ) : E_1 \to E$, where $\bar{E}$ denotes the given exact sequence (1), such that $\mathrm{Ker}(h_{\mu,E_1,E}) = \mathrm{Im}(h_{1,\bar{E},E_1})$ and $E_1 \geqslant E'$ in $\mathscr{C}_{A'}$. Given (4), form the commutative diagram

$$\begin{array}{rcccccccc}
 & & & & & & 0 & & \\
 & & & & & & \downarrow & & \\
\bar{E}:0 & \longrightarrow & A' & \xrightarrow{\mu} & A & \xrightarrow{\lambda} & A'' & \longrightarrow & 0 \\
 & & \| & & \downarrow{\scriptstyle \alpha} & & \downarrow & & \\
E_1:0 & \longrightarrow & A' & \xrightarrow{\alpha\mu} & Q & \longrightarrow & N & \longrightarrow & 0 \\
 & & \downarrow{\scriptstyle \mu} & & \| & & \downarrow & & \\
E:0 & \longrightarrow & A & \xrightarrow{\alpha} & Q & \longrightarrow & M & \longrightarrow & 0 \\
 & & & & & & \downarrow & & \\
 & & & & & & 0 & &
\end{array} \tag{5}$$

where N is the cokernel of $\alpha\mu$. By chasing the diagram one sees that the right column is exact. Furthermore, $E_1 \geqslant E'$ in $\mathscr{C}_{A'}$. Applying T to (5) and using the fact that $T(A'') \to T(N) \to T(M)$ is exact, another diagram chase shows that required exactness of the sequence $F_{\bar{E}} \to F_{E_1} \to F_E$.

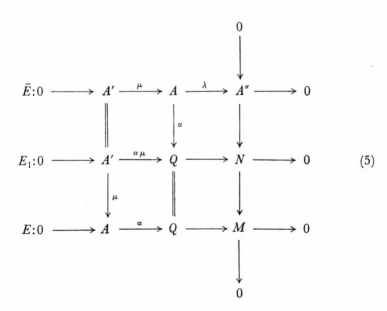

Finally we show kernel = image at position II. Because of C_3 it suffices to show that in any situation of the form

$$\begin{array}{ccccccccc}
\bar{E}:0 & \longrightarrow & A' & \xrightarrow{\mu} & A & \xrightarrow{\lambda} & A'' & \longrightarrow & 0 \\
 & & \| & & \downarrow{\scriptstyle\eta} & & \downarrow{\scriptstyle\epsilon} & & \\
E:0 & \longrightarrow & A' & \xrightarrow{\kappa} & Q & \xrightarrow{\tau} & M & \longrightarrow & 0
\end{array}$$

the sequence

$$T(A) \xrightarrow{T(\lambda)} T(A'') \xrightarrow{p_E T(\epsilon)} F_E \tag{6}$$

is exact, where $p_E : T(M) \to F_E$ is the cokernel of $T(\tau)$. We form the pushout diagram

$$\begin{array}{ccccccccc}
 & & 0 & & 0 & & & & \\
 & & \downarrow & & \downarrow & & & & \\
0 & \longrightarrow & A' & \xrightarrow{\mu} & A & \xrightarrow{\lambda} & A'' & \longrightarrow & 0 \\
 & & \downarrow{\scriptstyle\kappa} & & \downarrow{\scriptstyle\rho} & & \| & & \\
0 & \longrightarrow & Q & \underset{\delta}{\overset{\alpha}{\rightleftarrows}} & Q \oplus A'' & \underset{\gamma}{\overset{\beta}{\rightleftarrows}} & A'' & \longrightarrow & 0 \\
 & & \downarrow{\scriptstyle\tau} & & \downarrow{\scriptstyle\sigma} & & & & \\
 & & M & = & M & & & & \\
 & & \downarrow & & \downarrow & & & & \\
 & & 0 & & 0 & & & &
\end{array}$$

where α, γ and β, δ are injections and projections, respectively, for the coproduct, and $\delta\rho = \eta$. Recalling that $\alpha\delta + \gamma\beta = 1$ (I, 18.1) we have

$$\begin{aligned}
\sigma\gamma\lambda &= \sigma\gamma\beta\rho = \sigma(1 - \alpha\delta)\rho \\
&= -\sigma\alpha\delta\rho = -\sigma\alpha\eta = -\tau\eta = -\epsilon\lambda.
\end{aligned}$$

Since λ is an epimorphism, this shows that $\sigma\gamma = -\epsilon$. Therefore, exactness of (6) amounts to showing that $\operatorname{Im}(T(\lambda)) = \operatorname{Ker}(p_E T(\sigma) T(\gamma))$. Since T is half-exact, the sequence

$$T(A) \to T(Q \oplus A'') \to T(M)$$

is exact. Our result then follows from the following general lemma.

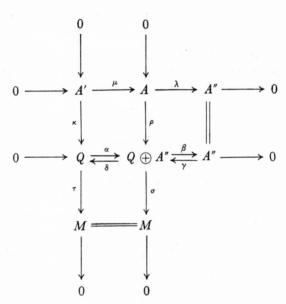

Lemma 3.3. *Consider a commutative diagram in an abelian category*

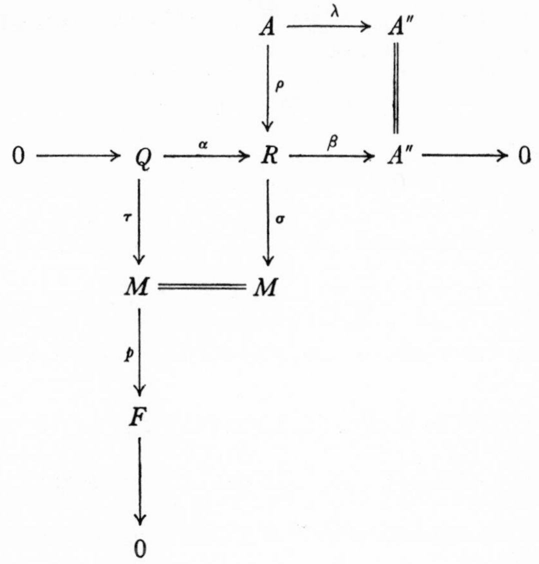

(7)

and suppose that all rows and columns are exact. If γ *is a splitting morphism for* β *(i.e.* $\beta\gamma = 1_{A''}$*), then* $\mathrm{Im}(\lambda) = \mathrm{Ker}(p\sigma\gamma)$.

Proof. Let $\delta : R \to Q$ be the projection from R, considered as the coproduct of Q and A'', so that in particular $\alpha\delta + \gamma\beta = 1$. Then it is easily checked that $p\sigma\gamma\lambda = 0$. It remains to be shown that $\mathrm{Ker}(p\sigma\gamma) \subset \mathrm{Im}(\lambda)$. We apply Metatheorem IV, 2.8; that is, we consider (7) as a diagram of abelian groups. Suppose that $x \in A''$, and $p\sigma\gamma(x) = 0$. Then $\sigma\gamma(x) = \tau(y)$ for some $y \in Q$, and using commutativity of (7) we then have $\sigma\gamma(x) = \sigma\alpha(y)$. Rewriting this, we have $\sigma(\gamma(x) - \alpha(y)) = 0$, and so $\gamma(x) - \alpha(y) = \rho(z)$ for some $z \in A$. Applying β to this last equation we have $x = \beta\rho(z) = \lambda(z)$. This proves that $\mathrm{Ker}(p\sigma\gamma) \subset \mathrm{Im}(\lambda)$ as required. ∎

Remark. If $\mathscr{A}$ is a category with injectives and $\mathscr{B}$ is any category, then the proof of 3.2 goes through without resort to direct limits (see case 2 following 2.2). If $\mathscr{A}$ also has projectives, then the dual remark applies, so that in this case the connected sequence of functors

$$\ldots S_2T, S_1T, T, S^1T, S^2T, \ldots$$

is exact. Observe, however, that in general 3.1* applies to satellites of covariant functors where the range is a C_3^* category. In particular, 3.1* does not apply to group valued functors in the case where projectives do not exist in the domain.

4. Satellites of Group Valued Functors

Let $\mathscr{A}$ be a small category, and let $T : \mathscr{A} \to \mathscr{G}$ be a covariant group valued functor. For $A \in \mathscr{A}$ and $n \geqslant 0$ define

$$T_n(A) = [\mathrm{Ext}^n(A, \ ), T].$$

An exact sequence

$$0 \to A' \to A \to A'' \to 0$$

induces an order two sequence

$$\ldots T_n(A') \to T_n(A) \to T_n(A'') \to T_{n-1}(A') \to \ldots$$

and so $\{T_n\}$ is a negative connected sequence of functors. Furthermore, we have

$$T_0(A) = [\mathrm{Ext}^0(A, \ ), T] = [H^A, T] \approx T(A)$$

using IV, 2.1. Identifying T with T_0 in this way we have:

Theorem 4.1. *The connected sequence $\{T_n\}$ above is the sequence of satellites of the group valued functor T.*

Proof. First observe that for $\mathbf{E} \in \mathrm{Ext}^n(A, C)$ and $\eta \in [\mathrm{Ext}^n(A, \ ), T]$, the iterated connecting morphism

$$[\mathrm{Ext}^n(A, \ ), T] \to [\mathrm{Ext}^0(C, \ ), T] = T(C)$$

relative to $\mathbf{E}$ takes η into the element $\eta_C(\mathbf{E})$. Now, given a negative connected sequence $\{U_n\}$ and a natural transformation $\varphi_0 : U_0 \to T$, in order to have commutativity with the connecting morphisms we must define

$$\varphi_{nA}(x)_C(\mathbf{E}) = \varphi_{0C}\delta_{\mathbf{E}}(x) \tag{1}$$

where $x \in U_n(A)$, $\mathbf{E} \in \mathrm{Ext}^n(A, C)$, and $\delta_{\mathbf{E}}$ is the iterated connecting morphism relative to the sequence of U's. Hence if $\{\varphi_n\}$ defined by (1) actually gives a morphism of connected sequences of functors extending φ_0, then it is the only such extension. The following points must be verified.

(i) $\varphi_{nA}(x)_C$ is additive.
(ii) $\varphi_{nA}(x)$ is a natural transformation.
(iii) φ_{nA} is additive.
(iv) φ_n is a natural transformation.
(v) $\{\varphi_n\}$ commutes with the connecting morphisms.

We prove the assertions for $n = 1$. The general case is similar and is left to the reader.

(i) Consider the construction

$$\begin{array}{rcccccccc}
E+E':0 & \longrightarrow & C & \longrightarrow & B''' & \longrightarrow & A & \longrightarrow & 0 \\
 & & \nabla\uparrow & & \uparrow & & \| & & \\
0 & \longrightarrow & C\oplus C & \longrightarrow & B'' & \longrightarrow & A & \longrightarrow & 0 \\
 & & \| & & \downarrow & & \downarrow\Delta & & \\
E\oplus E':0 & \longrightarrow & C\oplus C & \rightarrow & B\oplus B' & \rightarrow & A\oplus A & \longrightarrow & 0
\end{array} \qquad (2)$$

giving the sum of two elements $E, E' \in \mathrm{Ext}^1(A, C)$. From (2) we obtain a diagram of connecting morphisms

$$\begin{array}{rccc}
\delta_{E+E'}: & U_1(A) & \longrightarrow & U_0(C) \\
 & \| & & \uparrow\nabla \\
 & U_1(A) & \longrightarrow & U_0(C)\oplus U_0(C) \\
 & \Delta\downarrow & & \| \\
\delta_{E\oplus E'}: & U_1(A)\oplus U_1(A) & \rightarrow & U_0(C)\oplus U_0(C)
\end{array}$$

Using the relation $\delta_{E\oplus E'} = \delta_E \oplus \delta_{E'}$ (exercise 1), the equality

$$\varphi_{1A}(x)_C(E+E') = \varphi_{1A}(x)_C(E) + \varphi_{1A}(x)_C(E')$$

follows easily.

(ii) Given a morphism $C \to C_1$, we must show commutativity of the diagram

$$\begin{array}{ccc}
\mathrm{Ext}^1(A, C) & \longrightarrow & T(C) \\
\downarrow & & \downarrow \\
\mathrm{Ext}^1(A, C_1) & \longrightarrow & T(C_1)
\end{array}$$

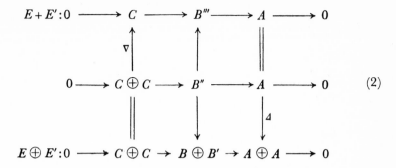

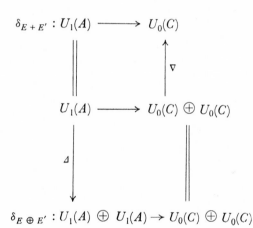

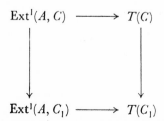

But this follows from commutativity of the diagram

$$\begin{array}{ccccc} U^1(A) & \longrightarrow & U^0(C) & \longrightarrow & T(C) \\ \| & & \downarrow & & \downarrow \\ U^1(A) & \longrightarrow & U^0(C_1) & \longrightarrow & T(C_1) \end{array}$$

which results from the commutative diagram

$$\begin{array}{ccccccccc} 0 & \longrightarrow & C & \longrightarrow & B & \longrightarrow & A & \longrightarrow & 0 \\ & & \downarrow & & \downarrow & & \| & & \\ 0 & \longrightarrow & C_1 & \longrightarrow & B' & \longrightarrow & A & \longrightarrow & 0 \end{array}$$

(iii) is purely algebraic. We have

$$\begin{aligned} \varphi_{1A}(x+y)_C(E) &= \varphi_{0C}\delta_E(x+y) = \varphi_{0C}\delta_E(x) + \varphi_{0C}\delta_E(y) \\ &= \varphi_{1A}(x)_C(E) + \varphi_{1A}(y)_C(E) = (\varphi_{1A}(x) + \varphi_{1A}(y))_C(E). \end{aligned}$$

(iv) Given $A \to A_1$ we must show commutativity of the diagram

$$\begin{array}{ccc} U_1(A) & \longrightarrow & U_1(A_1) \\ \downarrow & & \downarrow \\ [\mathrm{Ext}^1(A, \ ), T] & \rightarrow & [\mathrm{Ext}^1(A_1, \ ), T] \end{array}$$

But this follows from commutativity of the diagram

$$\begin{array}{ccccc} U_1(A) & \longrightarrow & U_0(C) & \longrightarrow & T(C) \\ \downarrow & & \| & & \| \\ U_1(A_1) & \longrightarrow & U_0(C) & \longrightarrow & T(C) \end{array}$$

which results from the commutative diagram

$$\begin{array}{ccccccccc} 0 & \longrightarrow & C & \longrightarrow & B' & \longrightarrow & A & \longrightarrow & 0 \\ & & \| & & \downarrow & & \downarrow & & \\ 0 & \longrightarrow & C & \longrightarrow & B & \longrightarrow & A_1 & \longrightarrow & 0 \end{array}$$

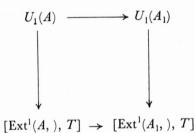

(v) Commutativity of φ_1 and φ_0 with the connecting morphisms is clear from the definition of φ_1. ▮

Corollary 4.2. *If T is an injective in the category $(\mathscr{A}, \mathscr{G})$, then the sequence of satellites of T is exact.* ▮

5. Projective Sequences

Let $\mathscr{A}$ be a small category and let $\mathrm{Seq}(\mathscr{A}, \mathscr{B})$ denote the class of all connected sequences of covariant functors from $\mathscr{A}$ to $\mathscr{B}$. Using morphisms of connected sequences as defined in §1 it is trivially verified that $\mathrm{Seq}(\mathscr{A}, \mathscr{B})$ is an abelian category possessing all of the properties C_i and C_i^* that $\mathscr{B}$ has. The same statement is true of the class of all positive connected sequences $\overset{+}{\mathrm{Seq}}(\mathscr{A}, \mathscr{B})$, and the class of all negative connected sequences $\overset{-}{\mathrm{Seq}}(\mathscr{A}, \mathscr{B}) = \overset{+}{\mathrm{Seq}}(\mathscr{A}^*, \mathscr{B}^*)$.

Consider the functors

$$F_i : \overset{+}{\mathrm{Seq}}(\mathscr{A}, \mathscr{B}) \rightarrow (\mathscr{A}, \mathscr{B})$$

defined for $i \geqslant 0$ by $F_i(T^n\}) = T^i$. Then the F_i's constitute a collectively faithful set of exact functors. If $\mathscr{B}$ is cocomplete, then a coadjoint for F_i is given by

$$G_i : (\mathscr{A}, \mathscr{B}) \rightarrow \overset{+}{\mathrm{Seq}}(\mathscr{A}, \mathscr{B})$$

where

$$\begin{aligned} G_i(T)^n &= S^{n-i}T \quad \text{for} \quad n \geqslant i \\ &= 0 \qquad\quad\ \text{for} \quad n < i. \end{aligned}$$

If $\mathscr{B}$ has a generator, then so does $(\mathscr{A}, \mathscr{B})$ by VI, 4.1. Choosing a generator $U_i \in (\mathscr{A}, \mathscr{B})$ for each i, we then see by V, 1.5, that $\bigoplus_{i \geqslant 0} G_i(U_i)$ is a generator for $\overset{+}{\mathrm{Seq}}(\mathscr{A}, \mathscr{B})$.

Consider now the functors

$$R_i : \overset{+}{\mathrm{Seq}}(\mathscr{A}, \mathscr{B}) \rightarrow (\mathscr{A}, \mathscr{B})$$

defined by

$$R_i(\{T^n\})(A) = T^i(A) / \bigcup_{E \in \mathscr{C}_A} \mathrm{Im}(\delta_E^{i-1})$$

where $\delta_E^{i-1} : T^{i-1}(C) \rightarrow T^i(A)$ is the connecting morphism of the connected sequence $\{T^n\}$ relative to the short exact sequence $E : 0 \rightarrow A \rightarrow B \rightarrow C \rightarrow 0$. Then the relations

$$R_i S_j = 0 \qquad \text{for} \quad i \neq j, \quad R_i S_i = 1$$

follow easily using the construction of satellites given in 2.2. Consequently condition 1 of V, 7.5, is satisfied. Now clearly the R_i's collectively take nonzero objects into nonzero objects. Also an exact sequence of connected sequences

$$\{T'^n\} \rightarrow \{T^n\} \rightarrow \{T''^n\} \rightarrow 0$$

induces a commutative diagram

$$\begin{array}{ccccccc}
\bigoplus_{E\in\mathscr{C}_A} T'^{i-1}(C) & \longrightarrow & \bigoplus_{E\in\mathscr{C}_A} T^{i-1}(C) & \longrightarrow & \bigoplus_{E\in\mathscr{C}_A} T''^{i-1}(C) & \longrightarrow & 0 \\
\downarrow & & \downarrow & & \downarrow & & \\
T'^{i}(A) & \longrightarrow & T^{i}(A) & \longrightarrow & T''^{i}(A) & \longrightarrow & 0
\end{array}$$

for each $A \in \mathscr{A}$. The bottom row is exact by assumption and the top row is exact since coproducts preserve cokernels. Therefore the sequence of cokernels of the vertical morphisms is exact. In other words R_i is cokernel preserving. Therefore, using V, 7.6, and VI, 4.1, we have:

Theorem 5.1. *If $\mathscr{A}$ is a small category and $\mathscr{B}$ is a cocomplete category with projectives, then $\overset{+}{\mathrm{Seq}}(\mathscr{A}, \mathscr{B})$ has projectives. The projectives in $\overset{+}{\mathrm{Seq}}(\mathscr{A}, \mathscr{B})$ are the objects of the form $\bigoplus_{i\geqslant 0} G_i(P_i)$ where P_i is projective in $(\mathscr{A}, \mathscr{B})$ for all i.* ▮

6. Several Variables

A sequence of functors of several variables

$$T^n : \mathscr{A}_1 \times \mathscr{A}_2 \times \ldots \times \mathscr{A}_k \to \mathscr{B} \qquad (n \in \mathbf{Z})$$

is called a **multiply connected sequence** if each sequence of single variable functors obtained by keeping $k-1$ of the variables fixed is a connected sequence and if, furthermore, a morphism of the fixed variables induces a morphism of connected sequences. The latter condition is equivalent to the condition that the connecting morphism for each variable be a natural transformation of functors of the remaining variables. A **morphism** $\{T^n\} \to \{U^n\}$ of multiply connected sequences is a family of natural transformations of several variable functors $\varphi^n : T^n \to U^n$ which when restricted to the partial functors of one variable yield morphisms of connected sequences. A multiply connected sequence is called **positive, negative**, or **exact** if each of the partial one variable sequences has the corresponding property. Multiply connected pairs are defined just as in the one variable case. If (T, T^1) has the property that for every multiply connected pair (U, U^1) and every natural transformation $\varphi : T \to U$ there is a unique extension $\varphi^1 : U^1 \to T^1$ of φ, then $T^1 = S^1 T$ is called the first **cosatellite** of T. In general the partial one variable functors associated with $S^1 T$ will not be the first cosatellites of the partial one variable functors associated with T. The nth cosatellite of T is defined inductively as before.

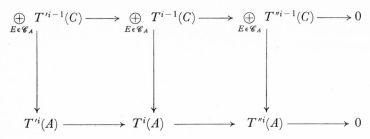

From VII, §5, we see that the sequence of two variable functors $\{\mathrm{Ext}^n\}_{n \geq 0}$ is a positive, exact, multiply connected sequence.

To simplify the notation we shall deal only with functors of two variables where both variables are covariant. However, our results will generalize to functors of any number of variables and arbitrary variance.

Given $T: \mathscr{A} \times \mathscr{C} \to \mathscr{B}$ and $C \in \mathscr{C}$, consider $T_C: \mathscr{A} \to \mathscr{B}$ defined by $T_C(A) = T(A, C)$. A morphism $C \to C'$ induces a natural transformation $T_C \to T_{C'}$, and hence a natural transformation $S^1 T_C \to S^1 T_{C'}$. Therefore, if $S^1 T_C$ is defined for all $C \in \mathscr{C}$, we have a two variable functor $S^1_{(1)} T$ defined by $S^1_{(1)} T(A, C) = S^1 T_C(A)$, and for an exact sequence $0 \to A' \to A \to A'' \to 0$ in $\mathscr{A}$ we have a connecting morphism

$$\delta_{(1)} : T(A'', C) \to S^1_{(1)} T(A', C) \tag{1}$$

which is natural with respect to the variable C. If (U, U^1) is a multiply connected pair and $\varphi : T \to U$ is a natural transformation of two variable functors, then by fixing the second variable we obtain a transformation $\varphi_{(1)} : S^1_{(1)} T \to U^1$ which is natural with respect to the first variable.

Lemma 6.1. *$\varphi_{(1)}$ is a natural transformation of two variable functors.*

Proof. Given an exact sequence $0 \to A' \to A \to A'' \to 0$, consider the commutative diagram

$$\begin{array}{ccc} T(A'', C) & \longrightarrow & S^1_{(1)} T(A', C) \\ \downarrow & & \downarrow \varphi_{(1)} \\ U(A'', C) & \longrightarrow & U^1(A', C), \end{array} \tag{2_C}$$

A morphism $C \to C'$ gives rise to morphisms from the vertices of (2_C) to the vertices of $(2_{C'})$, and from the resulting cube we see that the compositions $S^1_{(1)} T(\ , C) \to U^1(\ , C) \to U^1(\ , C')$ and $S^1_{(1)} T(\ , C) \to S^1_{(1)} T(\ , C') \to U^1(\ , C')$ extend the same transformation $T(\ , C) \to U(\ , C')$. Hence these compositions are the same, or in other words $\varphi_{(1)}$ is natural in the second variable. ∎

Similarly, by considering partial functors with respect to the second variable we can define a two variable functor $S^1_{(2)} T$ and connecting morphisms $\delta_{(2)}$. The above transformation φ then induces a natural transformation $\varphi_{(2)} : S^1_{(2)} T \to U^1$ of two variable functors. If $S^1_{(1)} S^1_{(2)} T$ is defined, we can define

$$\delta_{(21)} : S^1_{(2)} T(A'', C) \to S^1_{(1)} S^1_{(2)} T(A', C)$$

simply by replacing T by $S^1_{(2)} T$ in (1). On the other hand, if $S^1_{(2)} S^1_{(1)} T$ is defined we have

$$S^1_{(2)}(\delta_{(1)}) : S^1_{(2)} T(A'', C) \to S^1_{(2)} S^1_{(1)} T(A', C)$$

which is natural with respect to C, and which can be considered for fixed C as the connecting morphism of a pair $(S^1_{(2)}T(\ ,C), S^1_{(2)}S^1_{(1)}T(\ ,C))$. In the following we shall suppress the superscript 1.

Proposition 6.2. *If $S_{(2)}S_{(1)}T$ and $S_{(1)}S_{(2)}T$ are defined, then we have a natural equivalence of two variable functors*

$$\theta : S_{(1)}S_{(2)}T \to S_{(2)}S_{(1)}T$$

and a commutative diagram

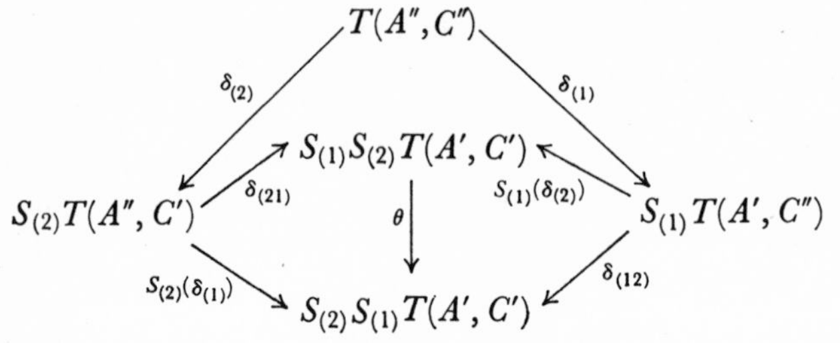

(3)

for exact sequences $0 \to A' \to A \to A'' \to 0$ and $0 \to C' \to C \to C'' \to 0$ in $\mathscr{A}$ and $\mathscr{C}$, respectively.

Proof. Replacing T by $S_{(2)}T$ and φ by the identity in 6.1 we obtain a natural transformation θ of two variable functors making the lower left-hand corner of (3) commutative. Interchanging the roles of the variables we obtain a natural transformation

$$\theta' : S_{(2)}S_{(1)}T \to S_{(1)}S_{(2)}T$$

making the lower right-hand corner of (3) commutative. Now we have

$$\begin{aligned}\theta'\theta\delta_{(21)}\delta_{(2)} &= \theta' S_{(2)}(\delta_{(1)})\delta_{(2)} = \theta'\delta_{(12)}\delta_{(1)} \\ &= S_{(1)}(\delta_{(2)})\delta_{(1)}.\end{aligned}$$

But also $\delta_{(21)}\delta_{(2)} = S_{(1)}(\delta_{(2)})\delta_{(1)}$, and so $\theta'\theta\delta_{(21)}$ and $\delta_{(21)}$ both extend $\delta_{(1)}$. Hence $\theta'\theta\delta_{(21)} = \delta_{(21)}$, or in other words $\theta'\theta$ extends the identity on $S_{(2)}T(\ ,C')$. Hence $\theta'\theta$ is the identity on $S_{(1)}S_{(2)}T$. Interchanging variables we see that $\theta\theta'$ is the identity on $S_{(2)}S_{(1)}T$. Thus θ is a natural equivalence as required. ∎

Proposition 6.3. *If $S^1_{(1)}T$ and $S^1_{(2)}T$ are defined, then the first cosatellite of the two-variable functor T is given by*

$$S^1T = S^1_{(1)}T \oplus S^1_{(2)}T.$$

The connecting morphism relative to a sequence $0 \to A' \to A \to A'' \to 0$ is given by the composition

$$T(A'', C) \xrightarrow{\delta_{(1)}} S^1_{(1)}T(A', C) \longrightarrow S^1_{(1)}T(A', C) \oplus S^1_{(2)}T(A', C),$$

with a similar definition for the connecting morphism of the second variable.

Proof. Consider a connected pair (U, U^1) and a natural transformation of two variable functors $\varphi : T \to U$. Then clearly

$$\varphi^1 = (\varphi_{(1)}, \varphi_{(2)}) : S^1_{(1)}T \oplus S^1_{(2)}T \to U^1$$

extends φ. On the other hand, using uniqueness of transformations induced on one variable cosatellites, it is easily seen that φ^1 is the only transformation extending φ. This proves the assertion. ▮

For an object A and an integer $n > 0$, let us define $nA = {}^nA$. Then using 6.2 and 6.3, we have the following corollary.

Corollary 6.4 (The Bifunctorial Theorem). *Let $\mathscr{A}$, $\mathscr{B}$, and $\mathscr{C}$ be categories which admit cosatellites for all one variable functors $\mathscr{A} \to \mathscr{B}$ and $\mathscr{C} \to \mathscr{B}$. Then the nth cosatellite of a two variable functor $T : \mathscr{A} \times \mathscr{C} \to \mathscr{B}$ is given by*

$$S^nT = \bigoplus_{i=0}^{n} \binom{n}{i} S^i_{(1)} S^{n-i}_{(2)} T. \qquad ▮$$

Exercises

1. Relative to an h.f. class $\mathscr{E}$ (V, exercise 5, and VII, exercise 6) develop a theory of satellites and prove generalizations for each of the numbers in this chapter with the exception of 3.2. Generalize 3.2 under the assumption that $\mathscr{E}$ has the following property: If in the exact commutative diagram

$$\begin{array}{ccccccccc}
 & & 0 & & 0 & & 0 & & \\
 & & \downarrow & & \downarrow & & \downarrow & & \\
0 & \longrightarrow & A' & \longrightarrow & A & \longrightarrow & A'' & \longrightarrow & 0 \\
 & & \downarrow & & \downarrow & & \downarrow & & \\
0 & \longrightarrow & B' & \longrightarrow & B & \longrightarrow & B'' & \longrightarrow & 0 \\
 & & \downarrow & & \downarrow{\scriptstyle \beta} & & \downarrow & & \\
0 & \longrightarrow & C' & \longrightarrow & C & \longrightarrow & C'' & \longrightarrow & 0 \\
 & & \downarrow & & \downarrow & & \downarrow & & \\
 & & 0 & & 0 & & 0 & &
\end{array}$$

all epimorphisms save possibly β are in $\mathscr{E}$, then β is also in $\mathscr{E}$. Show, in particular, that any closed class of epimorphisms has this property.

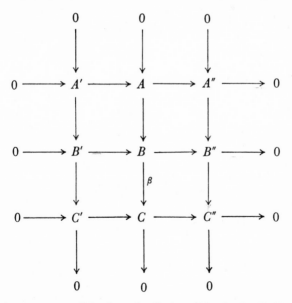

2. If $\{T^n\}$ is a connected sequence of functors from $\mathscr{A}$ to $\mathscr{B}$ with connecting morphisms δ^n, and if $\mathbf{E}$ and $\mathbf{F}$ are p-fold exact sequences in $\mathscr{A}$, then

$$\delta^n_{\mathbf{E}\oplus\mathbf{F}} = \delta^n_{\mathbf{E}} \oplus \delta^n_{\mathbf{F}}.$$

If $\mathscr{A}$ is a C_1 category and the T^n's are all coproduct preserving, then for any class of p-fold exact sequences $\{E_i\}$ we have

$$\delta^n_{\oplus\mathbf{E}_i} = \bigoplus \delta^n_{\mathbf{E}_i}.$$

3. Consider a connected sequence of covariant functors $\{T^n\}$ and the exact, 3 by 3 commutative diagram of exercise 1. Show that for any integer n the diagram of connecting morphisms

$$\begin{array}{ccc} T^n(C'') & \longrightarrow & T^{n+1}(C') \\ \downarrow & & \downarrow \\ T^{n+1}(A'') & \longrightarrow & T^{n+2}(A') \end{array}$$

is anticommutative: that is, the composition in one direction is the negative of the composition in the other direction. (Use VII, exercise 7.)

4. Consider exact, commutative diagrams $(i = 1, 2)$

$$\begin{array}{ccccccccc} & & & & & & 0 & & \\ & & & & & & \downarrow & & \\ & & & & & & K''_i & & \\ & & & & & & \downarrow & & \\ & & A'_i & \longrightarrow & A_i & \longrightarrow & A''_i & \longrightarrow & 0 \\ & & \downarrow & & \downarrow & & \downarrow & & \\ 0 & \longrightarrow & B'_i & \longrightarrow & B_i & \longrightarrow & B''_i & & \\ & & \downarrow & & & & & & \\ & & F'_i & & & & & & \\ & & \downarrow & & & & & & \\ & & 0 & & & & & & \end{array} \qquad (D_i)$$

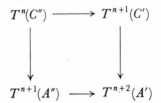

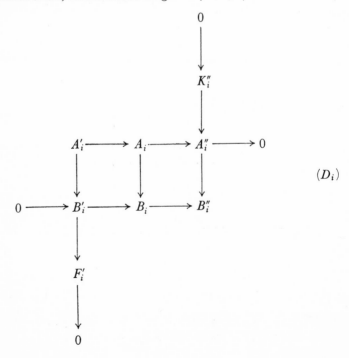

A morphism $D_1 \to D_2$ induces a commutative diagram

$$\begin{array}{ccc} K_1'' & \longrightarrow & F_1' \\ \downarrow & & \downarrow \\ K_2'' & \longrightarrow & F_2' \end{array}$$

where the horizontal arrows are the connecting morphisms defined in IV, §1. Hence the homology functors $H^n = H_{-n} : \mathscr{C}(\mathscr{A}) \to \mathscr{A}$, together with the connecting morphisms defined in VI, §8, comprise a connected sequence of functors.

5. Let $\mathscr{A}$ be a small category and let $\mathscr{B}$ and $\mathscr{C}$ be cocomplete. Consider covariant functors $U : \mathscr{A} \to \mathscr{B}$ and $T : \mathscr{B} \to \mathscr{C}$ with T cokernel preserving. Then $S^n(TU) = T(S^nU)$ for all $n \geqslant 0$.

6. For $T : \mathscr{A} \to {}^{\mathbf{R}}\mathscr{B}$ let $\bar{T}$ be the functor with values in $\mathscr{B}$ obtained by composing T with the forgetful functor ${}^{\mathbf{R}}\mathscr{B} \to \mathscr{B}$. Then the elements r of R induce natural transformations $\bar{r} : \bar{T} \to \bar{T}$. Hence if $S^1\bar{T}$ is defined, we have natural transformations $S^1(\bar{r}) : S^1\bar{T} \to S^1\bar{T}$. In this way $S^1\bar{T}$ may be regarded as having values in ${}^{\mathbf{R}}\mathscr{B}$, and as such it is the first cosatellite of T.

7. In the category $\mathscr{C}(\mathscr{A})$ of complexes in $\mathscr{A}$, every object X' admits a monomorphism into a complex X such that $H^n(X) = 0$ for all n. (Consider the projective class $\mathscr{E}_0\mathscr{C}(\mathscr{A})$ of VI, §8, and apply duality.) Hence use exercise 4, case 3 following 2.2, exercise 22 of Chapter VI, and duality to show the following:

$$\begin{array}{ll} S^1H^n = H^{n+1} & S_1H^n = H^{n-1} \\ S^1Z^n = H^{n+1} & S_1Z^n = 0 \\ S^1Z'^n = 0 & S_1Z'^n = H^{n-1} \\ S^1B^n = 0 & S_1B^n = 0. \end{array}$$

8. For any small category $\mathscr{A}$, $\mathrm{Seq}(\mathscr{A}, \mathscr{G})$ has an injective cogenerator and $\overset{+}{\mathrm{Seq}}(\mathscr{A}, \mathscr{G})$ has a projective generator. Furthermore $\overset{+}{\mathrm{Seq}}(\mathscr{A}, \mathscr{G})$ has an injective cogenerator. Every member of $\overset{+}{\mathrm{Seq}}(\mathscr{A}, \mathscr{G})$ is the quotient of an exact, positive connected sequence and every member of $\overset{-}{\mathrm{Seq}}(\mathscr{A}, \mathscr{G})$ admits a monomorphism into an exact, negative connected sequence.

9. Let $J_{A,E}$ be as defined in IV, §3. Establish a natural equivalence

$$[\mathrm{Ext}^n(C, \ ), J_{A,E}] \approx [\mathrm{Ext}^n(C, A), E]$$

to show that the right-hand side is the nth satellite of $J_{A,E}$ evaluated at C. Prove the latter fact directly, and then using the fact that satellites preserve products give another proof of 5.2.

[CHAPTER IX]

Global Dimension

Introduction

In 1957, Eilenberg, Rosenberg, and Zelinsky [13] showed that for any ring $\mathbf{R}$, the (right or left) global dimension of the polynomial ring $\mathbf{R}[X_1, \ldots, X_k]$ is k + gl. dim. $\mathbf{R}$. Hochschild [23] generalized this result by showing that the free ring over $\mathbf{R}$ on any set of letters has global dimension 1 + gl. dim. $\mathbf{R}$. In §1 we put this last result in the setting of a fairly general abelian category. For the most part our approach follows that of Hochschild. The proof of 1.4 is modelled after a proof of Kaplansky.

In §4–§6 we generalize the notion of graded module over a graded ring in the cases of free rings, polynomial rings, and exterior rings. This gives rise to more applications of the projective class theory of V, §7. The main results here generalize theorem 6.1 of [6, Chapter VIII], concerning freeness of gradable projectives, in the cases of the three rings cited above. In particular, this enables us to draw Hilbert's theorem on chains of syzygies in its original form [21].

In §7 we study the functor category $[I, \mathscr{A}]$ where I is a finite ordered set. Specializing to the case where $\mathscr{A} = \mathscr{G}^{\mathbf{R}}$, in §8 we see that the category $[I, \mathscr{G}^{\mathbf{R}}]$ is equivalent to the category of modules over a certain ring of matrices over $\mathbf{R}$. This enables us to obtain results on global dimension for such a ring. One would like to prove that associated with each finite ordered set I, there is a number m such that

$$\text{gl. dim.}[I, \mathscr{G}^{\mathbf{R}}] = m + \text{gl. dim. } \mathbf{R}$$

for all rings $\mathbf{R}$. However, we have been able to show this only for some special sets I.

1. Free Categories

Throughout this chapter $\mathscr{A}$ will denote a nontrivial abelian category and $\mathbf{R}$ will denote a nontrivial ring.

Given a category $\mathscr{A}$ and a set I, we define the **free category on I letters over $\mathscr{A}$** as the category $F_{\mathscr{A}}(\{x_i\}_{i\in I})$ of diagrams in $\mathscr{A}$ over the scheme consisting of one vertex and I arrows. Thus an object D in $F_{\mathscr{A}}(\{x_i\})$ is an object A together with a family of I endomorphisms $x_i : A \to A$. A morphism $D \to D'$ is a morphism $A \to A'$ such that for each $i \in I$ the diagram

$$\begin{array}{ccc} A & \longrightarrow & A' \\ {\scriptstyle x_i}\downarrow & & \downarrow{\scriptstyle x_i} \\ A & \longrightarrow & A' \end{array}$$

is commutative. If we define $T(D) = A$, then T is an exact, faithful functor from $F_{\mathscr{A}}(\{x_i\})$ to $\mathscr{A}$.

Let ρ denote the maximum of the cardinal number of I and the cardinal number of the integers. If $\mathscr{A}$ has coproducts indexed over ρ, then a coadjoint for T is given as follows. For $A \in \mathscr{A}$, let $S(A)$ be such that

$$TS(A) = \bigoplus_{(i_1 \ldots i_t)} A_{i_1 \ldots i_t}$$

where the coproduct is over all finite sequences $(i_1, \ldots, i_t)$ in I $(0 \leqslant t < \infty)$ and $A_{i_1 \ldots i_t} = A$. Denoting the injection of $A_{i_1 \ldots i_t}$ into the coproduct by $u_{i_1 \ldots i_t}$, we define $x_j : TS(A) \to TS(A)$ by

$$x_j u_{i_1 \ldots i_t} = u_{j i_1 \ldots i_t}, \qquad j \in I.$$

A morphism $S(A) \to D$ in $F_{\mathscr{A}}(\{x_i\})$ is completely determined by a morphism $A \to T(D)$. From this follows an adjoint relation

$$[S(A), D] \approx [A, T(D)].$$

Therefore by V, 7.2, if $\mathscr{A}$ has projectives then so does $F_{\mathscr{A}}(\{x_i\})$, and the projectives in the latter are the objects of the form $S(P)$ and their retracts, where P is projective in $\mathscr{A}$.

Lemma 1.1. *If $\mathscr{A}$ has projectives and exact coproducts over ρ, then for any $A \in \mathscr{A}$ we have*

$$\text{h.d. } S(A) \leqslant \text{h.d. } A.$$

Proof. From the hypothesis on $\mathscr{A}$ it follows that S is exact, and so S preserves projective resolutions. The conclusion then follows from VII, 6.4. ▌

Lemma 1.2. *Let $\mathscr{A}$ be a category with coproducts over ρ. If I is finite, then for any object D in $F_{\mathscr{A}}(\{x_i\})$, we have*

$$\text{h.d. } D \leqslant 1 + \text{h.d. } ST(D). \tag{1}$$

If $\mathscr{A}$ has projectives and exact coproducts over ρ, then (1) *is valid for any I.*

Proof. Let $T(D) = A$, and consider the sequence in $\mathscr{A}$

$$0 \to \bigoplus_{j \in I} \left(\bigoplus_{(i_1 \ldots i_t)} A_{i_1 \ldots i_t j} \right) \underset{\gamma}{\overset{\alpha}{\rightleftarrows}} \bigoplus_{(i_1 \ldots i_t)} A_{i_1 \ldots i_t} \underset{u}{\overset{\beta}{\rightleftarrows}} A \to 0 \qquad (2)$$

defined as follows. Denote the injections for the middle and left-hand coproducts by $u_{i_1 \ldots i_t}$ and $u'_{i_1 \ldots i_t j}$ respectively. (In particular, this defines u.) Then we define

$$\beta u = 1_A \qquad (3)$$

$$\beta u_{i_1 \ldots i_t} = x_{i_1} x_{i_2} \cdots x_{i_t} : A \to A \qquad (t > 0) \qquad (4)$$

$$\alpha u'_{i_1 \ldots i_t j} = u_{i_1 \ldots i_t j} - u_{i_1 \ldots i_t} x_j \qquad (5)$$

$$\gamma u = 0 \qquad (6)$$

$$\gamma u_{i_1 \ldots i_t} = \sum_{p=1}^{t} u'_{i_1 \ldots i_p} x_{i_{p+1}} \cdots x_{i_t} \qquad (t > 0). \qquad (7)$$

The morphisms α and β give us a sequence

$$0 \to {}^I S(A) \to S(A) \to D \to 0 \qquad (8)$$

in $F_{\mathscr{A}}(\{x_i\})$. We wish to show that (8) is exact. Since T is faithful, it suffices to show that (2) is exact in $\mathscr{A}$. We shall actually show that u, α, and β, γ are the injections and projections for a coproduct. Using (5), (6), and (7), it is straightforward to verify the relation $\gamma \alpha u'_{i_1 \ldots i_t j} = u'_{i_1 \ldots i_t j}$, and so it follows that $\gamma \alpha = 1$. Similarly, we have $\alpha \gamma + u \beta = 1$. Using Eq. (3), our assertion then follows from the remark after I, 18.1. Now if I is finite, then we see from the fact that Ext preserves finite coproducts that

$$\text{h.d. } {}^I S(A) = \text{h.d. } S(A). \qquad (9)$$

On the other hand, if $\mathscr{A}$ has projectives and exact coproducts over ρ, then $F_{\mathscr{A}}(\{x_i\})$ has exact coproducts over I, and we can use the coproduct of I copies of a projective resolution for $S(A)$ as a projective resolution for ${}^I S(A)$. Consequently, using VII, 6.4, we again have Eq. (9). Then applying VII, 6.1, 1 to the exact sequence (8), we obtain the inequality (1). ∎

Lemma 1.3. *If D is projective in $F_{\mathscr{A}}(\{x_i\})$, and $T(D) = A$, then $x_i : A \to A$ is a monomorphism for all $i \in I$.*

Proof. If D is projective, then it is a retract of $S(A)$. Since x_i is a monomorphism for $S(A)$, the same must be true of D. ∎

Consider the case where I consists of only one element, and let $L : F_{\mathscr{A}}(x) \to \mathscr{A}$ be defined by $L(D) = T(D)/xT(D)$, where $xT(D)$ denotes the image of the morphism $x : T(D) \to T(D)$. If $\mathscr{A}$ has countable coproducts (so that S is defined), then we have $LS(A) = A$. From this it follows that if $\mathscr{A}$ has projectives, then L preserves projectives. We shall also consider the functor $M : \mathscr{A} \to F_{\mathscr{A}}(x)$ defined by $TM(A) = A$ and $0 = x : A \to A$.

Lemma 1.4. *Let $\mathscr{A}$ be a category with projectives and countable coproducts. If A is a nonzero object in $\mathscr{A}$ and* h.d. $A = m$, *then* h.d. $M(A) = m + 1$.

Proof. If P is projective in $\mathscr{A}$, then $T(S(P))$, being a coproduct of copies of P, is also projective in $\mathscr{A}$. From this it follows that T preserves projectives, and since T is also exact it preserves projective resolutions. Therefore for any D in $F_{\mathscr{A}}(x)$ we have h.d. $D \geqslant$ h.d. $T(D)$. In particular this gives us the desired result if $m = \infty$.

If $m = 0$ then A is projective. Therefore by 1.2, h.d. $M(A) \leqslant 1$. But if h.d. $M(A)$ were zero, then $M(A)$ would be projective, and this is impossible by 1.3 since $A \neq 0$. Hence h.d. $M(A) = 1$.

For $m \geqslant 1$ form an exact sequence in $F_{\mathscr{A}}(x)$

$$0 \to K \to F \to M(A) \to 0 \tag{10}$$

with F projective. Since $xA = 0$ we have $xT(F) \subset T(K)$. Hence using the first Noether isomorphism theorem (I, 16.2) we have an exact sequence

$$0 \to T(K)/xT(F) \to T(F)/xT(F) \to A \to 0 \tag{11}$$

in $\mathscr{A}$. Now since F is projective, $L(F)$ is projective. From (11) we then have

$$\text{h.d. } T(K)/xT(F) = m - 1. \tag{12}$$

Assuming the lemma is true for $m = 1$, we can now prove the general case by induction. For we have h.d. $M(T(K)/xT(F)) = m$ and

$$\text{h.d. } M(T(F)/xT(F)) = 1.$$

Applying M to (11) and using VII, 6.1, 2, we see that h.d. $M(A) = m + 1$. Hence we have only to prove the case $m = 1$. Consider the commutative diagram

$$\begin{array}{ccc} T(K) & \longrightarrow & T(F) \\ \downarrow & & \downarrow \\ xT(K) & \longrightarrow & xT(F) \end{array}$$

Since x is a monomorphism on $T(F)$ (1.3), it follows that the vertical arrows are isomorphisms. Hence $A = T(F)/T(K) = xT(F)/xT(K)$. Using the first Noether isomorphism theorem we can then form an exact sequence

$$0 \to A \to T(K)/xT(K) \to T(K)/xT(F) \to 0. \tag{13}$$

Since h.d. $A = 1$ and h.d. $T(K)/xT(F) = 0$ by (12), we see from (13) that h.d. $L(K) =$ h.d. $T(K)/xT(K) = 1$. Now applying M to (11) and using the result already proved for $m = 0$ we see by VII, 6.1, 1 that h.d. $M(A)$ is 1 or 2. But if it were 1, then (10) shows that K would be projective, hence h.d. $L(K) = 0$. This contradiction completes the proof. ▮

Let $j \in I$, and consider the forgetful functor $U : F_{\mathscr{A}}(\{x_i\}) \to F_{\mathscr{A}}(x_j)$ where $\mathscr{A}$ has projectives and coproducts over ρ. Denoting the coadjoint $\mathscr{A} \to F_{\mathscr{A}}(x_j)$ by S', we have $US(A) = {}^J S'(A)$ where J is the set of all finite sequences in I which do not begin with j. From this it follows that U preserves projectives.

Lemma 1.5. *Let $\mathscr{A}$ have projectives and exact coproducts over ρ. If $D \in F_{\mathscr{A}}(\{x_i\})$ is such that $x_j A = 0$ for some $j \in I$ where $T(D) = A$, then* h.d. $D = 1 +$ h.d. A.

Proof. From 1.1 and 1.2 it follows that h.d. $D \leqslant 1 +$ h.d. A. If

$$\text{h.d. } D < 1 + \text{h.d. } A,$$

then since U preserves projective resolutions, we have h.d. $U(D) < 1 +$ h.d. A. But this contradicts 1.4 since $U(D) = M(A)$. ∎

Lemma 1.5 implies in particular that if we start with $A \in \mathscr{A}$ and define $D \in F_{\mathscr{A}}(\{x_i\})$ such that $T(D) = A$ with $x_i = 0$ for all $i \in I$, then

$$\text{h.d. } D = 1 + \text{h.d. } A.$$

Combining this with 1.1 and 1.2 we obtain:

Theorem 1.6. *If $\mathscr{A}$ is a category with projectives and exact coproducts over ρ, then*

$$\text{gl. dim. } F_{\mathscr{A}}(\{x_i\}) = 1 + \text{gl. dim. } \mathscr{A}. \qquad ∎$$

In the case where $\mathscr{A}$ is the category $\mathscr{G}^{\mathbf{R}}$, we see from V, 1.5 that $S(\mathbf{R})$ is a small projective generator for $F_{\mathscr{A}}(\{x_i\})$. Hence the latter is equivalent to the category of right modules over the endomorphism ring of $S(\mathbf{R})$. Using the fact that an endomorphism of $S(\mathbf{R})$ is completely determined by a morphism $\mathbf{R} \to TS(\mathbf{R})$ of right $\mathbf{R}$-modules which, in turn, is completely determined by the image of the identity element of $\mathbf{R}$, it is not difficult to show that this endomorphism ring is isomorphic to the free ring over $\mathbf{R}$ on I letters $F_{\mathbf{R}}(\{X_i\})$. The latter is defined as the free $\mathbf{R}$-module having as base the elements 1 and $X_{i_1} X_{i_2} \ldots X_{i_t}$, where the subscripts run through all finite sequences in I, and where multiplication is defined by the rule

$$(r_1 X_{i_1} \ldots X_{i_s})(r_2 X_{j_1} \ldots X_{j_t}) = r_1 r_2 X_{i_1} \ldots X_{i_s} X_{j_1} \ldots X_{j_t}.$$

This gives us:

Corollary 1.7. *For any ring* $\mathbf{R}$ *we have*

$$\text{r. gl. dim. } F_{\mathbf{R}}(\{X_i\}) = 1 + \text{r. gl. dim. } \mathbf{R}. \qquad ∎$$

The opposite ring of $F_{\mathbf{R}}(\{X_i\})$ is easily shown to be ring isomorphic to $F_{\mathbf{R}^*}(\{X_i\})$. From this it follows that 1.7 is also valid for left global dimension.

2. Polynomial Categories

The **polynomial category** on k letters over $\mathscr{A}$ is the full subcategory $\mathscr{A}[x_1, \ldots, x_k]$ of $F_{\mathscr{A}}(x_1, \ldots, x_k)$ consisting of all diagrams D satisfying the commutativity relations $x_i x_j = x_j x_i$. If $T(D) = A$, then the morphism $x_k : A \to A$ may be considered as an endomorphism of the object of $\mathscr{A}[x_1,\ldots, x_{k-1}]$ consisting of the $k-1$ endomorphisms $x_1,\ldots, x_{k-1} : A \to A$. In this way we obtain an isomorphism of categories

$$\mathscr{A}[x_1,\ldots, x_k] \approx \mathscr{A}[x_1,\ldots, x_{k-1}][x_k].$$

Using this, together with the fact that $\mathscr{A}[x_1] = F_{\mathscr{A}}(x_1)$, we have inductively from 1.6:

Theorem 2.1. *If $\mathscr{A}$ is a category with projectives and exact countable coproducts, then*

$$\text{gl. dim. } \mathscr{A}[x_1,\ldots, x_k] = k + \text{gl. dim. } \mathscr{A}. \qquad \blacksquare$$

If $\mathscr{A}$ has countable coproducts, then a coadjoint S for the evaluation functor $T : \mathscr{A}[x_1,\ldots, x_k] \to \mathscr{A}$ is given by

$$TS(A) = \bigoplus_{i_1 \leqslant i_2 \leqslant \ldots \leqslant i_t} A_{i_1 i_2 \ldots i_t}$$

where the coproduct is over all finite nondecreasing sequences $i_1 \leqslant i_2 \ldots \leqslant i_t$ of the integers $1, 2,\ldots, k$ $(0 \leqslant t < \infty)$, and where $A_{i_1 \ldots i_t} = A$. The morphisms $x_j : TS(A) \to TS(A)$ are defined by

$$x_j u_{i_1 \ldots i_t} = u_{|j i_1 \ldots i_t|} \qquad (1 \leqslant j \leqslant k),$$

where in general $|j_1 j_2 \ldots j_s|$ denotes the sequence obtained by putting the s numbers $j_1, j_2,\ldots, j_s$ in their natural order. If $\mathscr{A}$ has projectives, then so does $\mathscr{A}[x_1,\ldots, x_k]$, and the projectives are the objects of the form $S(P)$ and their retracts, where P is projective in $\mathscr{A}$. If $\mathscr{A}$ is $\mathscr{G}^{\mathbf{R}}$, then $S(\mathbf{R})$ is a small projective generator for $\mathscr{A}[x_1,\ldots, x_k]$. Thus $\mathscr{A}[x_1,\ldots, x_k]$ is equivalent to the category of right modules over the endomorphism ring of $S(\mathbf{R})$, which is easily shown to be isomorphic to the polynomial ring over $\mathbf{R}$ on k letters $\mathbf{R}[X_1,\ldots, X_k]$. Thus we have:

Corollary 2.2. *For any ring* $\mathbf{R}$ *we have*

$$\text{r. gl. dim. } \mathbf{R}[X_1,\ldots, X_k] = k + \text{r. gl. dim. } \mathbf{R}. \qquad \blacksquare$$

The opposite ring of $\mathbf{R}[X_1,\ldots, X_k]$ is clearly isomorphic to $\mathbf{R}^*[X_1,\ldots, X_k]$. Hence 2.2 can be stated as well for left global dimension.

3. Grassmann Categories

The **Grassmann category** on k letters over $\mathscr{A}$ is the full subcategory $E_{\mathscr{A}}(x_1,\ldots, x_k)$ of $F_{\mathscr{A}}(x_1,\ldots, x_k)$ consisting of diagrams satisfying the relations $x_i x_j + x_j x_i = 0$ and $x_i x_i = 0$. The coadjoint S for $T : E_{\mathscr{A}}(x_1,\ldots, x_k) \to \mathscr{A}$ is given by

$$TS(A) = \bigoplus_{i_1 < i_2 < \ldots < i_t} A_{i_1 i_2 \ldots i_t}$$

where the coproduct is over all finite increasing sequences $i_1 < i_2 < \ldots < i_t$ of the integers $1, 2, \ldots, k$ $(0 \leqslant t \leqslant k)$. The morphisms $x_j : TS(A) \to TS(A)$ are defined by

$$\begin{aligned} x_j u_{i_1 \ldots i_t} &= 0 \quad \text{if} \quad j \in \{i_1, i_2, \ldots, i_t\} \\ &= \sigma(j, i_1, \ldots, i_t) u_{|ji_1 \ldots i_t|} \qquad \text{otherwise.} \end{aligned}$$

Here $\sigma(j, i_1, \ldots, i_t)$ denotes $(-1)^n$, where n is the number of transpositions required to reduce $(j, i_1, \ldots, i_t)$ to the natural order. If $\mathscr{A}$ has projectives, then so does $E_{\mathscr{A}}(x_1, \ldots, x_k)$, and the projectives are the objects of the form $S(P)$ and their retracts, where P is projective in $\mathscr{A}$. If $\mathscr{A}$ is $\mathscr{G}^{\mathbf{R}}$, then $S(\mathbf{R})$ is a small projective generator for $E_{\mathscr{A}}(x_1, \ldots, x_k)$. Consequently, the latter is equivalent to the category of right modules over the endomorphism ring of $S(\mathbf{R})$, which is isomorphic to the Grassmann (or exterior) ring over $\mathbf{R}$ on k letters $E_{\mathbf{R}}(X_1, \ldots, X_k)$.

Lemma 3.1. *For $A \in \mathscr{A}$ consider the morphism $d : S(A) \to S(A)$ defined by*

$$du_{i_1 \ldots i_t} = (-1)^t \sum_{j=1}^{k} x_j u_{i_1 \ldots i_t}.$$

Then the sequence

$$S(A) \xrightarrow{d} S(A) \xrightarrow{d} S(A) \tag{1}$$

is exact.

Proof. It is trivial to verify that d commutes with the x_i's; that is, that d is an endomorphism of $S(A)$. It also follows easily from the relations $x_i x_j + x_j x_i = 0$, $x_i x_i = 0$ that $dd = 0$. In order to prove that (1) is exact we need only prove that $TS(A) \to TS(A) \to TS(A)$ is exact since T is faithful. We construct a morphism $s : TS(A) \to TS(A)$ as follows:

$$\begin{aligned} su_{i_1 \ldots i_t} &= 0 \qquad\qquad \text{for} \quad i_1 \neq 1 \\ &= (-1)^{t-1} u_{i_2 \ldots i_t} \quad \text{for} \quad i_1 = 1. \end{aligned}$$

By examining separately the cases $i_1 = 1$ and $i_1 \neq 1$, one can verify the relation

$$(sd + ds) u_{i_1 \ldots i_t} = u_{i_1 \ldots i_t}.$$

In other words $sd + ds = 1$. The required exactness now follows from *I*, 19.4. ▌

4. Graded Free Categories

We define the **graded free category** on k letters over $\mathscr{A}$ as the category $GF_{\mathscr{A}}(x_1, \ldots, x_k)$ of diagrams in $\mathscr{A}$ over the scheme whose vertices are the integers $\geqslant 0$, and which has k arrows from vertex n to vertex $n+1$ for each $n \geqslant 0$. If D is such a diagram we shall denote the k morphisms $D_n \to D_{n+1}$ by $x_1, \ldots, x_k$

regardless of the vertex n. Coadjoints S_n for the evaluation functors T_n are given by

$$\begin{aligned} T_m S_n(A) &= 0 && \text{for} \quad m < n \\ &= \bigoplus_{(i_1 \ldots i_{m-n})} A_{i_1 \ldots i_{m-n}} && \text{for} \quad m \geqslant n \end{aligned}$$

where $A_{i_1 \ldots i_{m-n}} = A$, and where the coproduct is indexed over all $(m-n)$ term sequences of the integers $1, 2, \ldots, k$. The morphisms $x_j : T_m S_n(A) \to T_{m+1} S_n(A)$ are defined as before by

$$x_j u_{i_1 \ldots i_{m-n}} = u_{j i_1 \ldots i_{m-n}} \qquad (m \geqslant n).$$

Theorem 4.1. *Let $\mathscr{E}$ be a projective class in $\mathscr{A}$. Then the class $\mathscr{E}GF_{\mathscr{A}}(x_1, \ldots, x_k)$ of all morphisms in $GF_{\mathscr{A}}(x_1, \ldots, x_k)$ which are pointwise in $\mathscr{E}$ is a projective class whose projectives are of the form $\bigoplus_{n \geqslant 0} S_n(P_n)$, where P_n is $\mathscr{E}$-projective for each n.*

Proof. Since a coproduct of the form $\bigoplus_{n \geqslant 0} S_n(A_n)$ involves only a finite number of nonzero objects at each vertex n, it follows that the family $\{S_n\}$ is coproductive. Thus the first statement is a consequence of V, 7.4. To show that the projectives are as stated we define functors $R_n^q : GF_{\mathscr{A}}(x_1, \ldots, x_n) \to \mathscr{A}$ by

$$R_n^q(D) = D_n \Big/ \bigcup_{i=q+1}^{k} x_i D_{n-1} \qquad (n \geqslant 1,\ 0 \leqslant q \leqslant k).$$

Thus $R_n^k = T_n$. If we define $R_n = R_n^0$ for $n > 0$ and $R_0 = T_0$, then it is readily verified that the family $\{R_n\}_{n \geqslant 0}$ satisfies condition 1 of V, 7.5.

To show that condition 2 is also satisfied, consider $\alpha : D^1 \to D^2$ where D^1 and D^2 are $\mathscr{E}GF_{\mathscr{A}}(x_1, \ldots, x_k)$-projective, and suppose that $R_n(\alpha)$ is an isomorphism for all $n \geqslant 0$. We wish to show that $T_n(\alpha)$ is an isomorphism for all $n \geqslant 0$. We know that $T_0(\alpha)$ is an isomorphism. Assume that $R_n^{q-1}(\alpha)$ is an isomorphism and that $R_{n-1}^p(\alpha)$ is an isomorphism for $0 \leqslant p \leqslant k$. We show that $R_n^q(\alpha)$ is an isomorphism. Consider the sequence of natural transformations

$$0 \to T_{n-1} \to R_n^q \to R_n^{q-1} \to 0 \tag{1}$$

where the transformation on the right is the obvious epimorphism and the one on the left is induced by $x_q : D_{n-1} \to D_n$. The sequence (1) is exact when evaluated at an object of the form $\bigoplus_{n \geqslant 0} S_n(A_n)$ where A_n is any object in $\mathscr{A}$. Thus it follows from V, 7.4, that (1) is exact when evaluated at any $\mathscr{E}GF_{\mathscr{A}}(x_1, \ldots, x_n)$-projective. Therefore, applying α to (1) and using the inductive hypothesis and the 5-lemma, we see that $R_n^q(\alpha)$ is an isomorphism as required. ∎

Taking $\mathscr{E}$ to be the class $\mathscr{E}_0$ of all retractions in $\mathscr{A}$, we obtain:

Corollary 4.2. *Any retract of an object of the form $\bigoplus_{n \geqslant 0} S_n(A_n)$ in $GF_{\mathscr{A}}(x_1, \ldots, x_k)$ is of the same form.* ∎

Since the T_n's are exact functors we have:

Corollary 4.3. *If $\mathscr{A}$ has projectives, then so does $GF_{\mathscr{A}}(x_1,\ldots, x_k)$. The projectives in the latter are precisely the objects of the form $\bigoplus_{n\geqslant 0} S_n(P_n)$ where P_n is projective in $\mathscr{A}$ for all $n \geqslant 0$.* ▮

If $\mathscr{A}$ has countable coproducts, then we can define a functor

$$L : GF_{\mathscr{A}}(x_1,\ldots, x_k) \to F_{\mathscr{A}}(x_1,\ldots, x_k)$$

by $TL(D) = \bigoplus_{n\geqslant 0} D_n$ and $x_i v_n = v_{n+1} x_i$, where v_n denotes the nth injection for the coproduct. For any integer n we have $LS_n = S : \mathscr{A} \to F_{\mathscr{A}}(x_1,\ldots, x_k)$. Also L preserves coproducts, so that in particular we have

$$L\left(\bigoplus_{n\geqslant 0} S_n(A_n)\right) = \bigoplus_{n\geqslant 0} S(A_n) \tag{2}$$

for any family A_n of objects in $\mathscr{A}$. If the countable coproducts in $\mathscr{A}$ are exact, then L is an exact functor. An object in $F_{\mathscr{A}}(x_1,\ldots, x_k)$ which is isomorphic to an object of the form $L(D)$ is called a **gradable** object.

Proposition 4.4. *If $\mathscr{A}$ has countable coproducts and $L(D)$ is projective in $F_{\mathscr{A}}(x_1,\ldots, x_k)$, then D is projective in $GF_{\mathscr{A}}(x_1,\ldots, x_k)$.*

Proof. Consider an epimorphism $f : D^1 \to D^2$ and a morphism $g : D \to D^2$ in $GF_{\mathscr{A}}(x_1,\ldots, x_k)$. Since $L(D)$ is projective, this gives rise to a commutative diagram in $F_{\mathscr{A}}(x_1,\ldots x_k)$

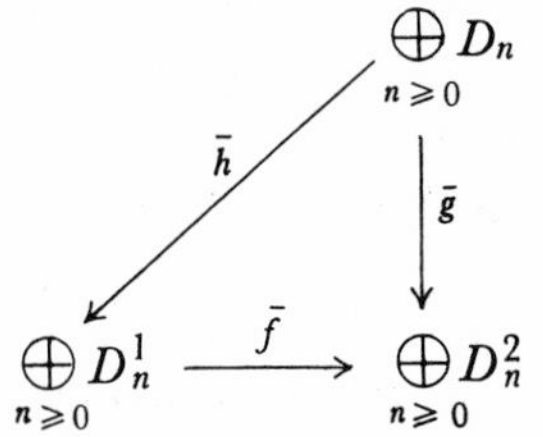

where $\bar{f} = \bigoplus_{n\geqslant 0} f_n$, $\bar{g} = \bigoplus_{n\geqslant 0} g_n$, and $\bar{h}$ commutes with the x_i's. Denote the injections and projections for $\bigoplus_{n\geqslant 0} D_n^1$ by u_n and p_n, and for $\bigoplus_{n\geqslant 0} D_n^2$ by v_n and q_n. Also denote the injections for $\bigoplus_{n\geqslant 0} D_n$ by w_n. Define $h_n = p_n \bar{h} w_n$. Then we have

$$f_n h_n = f_n p_n \bar{h} w_n = q_n \bar{f} \bar{h} w_n = q_n \bar{g} w_n = g_n$$

and

$$\begin{aligned} x_i h_n &= x_i p_n \bar{h} w_n = p_{n+1} x_i \bar{h} w_n = p_{n+1} \bar{h} x_i w_n \\ &= p_{n+1} \bar{h} w_{n+1} x_i = h_{n+1} x_i. \end{aligned}$$

Therefore the h_n's define a morphism h in $GF_{\mathscr{A}}(x_1,\ldots, x_k)$ and $fh = g$. This proves that D is projective. ▮

The converse of 4.4 is also true (see exercise 3).

From 4.4 we see that any gradable projective in $F_{\mathscr{A}}(x_1,\ldots, x_k)$ must be of the form $\bigoplus_{n\geqslant 0} S(P_n)$ where P_n is projective in $\mathscr{A}$ for all n. In particular, let $\mathscr{A}$ be $\mathscr{G}^{\mathbf{R}}$, where $\mathbf{R}$ is a ring with the property that every projective right $\mathbf{R}$-module is free (i.e., isomorphic to a coproduct of copies of $\mathbf{R}$). Then each P_n is free, and so since S preserves coproducts it follows that every gradable, projective right module over the free ring $F_{\mathbf{R}}(X_1,\ldots, X_k)$ is a free module. A consideration of opposite rings shows that we can replace "right" by "left" in the above discussion.

5. Graded Polynomial Categories

The full subcategory $G\mathscr{A}[x_1,\ldots, x_n]$ of $GF_{\mathscr{A}}(x_1,\ldots, x_n)$ consisting of all diagrams D satisfying the relations $x_ix_j = x_jx_i$ is called the **graded polynomial category** on k letters over $\mathscr{A}$. In this case the functors S_n are given by

$$\begin{aligned} T_mS_n(A) &= 0 \qquad \text{for} \qquad m < n, \\ &= \bigoplus_{i_1\leqslant\ldots\leqslant i_{m-n}} A_{i_1\ldots i_{m-n}} \qquad \text{for} \quad m \geqslant n, \\ x_ju_{i_1\ldots i_{m-n}} &= u_{|ji_1\ldots i_{m-n}|}. \end{aligned}$$

Theorem 5.1. *Let $\mathscr{E}$ be a projective class in $\mathscr{A}$. Then the class $\mathscr{E}G\mathscr{A}(x_1,\ldots, x_k)$ of all morphisms in $G\mathscr{A}(x_1,\ldots, x_k)$ which are pointwise in $\mathscr{E}$ is a projective class whose projectives are of the form $\bigoplus_{n\geqslant 0} S_n(P_n)$, where P_n is $\mathscr{E}$-projective for each n.*

Proof. The proof is identical to that of 4.1, except that the sequence (1) must be replaced here by

$$0 \to R^q_{n-1} \to R^q_n \to R^{q-1}_n \to 0. \qquad ▌$$

Corollary 5.2. *Any retract of an object of the form $\bigoplus_{n\geqslant 0} S_n(A_n)$ in $G\mathscr{A}[x_1,\ldots, x_n]$ is of the same form.* ▌

Corollary 5.3. *If $\mathscr{A}$ has projectives, then so does $G\mathscr{A}[x_1,\ldots, x_k]$. The projectives in the latter are precisely the objects of the form $\bigoplus_{n\geqslant 0} S_n(P_n)$ where P_n is projective in $\mathscr{A}$ for all $n \geqslant 0$.* ▌

If $\mathscr{A}$ has countable coproducts, then we have the functor

$$L: G\mathscr{A}[x_1,\ldots, x_k] \to \mathscr{A}[x_1,\ldots, x_k]$$

just as before, and the proof of 4.4 applies to the following.

Proposition 5.4. *If $\mathscr{A}$ has countable coproducts and $L(D)$ is projective in $\mathscr{A}[x_1,\ldots, x_k]$, then D is projective in $G\mathscr{A}[x_1,\ldots, x_k]$.* ▌

Again it follows from 5.4 that if $\mathbf{R}$ is a ring over which any projective module is free (such as a field), then any gradable module over the polynomial ring $\mathbf{R}[X_1,\ldots, X_k]$ is free. Theorem 2.1 combined with this fact contains Hilbert's theorem on chains of syzygies [21].

6. Graded Grassmann Categories

We define the **graded Grassmann category** on k letters over $\mathscr{A}$ as the category $GE_{\mathscr{A}}(x_1,\ldots, x_k)$ of diagrams in $\mathscr{A}$ over the scheme whose vertices are the integers (positive and negative) and which has k arrows $x_1,\ldots, x_k$ from vertex n to vertex $n+1$ for each $n \in \mathbf{Z}$, subject to the conditions $x_ix_j + x_jx_i = 0$ and $x_ix_i = 0$. Thus $GE(x_1)$ is just the category $\mathscr{C}(\mathscr{A})$ of complexes in $\mathscr{A}$. Coadjoints S_n for the evaluation functors are given by

$$\begin{aligned} T_mS_n(A) &= 0 && \text{for} \quad m < n, \\ &= \bigoplus_{i_1<\ldots<i_{m-n}} A_{i_1\ldots i_{m-n}} && \text{for} \quad m \geqslant n, \\ x_ju_{i_1\ldots i_{m-n}} &= \sigma(j, i_1,\ldots, i_{m-n})u_{|ji_1\ldots i_{m-n}|}. \end{aligned}$$

Theorem 6.1. *Let $\mathscr{E}$ be a projective class in $\mathscr{A}$. Then the class $\mathscr{E}GE_{\mathscr{A}}(x_1,\ldots, x_k)$ of all morphisms in $GE_{\mathscr{A}}(x_1,\ldots, x_k)$ which are pointwise in $\mathscr{E}$ is a projective class whose projectives are of the form $\bigoplus_{n\in\mathbf{Z}} S_n(P_n)$ where P_n is $\mathscr{E}$-projective for each n.*

Proof. A coproduct $\bigoplus_{n\in\mathbf{Z}} S_n(A_n)$ involves only a finite number of nonzero objects at each vertex n, and so the family $\{S_n\}$ is coproductive. Hence, again, the first statement follows from V, 7.4. To prove the second statement we define R_n^q as in 4.1. In this case we have the sequence

$$0 \to R_{n-1}^{q-1} \xrightarrow{x_q} R_n^q \to R_n^{q-1} \to 0$$

which is exact when evaluated at any $\mathscr{E}GE_{\mathscr{A}}(x_1,\ldots, x_k)$-projective. Therefore we can apply induction on q alone to show that if $R_n(\alpha) = R_n^0(\alpha)$ is an isomorphism for all n, then $T_n(\alpha) = R_n^k(\alpha)$ is an isomorphism. ▮

Corollary 6.2. *Any retract of an object of the form $\bigoplus_{n\in\mathbf{Z}} S_n(A_n)$ in $GE_{\mathscr{A}}(x_1,\ldots, x_k)$ is of the same form.* ▮

Corollary 6.3. *If $\mathscr{A}$ has projectives, then so does $GE_{\mathscr{A}}(x_1,\ldots, x_k)$. The projectives in the latter are precisely the objects of the form $\bigoplus_{n\in\mathbf{Z}} S_n(P_n)$ where P_n is projective in $\mathscr{A}$ for all n.* ▮

Let $\bar{G}E_{\mathscr{A}}(x_1,\ldots, x_k)$ be the full subcategory of $GE_{\mathscr{A}}(x_1,\ldots, x_k)$ consisting of all bounded objects; that is, objects D for which there exist integers p and q such that $D_n = 0$ for $n > q$ and $n < p$. Then we have the functor

$$L : \bar{G}E_{\mathscr{A}}(x_1,\ldots, x_k) \to E_{\mathscr{A}}(x_1,\ldots, x_k)$$

defined by $TL(D) = \bigoplus_{n\in\mathbf{Z}} D_n$. If $\mathscr{A}$ has coproducts, then L can be defined on all of $GE_{\mathscr{A}}(x_1,\ldots, x_k)$ as before.

Proposition 6.4. *If D is bounded and $L(D)$ is projective in $E_{\mathscr{A}}(x_1,\ldots, x_k)$, then D is projective in $GE_{\mathscr{A}}(x_1,\ldots, x_k)$. If $\mathscr{A}$ has countable coproducts, then the same statement is true for any D in $GE_{\mathscr{A}}(x_1,\ldots, x_k)$.*

Proof. If $\mathscr{A}$ has countable coproducts and $L(D)$ is projective, then the proof of 4.4 applies to show that D is projective. Thus, suppose that D is bounded and $L(D)$ is projective, but $\mathscr{A}$ does not necessarily have countable coproducts. Assume that $D_n = 0$ for $n < p$ and $n > q$. Associated with an object D^1 in $GE_{\mathscr{A}}(x_1,\ldots, x_k)$ we have the truncated object $\bar{D}^1$ defined by $\bar{D}^1_n = 0$ for $n < p$ and $n > q + 1$ and $\bar{D}^1_n = D^1_n$ for $p \leqslant n \leqslant q + 1$. Given an epimorphism $f : D^1 \to D^2$ and a morphism $g : D \to D^2$ we consider the diagram

$$\begin{array}{ccc} & & \bigoplus\limits_{n=p}^{q+1} D_n \\ & & \Big\downarrow \bar{g} \\ \bigoplus\limits_{n=p}^{q+1} D^1_n & \xrightarrow{\ \bar{f}\ } & \bigoplus\limits_{n=p}^{q+1} D^2_n \end{array}$$

where $\bar{f} = \bigoplus\limits_{n=p}^{q+1} f_n$ and $\bar{g} = \bigoplus\limits_{n=p}^{q+1} g_n$. Then $\bar{f}$ and $\bar{g}$ can be considered as morphisms from $L(\bar{D}^1)$ to $L(\bar{D}^2)$ and $L(D)$ to $L(\bar{D}^2)$, respectively. Therefore, since $L(D)$ is projective we obtain $\bar{h}$ such that $\bar{f}\bar{h} = \bar{g}$, and $h : D \to D^1$ can be defined from $\bar{h}$ just as in 4.4 to show that D is projective. ▮

Theorem 6.5. *If $\mathscr{A}$ is any abelian category with projectives, then*

$$\text{gl. dim. } E_{\mathscr{A}}(x_1,\ldots, x_k) = \infty.$$

Proof. Let A be any nonzero projective in $\mathscr{A}$, and consider the morphism $d : S(A) \to S(A)$ of 3.1. Clearly d is of the form $L(\delta)$ where $\delta : S_1(A) \to S_0(A)$. The kernel K of δ is such that $K_{n+1} \neq 0$, hence $K \neq 0$. On the other hand we have $x_1 x_2 \ldots x_k \delta = 0$, and so the image I of δ has the property

$$x_1 x_2 \ldots x_k I = 0. \tag{1}$$

Now since L is exact we have $L(I) = L(K)$ by 3.1. If we can show that $L(I)$ is not projective, then 3.1 will furnish us with an infinite projective resolution of $L(I)$ for which the kernel is never projective. By VII, 6.4, this will show that $L(I)$ has infinite homological dimension.

Suppose that $L(I)$ is projective. Then by 6.4, I is projective. Thus I is of the form $\bigoplus\limits_{n \in \mathbf{Z}} S_n(P_n)$. Using (1) it follows that $P_n = 0$ for all n. Thus $I = 0$, and so $L(K) = L(I) = 0$. Consequently $K = 0$, a contradiction. ▮

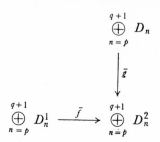

Corollary 6.6. *For any ring* **R** *we have*

$$\text{r. gl. dim. } E_{\mathbf{R}}(X_1,\ldots, X_k) = \infty. \qquad \blacksquare$$

Since the opposite ring of $E_{\mathbf{R}}(X_1,\ldots, X_k)$ is isomorphic to $E_{\mathbf{R}^*}(X_1,\ldots, X_k)$, Corollary 6.6 can also be stated for left global dimension.

7. Finite Commutative Diagrams

Let Σ be a diagram scheme and let $\sim$ be the largest commutativity relation on Σ. Thus $[\Sigma/\sim, \mathscr{A}]$ is the category of commutative diagrams in $\mathscr{A}$ over Σ, and $\Sigma/\sim$, viewed as a category, is simply an ordered set. Since any ordered set is equivalent as a category to an ordered set with the property that any two members which precede each other are equal, we shall assume this to be true of all ordered sets in the sequel. Furthermore, unless otherwise specified, all ordered sets will be finite.

If $i < j$ in an ordered set I, then we shall say that i **immediately** precedes j or that j **immediately** follows i if there is no k such that $i < k < j$. The **order** of an element i is the length n of the longest chain of the form

$$i_0 < i_1 < \ldots < i_{n-1} < i_n = i.$$

If $i < j$, then clearly the order of i is less than the order of j. We say that i and j are **compatible** if one precedes the other. If i and j have the same order, then they cannot be compatible.

If $D \in [I, \mathscr{A}]$ and $i \leqslant j$, then the morphism from D_i to D_j will be denoted by D_{ij}. The morphisms D_{ij} can be considered collectively as a natural transformation from T_i to T_j (where $T_i(D) = D_i$). A coadjoint S_i for T_i is given by

$$\begin{aligned}
T_jS_i(A) &= A && \text{for } i \leqslant j\\
&= 0 && \text{otherwise;}\\
S_i(A)_{jk} &= 1_A && \text{for } i \leqslant j \leqslant k\\
&= 0 && \text{otherwise;}\\
T_jS_i(\alpha) &= \alpha && \text{for } i \leqslant j\\
&= 0 && \text{otherwise.}
\end{aligned}$$

When there is more than one ordered set in question we shall denote S_i by S_i^I. Observe that the finiteness condition on I is not needed in defining S_i.

We also define functors $R_i = R_i^I : [I, \mathscr{A}] \to \mathscr{A}$ by

$$R_i(D) = D_i/\bigcup_{j<i} \text{Im}(D_{ji}).$$

If I' is a subcategory of I, we let $F : [I, \mathscr{A}] \to [I', \mathscr{A}]$ be the restriction functor.

Theorem 7.1. *Let I be a finite ordered set and let $\mathscr{E}$ be a projective class in $\mathscr{A}$. Then the class $\mathscr{E}[I, \mathscr{A}]$ of morphisms in $[I, \mathscr{A}]$ which are pointwise in $\mathscr{E}$ is a projective class whose* *projectives are the objects of the form* $\bigoplus_{i \in I} S_i(P_i)$ *where* P_i *is* $\mathscr{E}$*-projective for all* $i \in I$. *If* D *and* E *are* $\mathscr{E}[I, \mathscr{A}]$*-projective and* $\alpha : D \to E$ *is such that* $R_i(\alpha)$ *is an isomorphism for all* $i \in I$, *then* α *is an isomorphism.*

Proof. By V, 7.5, it suffices to show that the last assertion is true. We wish to show that if $R_i(\alpha)$ is an isomorphism for all i, then $\alpha_i : D_i \to E_i$ is an isomorphism for all i. We proceed by induction on the number n of objects plus morphisms in I. If I has only identity morphisms (in particular, if $n = 2$) then $R_i = T_i$ for all i, and so the condition is trivially satisfied. Otherwise we can find members p, q of I such that q is maximal in I and p immediately precedes q. First we take I' to be the full subcategory of I consisting of all objects i such that $i < q$. Then for $i \in I'$ we have $FS_i^I = S_i^{I'}$, and so it follows from V, 7.4, that F takes $\mathscr{E}[I, \mathscr{A}]$-projectives into $\mathscr{E}[I', \mathscr{A}]$-projectives. Also we have $R_i^{I'}F = R_i^I$ for all $i \in I'$, and so our induction allows us to assert that α_i is an isomorphism for all $i < q$.

Now let J be the set of all elements $j \in I$ such that $j \leqslant p$ but j precedes no other element which immediately precedes q. Let I' be the subcategory of I obtained by omitting the morphism from j to q for all $j \in J$. If $i \notin J$ then $FS_i^I = S_i^{I'}$, whereas if $i \in J$, then $FS_i^I = S_i^{I'} \oplus S_q^{I'}$. In any case it follows again that F takes $\mathscr{E}[I, \mathscr{A}]$-projectives into $\mathscr{E}[I', \mathscr{A}]$-projectives. For $i \neq q$ we have $R_i^{I'}F = R_i^I$, and so $R_i^{I'}F(\alpha)$ is an isomorphism. Furthermore, we have a sequence of natural transformations

$$\bigoplus_{\substack{j<p \\ j \notin J}} T_j \to T_p \to R_q^{I'}F \to R_q^I \to 0 \tag{1}$$

which is easily seen to be exact when evaluated at any object of the form $S_i^I(A)$ for any i. Consequently, (1) is exact when evaluated at any $\mathscr{E}[I,\mathscr{A}]$-projective. Now applying α to (1) and using 5-lemma and what we have already proved, we see that $R_q^{I'}F(\alpha)$ is also an isomorphism. Hence by induction, α_i is an isomorphism for all $i \in I$. ∎

Corollary 7.2. *Any retract of an object of the form* $\bigoplus_{i \in I} S_i(A_i)$ *in* $[I, \mathscr{A}]$ *is isomorphic to an object of the same form.* ∎

Corollary 7.3. *If* $\mathscr{A}$ *has projectives, then so does* $[I, \mathscr{A}]$. *An object in the latter is projective if and only if it is isomorphic to an object of the form* $\bigoplus_{i \in I} S_i(P_i)$ *where* P_i *is projective in* $\mathscr{A}$ *for all* i. ∎

Corollary 7.4. *Let* D *be an object of the form* $\bigoplus_{i \in I} S_i(A_i)$ *in* $[I, \mathscr{A}]$, *and for each* $i \in I$ *let* $A_i' \subset D_i$ *be such that*

$$D_i = A_i' \oplus \left(\bigcup_{j<i} \operatorname{Im} D_{ji} \right).$$

(In particular this means that A_i' is isomorphic to A_i, but not necessarily as a subobject of D_i.) Then for each i we have

$$\bigcup_{j<i} \operatorname{Im}(D_{ji}) = \bigcup_{j<i} D_{ji}(A_j')$$

and the union on the right side is a coproduct.

Proof. It suffices to prove that the morphism

$$\alpha : \bigoplus_{i \in I} S_i(A_i') \to D$$

induced by the inclusions $A_i' \subset D_i$ is an isomorphism. But this follows from 7.1 since for each i, the morphism $R_i(\alpha)$ is just the identity morphism on A_i'. ∎

If $\mathscr{A}$ has projectives, then a projective resolution for D in $[I, \mathscr{A}]$ can be constructed as follows. For each D_i choose an epimorphism $P_i \to D_i$ in $\mathscr{A}$ with P_i projective. This induces morphisms $S_i(P_i) \to D$ which are the coordinates of an epimorphism

$$D^0 = \bigoplus_{i \in I} S_i(P_i) \to D$$

in $[I, \mathscr{A}]$. Letting K^1 denote the kernel, we repeat the process using K^1 instead of D. This iterative procedure then gives a projective resolution for D.

8. Homological Tic Tac Toe

We consider here the case where $\mathscr{A}$ is the category $\mathscr{G}^{\mathbf{R}}$. Since I is finite, we see from V, 1.5, that $S(\mathbf{R}) = \bigoplus_{i \in I} S_i(\mathbf{R})$ is a small projective generator for $[I, \mathscr{G}^{\mathbf{R}}]$, and consequently $[I, \mathscr{G}^{\mathbf{R}}]$ is equivalent to the category of right modules over the endomorphism ring of $S(\mathbf{R})$. Consider the right module $U = \bigoplus_{i \in I} \mathbf{R}_i$ where $\mathbf{R}_i = \mathbf{R}$ for all $i \in I$. Then we can regard $S(\mathbf{R})$ as a network of submodules of U. Explicitly, we have $S(\mathbf{R})_j = \bigoplus_{i \leqslant j} \mathbf{R}_i \subset U$, and for $j \leqslant k$ the morphism $S(\mathbf{R})_{jk}$ can be considered simply as the inclusion

$$\bigoplus_{i \leqslant j} \mathbf{R}_i \to \bigoplus_{i \leqslant k} \mathbf{R}_i.$$

In this light, an endomorphism of $S(\mathbf{R})$ is simply an endomorphism of the free module U which takes every submodule in the network into itself. Such an endomorphism can be identified with an $I \times I$ matrix over $\mathbf{R}$ of the form (r_{ij}) where $r_{ij} = 0$ if $i \nless j$. This identification being clearly an isomorphism of rings, we have:

Theorem 8.1. *The category $[I, \mathscr{G}^{\mathbf{R}}]$ is equivalent to the category $\mathscr{G}^{\Lambda}$ where Λ is the ring of $I \times I$ matrices over $\mathbf{R}$ of the form (r_{ij}) such that $r_{ij} = 0$ for $i \nless j$.* ∎

For left $\mathbf{R}$-modules we have

$$[I, {}^{\mathbf{R}}\mathscr{G}] = [I, \mathscr{G}^{\mathbf{R}^*}].$$

By 8.1 the right side is equivalent to the category $\mathcal{G}^{\Gamma^*}$ where Γ^* is the ring of matrices over $\mathbf{R}^*$ of the form (r_{ij}) such that $r_{ij} = 0$ for $i \not< j$. Now the opposite ring Γ of Γ^* is given by the transpose operation on matrices. Hence we have:

Theorem 8.1*. *The category $[I, {}^{\mathbf{R}}\mathcal{G}]$ is equivalent to the category ${}^{\Gamma}\mathcal{G}$ where Γ is the ring of $I \times I$ matrices over $\mathbf{R}$ of the form (r_{ij}) such that $r_{ij} = 0$ for $j \not< i$.* ▌

We now consider some examples.

1. The **discrete** set of n elements is the category I with n objects and whose only morphisms are identities. In this case the endomorphism ring of $S(\mathbf{R})$ is just the ring of $n \times n$ diagonal matrices, which is ring isomorphic to the product of n copies of $\mathbf{R}$. However it is clear that $[I, \mathcal{G}^{\mathbf{R}}]$ is simply the product (of categories) of n copies of $\mathcal{G}^{\mathbf{R}}$. Hence the category of right modules over $\mathbf{R}^n$ is equivalent to the product of n copies of $\mathcal{G}^{\mathbf{R}}$.

2. If I_1 is the ordered set defined schematically by $1 \to 2$, then $S(\mathbf{R})$ is given by the diagram

$$\mathbf{R}_1 \to \mathbf{R}_1 \oplus \mathbf{R}_2.$$

Here $S(\mathbf{R})_{12}(r) = (r, 0)$ for $r \in \mathbf{R}$. The category $[I_1, \mathcal{G}^{\mathbf{R}}]$ is equivalent to the category of right modules over the ring of matrices over $\mathbf{R}$ of the form

$$\begin{pmatrix} x & x \\ 0 & x \end{pmatrix}$$

where we have put an x in any position where we are free to enter arbitrary elements of $\mathbf{R}$. More generally, if I is the linearly ordered set of n elements

$$1 \to 2 \to 3 \to \dots \to n-1 \to n,$$

then $[I, \mathcal{G}^{\mathbf{R}}]$ is equivalent to the category of right modules over the ring of $n \times n$ matrices which have 0's at every position below the main diagonal; that is, the ring of $n \times n$ triangular matrices.

3. For the square

$$\begin{array}{cccc} I_1 \times I_1: & 1 & \longrightarrow & 2 \\ & \downarrow & & \downarrow \\ & 3 & \longrightarrow & 4 \end{array}$$

$S(\mathbf{R})$ takes the form

$$\begin{array}{ccc} \mathbf{R}_1 & \longrightarrow & \mathbf{R}_1 \oplus \mathbf{R}_2 \\ \downarrow & & \downarrow \\ \mathbf{R}_1 \oplus \mathbf{R}_3 & \longrightarrow & \mathbf{R}_1 \oplus \mathbf{R}_2 \oplus \mathbf{R}_3 \oplus \mathbf{R}_4 \end{array}$$

where

$$S(\mathbf{R})_{12}(r) = (r, 0) \qquad S(\mathbf{R})_{24}(r, s) = (r, s, 0, 0)$$
$$S(\mathbf{R})_{13}(r) = (r, 0) \qquad S(\mathbf{R})_{34}(r, s) = (r, 0, s, 0).$$

The category $[I_1 \times I_1, \mathscr{G}^{\mathbf{R}}]$ is equivalent to the category of right modules over the ring of matrices over $\mathbf{R}$ of the form

$$\begin{pmatrix} x & x & x & x \\ 0 & x & 0 & x \\ 0 & 0 & x & x \\ 0 & 0 & 0 & x \end{pmatrix}$$

This last fact could also be obtained from example 2 using the isomorphism of categories

$$[I_1 \times I_1, \mathscr{G}\ ] \qquad [I_1, [I_1, \mathscr{G}^{\mathbf{R}}]].$$

We return now to the general case. If, instead of using $S(\mathbf{R}) = \bigoplus_{i \in I} S_i(\mathbf{R})$ as a small projective generator, we take $\bigoplus_{i \in I} S_i(\mathbf{R}^{n_i})$ where $n_i > 0$ for all i (V, 1.5), then we find that the corresponding endomorphism ring is isomorphic to a certain ring of $n \times n$ matrices over $\mathbf{R}$ where $n = \sum_{i \in I} n_i$. Thus in example 3 above, if we take $n_1 = 2$, $n_2 = 1$, $n_3 = 3$, and $n_4 = 2$, then the matrix pattern becomes

$$\begin{pmatrix} x & x & x & x & x & x & x & x \\ x & x & x & x & x & x & x & x \\ 0 & 0 & x & 0 & 0 & 0 & x & x \\ 0 & 0 & 0 & x & x & x & x & x \\ 0 & 0 & 0 & x & x & x & x & x \\ 0 & 0 & 0 & x & x & x & x & x \\ 0 & 0 & 0 & 0 & 0 & 0 & x & x \\ 0 & 0 & 0 & 0 & 0 & 0 & x & x \end{pmatrix}$$

In the case where I consists of a single element, taking $\mathbf{R}^n$ as a projective generator we have the following result.

Proposition 8.2. *For any integer $n > 0$, the category $\mathscr{G}^{\mathbf{R}}$ is equivalent to the category $\mathscr{G}^{M_n(\mathbf{R})}$ where $M_n(\mathbf{R})$ is the full ring of $n \times n$ matrices over $\mathbf{R}$.* ∎

Let Λ be any subring of $M_n(\mathbf{R})$ defined by requiring that 0's appear in certain positions in the matrix and arbitrary elements of $\mathbf{R}$ elsewhere. We call the corresponding array of x's and 0's a **pattern**, and we say that Λ is defined by an $n \times n$ pattern over $\mathbf{R}$. Since Λ must contain the identity element of $M_n(\mathbf{R})$, a pattern must have x's at every position along the main diagonal.

(Thus, x always wins. . . .) Furthermore, patterns cannot be too random since Λ must be closed under multiplication. Explicitly, if x appears in both positions (i, j) and (j, k) then x must also appear in position (i, k). A permutation of the integers 1 to n induces an isomorphism from Λ onto another ring defined by a pattern. Consequently, we can alter a pattern by interchanging rows and the corresponding columns without changing any property of Λ. We now prove the converse of 8.1.

Theorem 8.3. *Let Λ be a ring defined by an $n \times n$ pattern over* $\mathbf{R}$. *Then $\mathcal{G}^{\Lambda}$ is equivalent to the category $[I, \mathcal{G}^{\mathbf{R}}]$ for some finite ordered set I.*

Proof. By an interchange of columns (taking care to interchange the corresponding rows) we may assume that the first column is the one with the least number, say n_1 of x's. Now the main diagonal must have x at every position, and so in particular we must have x in the northwest corner of the pattern. Making interchanges among rows 2 to n (and the corresponding columns) we may assume that x appears at each of the first n_1 positions of the first column, and consequently that 0 appears in the last $n - n_1$ positions. Then, using the fact that matrix multiplication must preserve the pattern, we find that 0 must appear in the last $n - n_1$ positions of each of the first n_1 columns. But since the first column had the least number of x's, this means that x must appear at each position of the $n_1 \times n_1$ block in the northwest corner. This will be referred to as the block in position (1, 1).

Of the remaining $n - n_1$ columns we interchange so that column $n_1 + 1$ has the least number of x's. Note that such an interchange will not affect the pattern already established in the first n_1 columns. We then make interchanges among the last $n - n_1$ rows so as to have x appear at every position from $n_1 + 1$ to $n_1 + n_2$, say, in column $n_1 + 1$, and so as to have 0 appear below position $n_1 + n_2$. Again, by closure of multiplication we see that we must have 0 below position $n_1 + n_2$ in each of the columns $n_1 + 1$ to $n_1 + n_2$. For the same reason it follows that there must be either all x's or all 0's in positions 1 to n_1 in column $n_1 + 1$. In the case where there are all 0's, one again uses closure of multiplication to show that there are 0's in every position of the $n_1 \times n_2$ block formed by the intersection of the first n_1 rows with columns $n_1 + 1$ to $n_1 + n_2$ (called the block in the position (1,2)). Then since column $n_1 + 1$ had the least number of x's, it follows that there must be an x in every position of the $n_2 \times n_2$ block touching the block in position (1,1) at its southeast corner (the block in position (2, 2)). The same reason shows that in the case where there are x's at each of positions 1 to n_1 in column $n_1 + 1$ there must be x's throughout the blocks in positions (1, 2) and (2, 2).

Continuing in this way we get a string of say k square blocks along the main diagonal (the blocks in position (i, i) for $i = 1, 2, \ldots, k$) consisting entirely of x's. Suppose that the length of the block in position (i, i) is n_i, so that $\sum_{i=1}^{k} n_i = n$.

Then for $i < j$ the $n_i \times n_j$ block in position (i, j) formed by intersecting the n_i rows passing through the ith diagonal block with the n_j columns passing through the jth diagonal block will consist either entirely of x's or entirely of 0's. All blocks below the diagonal consist entirely of 0's. Furthermore, another consequence of closure of multiplication is that if the blocks in positions (i, j) and (j, k) consist entirely of x's, then the same is true of the block in position (i, k). Let I be the ordered set consisting of the integers $1, 2, \ldots, k$ with $i \leqslant j$ if and only if the block in position (i, j) consists entirely of x's. Then $\bigoplus_{i \in I} S_i(\mathbf{R}^{n_i})$ is a small projective generator for $[I, \mathscr{G}^{\mathbf{R}}]$ whose endomorphism ring is isomorphic to Λ. ∎

Corollary 8.4. *Let Λ be a ring defined by an $n \times n$ pattern over* **R**. *Then for some $k \leqslant n$, $\mathscr{G}^{\Lambda}$ is equivalent to $\mathscr{G}^{\Lambda_0}$ where Λ_0 is defined by a $k \times k$ pattern over* **R** *and is a subring of the $k \times k$ triangular matrices.* ∎

Left Λ-modules are right Λ^*-modules, and Λ^* is isomorphic to the ring of transposes of members of Λ. It follows that if I is the ordered set obtained in 8.3 for right Λ-modules, then ${}^{\Lambda}\mathscr{G}$ is equivalent to $[I^*, {}^{\mathbf{R}}\mathscr{G}]$.

9. Normal Subsets

Given $I' \subset I$, we define the following two subsets of $I - I'$:

$$X(I, I') = \{i \mid i \text{ follows no member of } I'\}$$
$$Y(I, I') = \{i \mid i \in I - I' \text{ and } j < i \text{ for some } j \in I'\}.$$

We say that i_0 is a **minimal element of I' following** i if $i_0 \in I'$, $i \leqslant i_0$, and for no member j of I' do we have $i \leqslant j \leqslant i_0$. Considering I' as an ordered subset (that is, a full subcategory) of I, we say that I' is a **normal** subset of I if the following condition holds: For each $i \in Y(I, I')$ and each pair i_0, i_1 of minimal elements of I' following i there exists no member k of I' such that $i_0 < k$ and $i_1 < k$. As before, we shall denote the restriction functor $[I, \mathscr{A}] \to [I', \mathscr{A}]$ by F.

Lemma 9.1. *If $\mathscr{A}$ has projectives and $D \in [I, \mathscr{A}]$ is such that $D_j = 0$ for all $j \in X(I, I')$, then there exists a projective resolution for D every term of which also has this property.*

Proof. If $D_j = 0$, then we can take $P_j = 0$ in the discussion at the end of §7. Now for $j \in X(I, I')$ there is no element $i < j$ for which $D_i \neq 0$. Consequently, $T_j\left(\bigoplus_{i \in I} S_i(P_i)\right) = 0$ for $j \in X(I, I')$, and so $K_j^1 = 0$ for all $j \in X(I, I')$. The result now follows by iteration. ∎

Lemma 9.2. *Let I' be a normal subset of I and suppose that $\mathscr{A}$ has projectives. If D is projective in $[I, \mathscr{A}]$ and is such that $D_j = 0$ for all $j \in X(I, I')$, then $F(D)$ is projective in $[I', \mathscr{A}]$.*

Proof. By 7.3 it suffices to consider D of the form $S_i^I(P)$ where P is projective in $\mathscr{A}$ and where i is in I' or $Y(I, I')$. In the first case we have $FS_i^I(P) = S_i^{I'}(P)$. In the second case we have

$$FS_i^I(P) = \bigoplus_{j\in J} S_j^{I'}(P)$$

where J is the set of minimal elements of I' following i. Hence, in either case, $FS_i^I(P)$ is projective. ∎

Lemma 9.3. *Let I' be any ordered subset of I. Then there is a functor*

$$E : [I', \mathscr{A}] \to [I, \mathscr{A}]$$

such that $T_jE = 0$ for all $j \in X(I, I')$ and such that FE is the identity functor on $[I', \mathscr{A}]$.

Proof. For $i \in I$, let $Y(i)$ be the ordered subset of I consisting of all members j of I' such that $i \leqslant j$. Given $D' \in [I', \mathscr{A}]$ we define $E(D')_i = 0$ for $i \in X(I, I')$, and otherwise we take $E(D')_i$ as the limit of the restriction of D' to $Y(i)$. The limit exists by II, 2.7, since I is finite. For $i \leqslant j$ and $i \notin X(I, I')$ we have a compatible family $\{E(D')_i \to D'_k\}_{k\in Y(j)}$ which gives rise to a limit morphism $E(D')_{ij} : E(D')_i \to E(D')_j$. Likewise for $i \notin X(I, I')$, the morphism $E(\alpha)_i$ relative to a morphism α in $[I', \mathscr{A}]$ can be defined as the limit morphism of the family $\{\alpha_j\}_{j\in Y(i)}$. In this way E becomes a functor with the required properties. ∎

Proposition 9.4. *If I' is a normal subset of I and $\mathscr{A}$ has projectives, then*

$$\text{gl. dim. } [I', \mathscr{A}] \leqslant \text{gl. dim.}[I, \mathscr{A}]. \tag{1}$$

Proof. Given $D' \in [I', \mathscr{A}]$, by 9.1 and 9.3 we can construct a projective resolution for $E(D')$ every term of which is zero over j for all $j \in X(I, I')$. Applying F to this resolution and using 9.2 we obtain a projective resolution for $FE(D') = D'$. Hence we have h.d. $D' \leqslant$ h.d. $E(D')$, and so (1) follows. ∎

10. Dimension for Finite Ordered Sets

Throughout this section $\mathscr{A}$ will denote an abelian category with projectives.

Lemma 10.1. *Consider $D \in [I, \mathscr{A}]$ and suppose that* h.d. $D_i \leqslant n < \infty$ *for some $i \in I$.* If

$$0 \to K^{n+r+1} \to D^{n+r} \to D^{n+r-1} \cdots \xrightarrow{d^2} D^1 \xrightarrow{d^1} D^0 \to D \to 0 \tag{1}$$

is an exact sequence with D^k projective for $0 \leqslant k \leqslant n + r$ and $r \geqslant 0$, then K_{ij}^{n+r+1} is a coretraction for all $j > i$.

Proof. Since h.d. $D_i \leqslant n$ we see that $\text{Im}(d_i^{n+r}) = \text{Ker}(d_i^{n+r-1})$ is projective in $\mathscr{A}$, hence d^{n+r+1} is a coretraction. Since D^{n+r} is projective we know also by 7.1 that D_{ij}^{n+r} is a coretraction. Hence since

$$d_j^{n+r+1} K_{ij}^{n+r+1} = D_{ij}^{n+r} d_i^{n+r+1}$$

it follows that K_{ij}^{n+r+1} is a coretraction. ∎

Lemma 10.2. *If* $D \in [I, \mathscr{A}]$ *and* h.d. $D_i \leqslant n < \infty$ *for all* $i \in I$, *then there is an exact sequence* (1) *with* D^k *projective for* $0 \leqslant k \leqslant n+r$ *and such that* $K_i^{n+r+1} = 0$ *for all elements* i *of order* $\leqslant r$ *in* I $(r \geqslant 0)$. *If, furthermore,* $r \geqslant 1$ *and* i_0 *is an element of order* $r+1$ *which is preceded by only one element of order* r, *then we can take* $K_{i_0}^{n+r+1} = 0$ *as well.*

Proof. Construct an exact sequence in $[I, \mathscr{A}]$

$$0 \to K^n \to D^{n-1} \to D^{n-2} \to \ldots \to D^1 \to D^0 \to D \to 0$$

with D^k projective for $0 \leqslant k \leqslant n-1$. Then since h.d. $D_i \leqslant n$ we see that K_i^n is projective for all i. Consequently, $D^n = \bigoplus_{i \in I} S_i(K_i^n)$ is projective, and we have the obvious epimorphism $D^n \to K^n$. Letting K^{n+1} be its kernel, we see again that K_i^{n+1} is projective for all i, and furthermore $K_i^{n+1} = 0$ for all elements i of order 0. We define inductively

$$D^{n+r} = \bigoplus_{i \in I} S_i(K_i^{n+r}).$$

Then we have an epimorphism $D^{n+r} \to K^{n+r}$ whose kernel K^{n+r+1} is such that $K_i^{n+r+1} = 0$ for all elements i of order $\leqslant r$. If $r \geqslant 1$ and i_0 is an element of order $r+1$ which is preceded by only one element j of order r, then we apply 10.1 to write

$$K_{i_0}^{n+r} = \operatorname{Im}(K_{ji_0}^{n+r}) \oplus K_{i_0}^{n+r'}.$$

Then we can define D^{n+r} by

$$D^{n+r} = \left(\bigoplus_{i \neq i_0} S_i(K_i^{n+r}) \right) \oplus S_{i_0}(K_i^{n+r'}),$$

and the kernel K^{n+r+1} of the obvious epimorphism $D^{n+r} \to K^{n+r}$ will have the desired property. ▌

Corollary 10.3. *If* h.d. $D_i \leqslant n \leqslant \infty$ *for all* $i \in I$ *and the maximal order of a vertex in* I *is* m, *then* h.d. $D \leqslant m + n$. *Consequently*

$$\text{gl. dim.}[I, \mathscr{A}] \leqslant m + \text{gl. dim. } \mathscr{A}. \quad ▌$$

Consider the linearly ordered set I_1 of two elements. We define functors $M_1 : \mathscr{A} \to [I_1, \mathscr{A}]$ and $G : [I_1, \mathscr{A}] \to \mathscr{A}$ by $M_1(A) = (A \to 0)$ and $G(D) = D_2/\operatorname{Im} D_{12}$, respectively. Then from 7.1 we see that G preserves projectives.

Furthermore, an exact complex in $[I_1, \mathscr{A}]$ consisting of terms D such that D_{12} is a monomorphism is taken by G into an exact complex in $\mathscr{A}$. This is simply the statement that the quotient of an exact complex by an exact subcomplex is again exact (VI, §8).

Lemma 10.4. *If* h.d. $A = n \geqslant 0$, *then* h.d. $M_1(A) = n + 1$.

Proof. By 10.1 we have h.d. $M_1(A) \leqslant n+1$. Suppose that h.d. $M_1(A) < n+1$. If $n = 0$, then this means that $M_1(A)$ is projective, and it follows that $A \to 0$ is a monomorphism. Consequently, $A = 0$, a contradiction. If $n > 0$, consider an exact sequence in $[I_1, \mathscr{A}]$

$$\begin{array}{ccccccccc} 0 & \longrightarrow & K & \longrightarrow & P & \longrightarrow & A & \longrightarrow & 0 \\ & & \downarrow & & \| & & \downarrow & & \\ 0 & \longrightarrow & P & = & P & \longrightarrow & 0 & \longrightarrow & 0 \end{array}$$

with P projective in $\mathscr{A}$. Denoting $K \to P$ by K^1 we have h.d. $K^1 < n$. But if we apply G to a projective resolution for K^1 of length $< n$, then we obtain a projective resolution for $G(K^1) = A$ of length $< n$. Hence h.d. $A < n$, and so again we have a contradiction. Therefore, h.d. $M_1(A) = n + 1$. ∎

Corollary 10.5. *The m-cube I_1^m is such that*

$$\text{gl. dim.}[I_1^m, \mathscr{A}] = m + \text{gl. dim. } \mathscr{A}$$

for all $\mathscr{A}$.

Proof. For $m = 1$ this follows from 10.4 and 10.3. We then have inductively

$$\begin{aligned} \text{gl. dim. } [I_1^m, \mathscr{A}] &= \text{gl. dim.}[I_1^{m-1} \times I_1, \mathscr{A}] \\ &= \text{gl. dim.}[I_1^{m-1}, [I_1, \mathscr{A}]] \\ &= (m-1) + \text{gl. dim.}[I_1, \mathscr{A}] \\ &= (m-1) + (1 + \text{gl. dim. } \mathscr{A}) \\ &= m + \text{gl. dim. } \mathscr{A}. \qquad ∎ \end{aligned}$$

Corollary 10.6. *If I is nondiscrete, then*

$$\text{gl. dim.}[I, \mathscr{A}] \geqslant 1 + \text{gl. dim. } \mathscr{A}.$$

Proof. If I is nondiscrete, then I contains I_1 as a (necessarily normal) subset. Hence the result follows from 10.5 and 9.4. ∎

Corollary 10.7. *Let Λ be a ring of matrices over* **R** *defined by a pattern with zeros below the main diagonal and at least one x above the main diagonal. Then*

$$\text{r. gl. dim. } \Lambda \geqslant 1 + \text{r. gl. dim. } \mathbf{R}.$$

The same statement is true for left global dimension. ∎

We say that a member i of I is a **decision point** for i if there are members j, p, q of I such that $i < p < j$ and $i < q < j$ and p and q are incompatible. I is called **decision free** if it has no decision points.

Lemma 10.8. *Consider $D \in [I, \mathscr{A}]$ and suppose that* h.d. $D_i \leqslant n$ *in $\mathscr{A}$ for all $i \in I$. If I is decision free, then* h.d. $D \leqslant n + 1$.

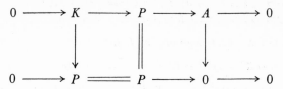

Proof. We proceed by induction on the number m of elements in I. If $m = 1$, then h.d. $D \leqslant n$. Otherwise let i_0 be maximal in I, and let J be the set of elements which immediately precede it. Then no two members of J are compatible. Consider an exact sequence in $[I, \mathscr{A}]$

$$0 \longrightarrow D^{n+1} \xrightarrow{dn+1} D^n \xrightarrow{dn} D^{n-1} \quad \ldots D^0 \longrightarrow D \longrightarrow 0 \tag{2}$$

with D^k projective for $0 \leqslant k \leqslant n$. We wish to show that D^{n+1} is projective. Write

$$D^n = \bigoplus_{i\in I} S_i(P_i) \tag{3}$$

where P_i is projective for each $i \in I$. We regard D^{n+1} and D^n as networks of subobjects of $\bigoplus_{i\in I} P_i$. Since h.d. $D_i \leqslant n$ we know that $\mathrm{Im}(d_i^n)$ is projective for all i. Hence d_i^{n+1} is a coretraction for all i. Since I is decision free we see that no two members of J can be preceded by a common element, and so it follows from (3) that the union $\bigcup_{j\in J} D_j^n$ is a coproduct. But then since D_j^{n+1} is a retract of D_j^n it follows that $\bigcup_{j\in J} D_j^{n+1}$ is a coproduct and is further a retract of $\bigcup_{j\in J} D_j^n$. Since the latter is a retract of $D_{i_0}^n$, we see that $\bigcup_{j\in J} D_j^{n+1}$ is a retract of $D_{i_0}^n$, hence of $D_{i_0}^{n+1}$. Now let I' be the ordered subset of I obtained by removing i_0. Applying the restriction functor F to (2) it follows by induction that $F(D^{n+1})$ is projective. This combined with what we have proved above then shows that D^{n+1} is projective. ∎

Theorem 10.9. *Let I be nondiscrete and decision free. Then for any $\mathscr{A}$ we have*

$$\text{gl. dim.}[I, \mathscr{A}] = 1 + \text{gl. dim. } \mathscr{A}. \tag{4}$$

Conversely, if gl. dim. $\mathscr{A}$ *is finite and* (4) *holds, then I is nondiscrete and decision free.*

Proof. The first statement is immediate from 10.6 and 10.8. Conversely, suppose that gl. dim. $\mathscr{A}$ is finite and that (4) holds. Then I cannot be discrete since otherwise we would have gl. dim.$[I, \mathscr{A}] =$ gl. dim. $\mathscr{A}$. On the other hand, suppose that I is not decision free and let i be a decision point in I of maximal order. Let I' be an ordered subset of I consisting of 4 elements i, j, p, q where $i < p < j$, $i < q < j$, and p and q are incompatible. Then I' must be a normal subset of I, since otherwise there would be a decision point in I of order greater than that of i. Hence, by 9.4 we have

$$\text{gl. dim.}[I', \mathscr{A}] \leqslant \text{gl. dim.}[I, \mathscr{A}]. \tag{5}$$

But I' is just I_1^2, and by 10.5 we have

$$\text{gl. dim.}[I', \mathscr{A}] = 2 + \text{gl. dim. } \mathscr{A}. \tag{6}$$

Combining (5) and (6) we obtain a contradiction to (4). Hence I is decision free. ∎

Corollary 10.10. *Let Λ be the ring of $m \times m$ triangular matrices over* $\mathbf{R}$ $(m > 1)$. *Then*

$$\text{r. gl. dim. } \Lambda = 1 + \text{r. gl. dim. } \mathbf{R}.$$

The same is true for left global dimension. ∎

Corollary 10.10 was obtained by Eilenberg, Rosenberg, and Zelinsky [13] using a spectral sequence.

For $m > 1$, let I_m denote the ordered set given schematically by

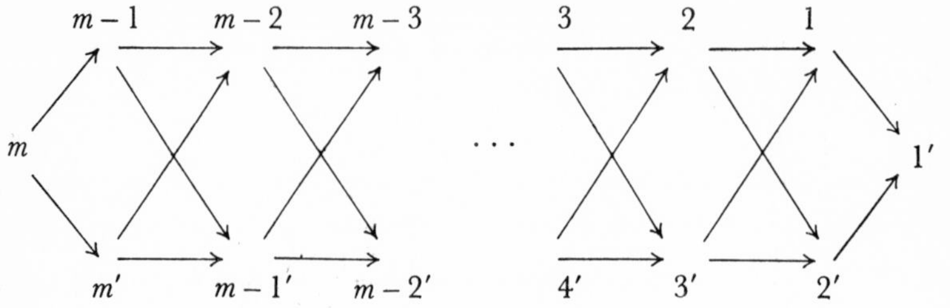

(7)

We have the functor $M_m : \mathscr{A} \to [I_m, \mathscr{A}]$ defined by

$$\begin{aligned} M_m(A)_i &= 0 \qquad \text{for} \quad i \neq m \\ &= A \qquad \text{for} \quad i = m. \end{aligned}$$

Also for $m \geqslant 2$ we define $L : [I_m, \mathscr{A}] \to [I_{m-1}, \mathscr{A}]$ by

$$\begin{aligned} L(D)_i &= D_i/\mathrm{Im}(D_{m',i}) \qquad &\text{for} \quad i \neq m-1 \\ &= D_{m-1}/\mathrm{Im}(D_{m,m-1}) \qquad &\text{for} \quad i = m-1. \end{aligned}$$

Then we have $LS_m^{I_m} = 0 = LS_{m'}^{I_m}$ and $LS_i^{I_m} = S_i^{I_{m-1}}$ for $i \neq m, m'$. Hence L preserves projectives. Also L preserves exact sequences consisting of terms D such that D_{ij} is a monomorphism for all $i \leqslant j$.

Lemma 10.11. *If* h.d. $A = n \geqslant 0$, *then* h.d. $M_m(A) = m + n$.

Proof. By 10.3 we have h.d. $M_m(A) \leqslant m + n$. The reverse inequality will be proved by induction on m. The case $m = 1$ has been handled in 10.4. Thus suppose $m > 1$, and take an exact sequence $0 \to K \to P \to A \to 0$ in $\mathscr{A}$ with P projective. This gives rise to an exact sequence

$$0 \to K^1 \to S_m^{I_m}(P) \to M_m(A) \to 0 \tag{8}$$

in $[I_m, \mathscr{A}]$, and we have $L(K^1) = M_{m-1}(A)$. If h.d. $M_m(A) < m + n$, then from (8) we have h.d. $K^1 < m + n - 1$. Applying L to a projective resolution for K^1 of length $< m + n - 1$ we obtain a projective resolution for $M_{m-1}(A)$ of length $< m + n - 1$. This contradicts the inductive hypothesis. ▌

Combining 10.11 and 10.3 we have the following theorem, which was conjectured by F. Linton.

Theorem 10.12. *For all* $\mathscr{A}$ *we have*

$$\text{gl. dim.}[I_m, \mathscr{A}] = m + \text{gl. dim. } \mathscr{A}. \qquad ▌$$

For $i \in \mathrm{I}$ we define $Z(i)$ as the ordered subset of I consisting of all elements j such that $j \leqslant i$.

Lemma 10.13. *Let $i_1, \ldots, i_p$ be the maximal elements of I. Then*

$$\text{gl. dim.}[I, \mathscr{A}] = \sup_{1 \leqslant k \leqslant p} \text{gl. dim.}[Z(i_k), \mathscr{A}].$$

Proof. Let D be an object in $[I, \mathscr{A}]$ with the property that its restriction to each of the sets $Z(i_k)$ is projective in $[Z(i_k), \mathscr{A}]$. Then for each $i \in I$ we can choose a subobject $A_i' \subset D_i$ such that

$$D_i = A_i' \oplus (\bigcup_{j<i} \text{Im } D_{ji}).$$

It then follows from 7.4 that we have for each i

$$D_i = \bigoplus_{j \leqslant i} D_{ji}(A_j'),$$

and consequently D is projective. On the other hand, if D is projective in $[I, \mathscr{A}]$ then clearly the restriction of D to any set of the form $Z(i)$ is projective in $[Z(i), \mathscr{A}]$. The lemma is an easy consequence of these two facts. ▌

Lemma 10.14. *Let i be a maximal element in I and suppose that i is immediately preceded by only one element j. If $I' = I - \{i\}$ is nondiscrete, then*

$$\text{gl. dim.}[I, \mathscr{A}] = \text{gl. dim.}[I', \mathscr{A}].$$

Proof. Clearly I' is a normal subset of I, and so by 9.4 we have only to show

$$\text{gl. dim.}[I, \mathscr{A}] \leqslant \text{gl. dim.}[I', \mathscr{A}].$$

If the right side is infinite there is nothing to prove. Thus suppose that we have

$$\text{gl. dim.}[I', \mathscr{A}] = n + r + 1 \tag{9}$$

where gl. dim. $\mathscr{A} = n$. Since I' is nondiscrete we know by 10.6 that $r \geqslant 0$. Given $D \in [I, \mathscr{A}]$, construct the exact sequence (1) of 10.1 with D^k projective for $0 \leqslant k \leqslant n + r$. Let F be the restriction functor from $[I, \mathscr{A}]$ to $[I', \mathscr{A}]$. Then applying F to (1) and using (9) we see that $F(K^{n+r+1})$ is projective. Also by 10.1 we know that K_{ji}^{n+r+1} is a coretraction. It follows that K^{n+r+1} is projective, and so h.d. $D \leqslant n + r + 1$ as required. ▌

Lemma 10.15. *Let i be a maximal element in I and let $I' = I - \{i\}$. If* gl. dim. $\mathscr{A} = n$ *and* gl. dim.$[I, \mathscr{A}] = m + n$, *then* gl. dim.$[I', \mathscr{A}] \geqslant m + n - 1$.

Proof. If $m < 2$, then this is trivial. Thus, suppose that gl. dim.$[I', \mathscr{A}] < m + n - 1$ where $m \geqslant 2$. Given $D \in [I, \mathscr{A}]$, construct an exact sequence in $[I, \mathscr{A}]$

$$0 \to K^{m+n-2} \to D^{m+n-3} \to \ldots \to D^1 \to D^0 \to D \to 0$$

where D^k is projective for $0 \leqslant k \leqslant m + n - 3$. Applying the restriction functor F, we see that $F(K^{m+n-2})$ is projective. Thus, by 7.1 we may write

$$F(K^{m+n-2}) = \bigoplus_{j \in I'} S_j^{I'}(P_j).$$

But also K_i^{m+n-2} is projective, and we have an epimorphism

$$\left(\bigoplus_{j\in I'} S_j^I(P_j)\right) \oplus S_i^I(K_i^{m+n-2}) \to K^{m+n-2}$$

whose kernel is zero over j for $j \in I'$ and is projective over i. Thus we obtain a projective resolution of length $\leqslant m+n-1$ for D. Consequently,

$$\text{gl. dim.}[I, \mathscr{A}] < m+n,$$

a contradiction. Hence gl. dim.$[I', \mathscr{A}] \geqslant m+n-1$. ▮

Theorem 10.16. *Suppose that* gl. dim. $\mathscr{A} = n < \infty$, *and that*

$$\text{gl. dim.}[I, \mathscr{A}] = m+n.$$

Then I has $\geqslant 2m$ elements, with equality holding if and only if $I = I_m$.

Proof. The proof is by induction on m. If $m = 1$, then I cannot be discrete, hence I has at least 2 elements. If I has precisely 2 elements, then it is clear that $I = I_1$. Supposing the theorem true for $m-1$, let gl. dim.$[I, \mathscr{A}] = m+n$. We shall use the notation of diagram (7). By 10.13 we may assume that I has a unique maximal element, say $1'$. If I has $< 2m$ elements, then $I' = I - \{1'\}$ has $\leqslant 2m-2$ elements, and by 10.15 we have gl. dim.$[I', \mathscr{A}] \geqslant (m-1)+n$. Hence, by induction, $I' = I_{m-1}$. It follows that $1'$ is immediately preceded by at most one element, and so by 10.14 we have gl. dim. $[I, \mathscr{A}] = (m-1)+n$. This contradiction shows that I has at least $2m$ elements.

Now suppose that I has precisely $2m$ elements. Let $1'$ and I' be as above. If I' has only one maximal element, then by 10.14,

$$\text{gl. dim.}[I', \mathscr{A}] = \text{gl. dim.}[I, \mathscr{A}] = m+n.$$

On the other hand, I' has $2m-1$ elements, contradicting what we have already proved. Therefore I' has at least two maximal elements. Among them let $2'$ be such that gl. dim.$[I', \mathscr{A}] =$ gl. dim.$[Z(2'), \mathscr{A}]$ (10.13). Then our induction shows that $Z(2') = I_{m-1}$, and consequently $I - Z(2')$ consists of $1'$ and one other element 1 immediately preceding $1'$. It remains to be shown that 1 follows both 2 and $3'$ (see diagram (7)). If 1 follows neither 2 nor $3'$, then 1 has order $< m-1$ in I. If 1 follows just one of 2 or $3'$, then 1 has order $m-1$ in I, but is immediately preceded by only one element in I. In either case one uses 10.2 to construct projective resolutions for all objects D in $[I, \mathscr{A}]$ of length $< m+n-1$. This contradiction shows that 1 follows both 2 and $3'$, and so $I = I_m$. ▮

Corollary 10.17. *Let Λ be defined by an $m \times m$ pattern over* **R**, *and suppose that* r. gl. dim. $\mathbf{R} < \infty$. *Then*

$$\text{r. gl. dim. } \Lambda \leqslant m/2 + \text{r. gl. dim. } \mathbf{R},$$

with equality holding if and only if the pattern is isomorphic to one with 0's everywhere below the main diagonal and x's everywhere above the main diagonal except in positions $(2, 3), (4, 5), (6, 7),\ldots, (m-2, m-1)$. ▮

Let us define the **dimension** of a finite ordered set I to be m if

$$\text{gl. dim.}[I, \mathscr{A}] = m + \text{gl. dim. } \mathscr{A}$$

for all categories $\mathscr{A}$ with both projectives and injectives. Clearly, discrete sets have dimension 0, and by 10.6 we see that these are the only such sets. By 10.9 we see that I has dimension 1 if and only if it is nondiscrete and decision free. If I has dimension m and J has dimension n, then it follows from the isomorphism of categories

$$[I \times J, \mathscr{A}] \approx [I, [J, \mathscr{A}]]$$

that $I \times J$ has dimension $m+n$. Thus from 10.12 we see that I_m^n has dimension $mn (m, n \geqslant 1)$. Furthermore, if I has dimension m, then we have

$$\begin{aligned} \text{gl. dim.}[I^*, \mathscr{A}] &= \text{gl. dim.}[I^*, \mathscr{A}^{**}] \\ &= \text{gl. dim.}[I, \mathscr{A}^*]^* \\ &= \text{gl. dim.}[I, \mathscr{A}^*] \\ &= m + \text{gl. dim. } \mathscr{A}^* \\ &= m + \text{gl. dim. } \mathscr{A}, \end{aligned}$$

and consequently I^* also has dimension m.

It is not known if this dimension is defined for all finite ordered sets.

Exercises

1. Show that when $\mathscr{A} = \mathscr{G}^{\mathbf{R}}$, then the category $F_{\mathscr{A}}(\{x_i\})$ is actually isomorphic to the category of right modules over the free ring $F_R(\{X_i\})$. Do likewise for $\mathscr{A}[x_1,\ldots, x_k]$ and $E_{\mathscr{A}}(x_1,\ldots, x_k)$.

2. Consider an adjoint situation $(\eta; S, T; \mathscr{A}, \mathscr{B})$ where T is exact and $\mathscr{A}$ and $\mathscr{B}$ are abelian categories (not necessarily with projectives). If P is projective in $\mathscr{B}$, then $S(P)$ is projective in $\mathscr{A}$.

For any abelian category $\mathscr{A}$, the evaluation functor $T_n : GF_{\mathscr{A}}(x_1,\ldots, x_k) \to \mathscr{A}$ has an exact adjoint for all $n \geqslant 0$. Hence, if D is projective in $GF_{\mathscr{A}}(x_1,\ldots, x_k)$, then D_n is projective for all n. Use 4.2 to show that for any abelian category $\mathscr{A}$ (not necessarily with projectives), the projectives in $GF_{\mathscr{A}}(x_1,\ldots, x_k)$ are precisely the objects of the form $\bigoplus_{n \geqslant 0} S_n(P_n)$ where P_n is projective in $\mathscr{A}$ for all $n \geqslant 0$ (cf. 4.3).

Obtain similar results for $G\mathscr{A}[x_1,\ldots, x_k]$, $GE_{\mathscr{A}}(x_1,\ldots, x_k)$, and $[I, \mathscr{A}]$ where I is any finite ordered set.

3. Suppose that $\mathscr{A}$ has countable coproducts. Use exercise 2 to prove the converse of 4.4; namely, if D is projective in $GF_{\mathscr{A}}(x_1,\ldots, x_k)$, then $L(D)$ is projective in $F_{\mathscr{A}}(x_1,\ldots, x_k)$. Hence show that if $\mathscr{A}$ has projectives and exact, countable coproducts, then

$$\text{gl. dim. } GF_{\mathscr{A}}(x_1,\ldots, x_k) = 1 + \text{gl. dim. } \mathscr{A}.$$

Show similarly that in this case we have

$$\text{gl. dim. } G\mathscr{A}[x_1,\ldots, x_k] = k + \text{gl. dim. } \mathscr{A}$$

and

$$\text{gl. dim. } GE_{\mathscr{A}}(x_1,\ldots, x_k) = \infty.$$

4. Show that if I is an infinite set, then for any category with projectives and exact coproducts indexed over $|I|$, the polynomial category $\mathscr{A}[\{x_i\}_{i\in I}]$ has infinite global dimension.

5. Use V, 7.6, to obtain 4.3 independently of 4.1. Do likewise for 5.3, 6.3, and 7.3.

6. Consider the functor $S : \mathscr{A} \to E_{\mathscr{A}}(x_1)$ of §3. In the case where $\mathscr{A}$ is $\mathscr{G}^{\mathbf{R}}$, show that the ring of endomorphisms of $S(\mathbf{R})$ is isomorphic to the ring of matrices over $\mathbf{R}$ of the form

$$\begin{pmatrix} a & 0 \\ b & a \end{pmatrix}$$

More generally, show that the exterior ring on any number generators $E_{\mathbf{R}}(x_1,\ldots, x_k)$ is isomorphic to a certain ring of triangular matrices.

7. Consider the diagram scheme consisting of two vertices i and j and two arrows m and d from i to j and from j to j respectively. The category of diagrams D of right $\mathbf{R}$-modules satisfying the relations

$$D(d)D(m) = 0 \qquad D(d)D(d) = 0$$

has as a small projective generator the diagram G defined as follows:

$$G_i = \mathbf{R} \qquad\qquad G_j = \mathbf{R} \oplus \mathbf{R} \oplus \mathbf{R}$$
$$G(m)(r) = (0, r, 0) \qquad G(d)(r, s, t) = (0, 0, r).$$

Hence this category is equivalent to the category of right modules over the ring of matrices of the form

$$\begin{pmatrix} a & 0 & 0 \\ b & c & 0 \\ d & e & a \end{pmatrix}$$

8. A **component** of an ordered set I is an equivalence class of elements of I under the equivalence relation generated by the compatibility relation. Let Λ be defined by a pattern over $\mathbf{R}$. Then the center of Λ is isomorphic to the product of m copies of the center of $\mathbf{R}$, where m is the number of components in the ordered set associated with Λ.

9. A full subcategory of an ordered set I can have dimension strictly greater than that of I. (Let I be defined by putting an object at the intersection of the two intersecting arrows of I_3 (see diagram (7) of §10).)

10. In an ordered set I, suppose that i_1 is immediately preceded by only one element i_0 and immediately followed by only one element i_2, and that i_2 is immediately preceded by only i_1 and is immediately followed by only one element i_3. If I' is the ordered subset of I obtained by omitting i_2, then for any category $\mathscr{A}$ with projectives we have

$$\text{gl. dim.}[I, \mathscr{A}] = \text{gl. dim.}[I', \mathscr{A}].$$

Hence if I is the union of two linearly ordered subsets which have at least three elements each and which have only their initial elements and terminal elements in common, then

$$\text{gl. dim.}[I, \mathscr{A}] = 2 + \text{gl. dim.}\ \mathscr{A}.$$

[CHAPTER X]

Sheaves

Introduction

Sheaves with values in sets, rings, and modules were defined by Godement in [18] in such a way as to open the road to a theory of sheaves with values in more general categories. This generalization has been carried out independently by J. Gray [19] and R. Deheuvels [7]. The treatment given here is a modification of the work of Gray. The proofs of 3.1 and 5.1 have been taken from [19].

After some preliminaries, the notion of an $\mathscr{F}$-category is introduced. The axioms for an $\mathscr{F}$-category are precisely the conditions needed to prove the important lemma 2.1. For abelian categories these axioms coincide with Grothendieck's axiom A.B.6 [20]. Using the techniques of adjoint functors, the notions of associated sheaves and direct and inverse images of sheaves as defined in [18] are generalized to sheaves with values in an $\mathscr{F}$-category $\mathscr{A}$. If, further, $\mathscr{A}$ is abelian, then the category of sheaves in $\mathscr{A}$ over a fixed topological space is a complete C_3 category (6.3). In this case the standard theorems concerning sheaves induced on locally closed subspaces can be proved (§8).

1. Preliminaries

Throughout the chapter, $\mathscr{A}$ will denote a complete, locally small category with direct limits. In particular, $\mathscr{A}$ has intersections, inverse images, and a null object (which we denote by 0). Also $\mathscr{A}$ has images (I, §10) and hence unions of naturally directed systems of subobjects (II, 2.8).

Let X be a topological space, and let $\mathscr{U}_X$ denote the family of open sets in X. We consider $\mathscr{U}_X$ as an ordered set by defining $U \leqslant V$ if and only if $V \subset U$. The functor category $[\mathscr{U}_X, \mathscr{A}]$ is called the **category of presheaves in $\mathscr{A}$ over** X, and is denoted by $\mathscr{P}(X, \mathscr{A})$. Thus a presheaf P assigns to each open set U in X an object $P(U)$ in $\mathscr{A}$, and to each inclusion $V \subset U$ of open sets a morphism $P_{UV} : P(U) \to P(V)$ such that if $W \subset V \subset U$, then $P_{VW}P_{UV} = P_{UW}$, and such that $P_{UU} = 1$ for all open U in X. A morphism $\alpha : P \to P'$ of presheaves is a family of morphisms $\alpha_U : P(U) \to P'(U)$ such that for each inclusion of open sets $V \subset U$ we have a commutative diagram

$$\begin{array}{ccc} P(U) & \xrightarrow{\alpha_U} & P'(U) \\ {\scriptstyle P_{UV}}\downarrow & & \downarrow{\scriptstyle P'_{UV}} \\ P(V) & \xrightarrow{\alpha_V} & P'(V) \end{array}$$

Let $\{U_i\}_{i\in I}$ be an open cover for an open set U (i.e., each U_i is open and $\bigcup_{i\in I} U_i = U$). Let $U_{jk} = U_j \cap U_k$, and for a presheaf P let p_i denote the ith projection from the product $\mathsf{X}_{i\in I} P(U_i)$. Then we have the morphism

$$u : P(U) \to \mathsf{X}_{i\in I} P(U_i) \tag{1}$$

such that $p_i u = P_{UU_i}$. Also we have morphisms

$$f, g : \mathsf{X}_{i\in I} P(U_i) \to \mathsf{X}_{(j,k)\in I\times I} P(U_{jk}). \tag{2}$$

The (j, k)th coordinate of f is $P_{U_jU_{jk}}p_j$ and the (j, k)th coordinate of g is $P_{U_kU_{jk}}p_k$. Clearly $fu = gu$. If P has the property that for every open set U and every open cover of U the morphism u is the equalizer of the two morphisms f and g, then P is called a **sheaf** in $\mathscr{A}$ over X. The full subcategory of $\mathscr{P}(X, \mathscr{A})$ consisting of all sheaves in $\mathscr{A}$ over X will be denoted by $\mathscr{F}(X, \mathscr{A})$.

Let P be the presheaf such that $P(U) = 0$ for all open sets U. Recalling that the product of any number of null objects is again a null object, we see that P is a sheaf. We call P the **null sheaf**, and we denote it also by 0.

A presheaf P will be called a **monopresheaf** if it satisfies the weaker condition that (1) be always a monomorphism. The full subcategory of $\mathscr{P}(X, \mathscr{A})$ consisting of all monopresheaves is denoted by $\mathscr{M}(X, \mathscr{A})$. If P is a monopresheaf, then by considering the empty covering of the empty set $\varnothing$, we see from (1) that $P(\varnothing)$ is a subobject of a null object, and hence is itself a null object.

Since the category $\mathscr{A}$ is complete, we know that limits in the functor category $\mathscr{P}(X, \mathscr{A})$ are computed pointwise (II, §11). Using the characterization of equalizers as limits (I, 17.4), it follows from II, 12.2, that the limit in $\mathscr{P}(X, \mathscr{A})$ of a diagram of sheaves is again a sheaf. In other words, $\mathscr{F}(X, \mathscr{A})$ is a complete subcategory of $\mathscr{P}(X, \mathscr{A})$. Likewise $\mathscr{M}(X, \mathscr{A})$ is a complete subcategory of $\mathscr{P}(X, \mathscr{A})$.

For each $x \in X$, the open sets in X which contain x form a directed subset of $\mathscr{U}_X$, and thus a presheaf P over X determines a direct system in $\mathscr{A}$. We denote

$$P_x = \varinjlim_{x\in U} P(U)$$

and we call P_x the **stalk** of P over x. The morphism from $P(U)$ to the direct limit is denoted by P_{Ux}. If $\alpha : P \to P'$ is a morphism of presheaves, then we have an induced morphism of stalks $\alpha_x : P_x \to P'_x$ in $\mathscr{A}$, and in this way the process of taking stalks becomes functorial. We let $S_x : \mathscr{P}(X, \mathscr{A}) \to \mathscr{A}$ be defined by $S_x(P) = P_x$ and $S_x(\alpha) = \alpha_x$. By II, 12.2*, it follows that if $\mathscr{A}$ is cocomplete, then S_x is a colimit preserving functor for all $x \in X$.

Given a family of objects $\{A_x\}_{x\in X}$, we form a presheaf $\bar{R}_X A$ as follows. For an open set U we define

$$\bar{R}_X A(U) = \bigtimes_{x\in U} A_x,$$

and for $V \subset U$ we have the morphism $\bigtimes_{x\in U} A_x \to \bigtimes_{x\in V} A_x$ which when composed with the xth projection from the codomain gives the xth projection from the domain. The rules for a presheaf are trivially satisfied.

Lemma 1.1. *$\bar{R}_X A$ is a sheaf.*

Proof. Relative to an open cover $U = \bigcup_{i\in I} U_i$, consider the diagram

$$\begin{array}{ccccc} & & B & & \\ & & \big\downarrow v & & \\ \bigtimes_{x\in U} A_x & \xrightarrow{\ u\ } & \bigtimes_{i\in I}\Big(\bigtimes_{x\in U_i} A_x\Big) & \xrightarrow{\ f,g\ } & \bigtimes_{(j,k)\in I\times I}\Big(\bigtimes_{x\in U_{jk}} A_x\Big) \end{array}$$

where u, f, and g are defined by (1) and (2), and v is such that $fv = gv$. We wish to find a morphism $h : B \to \bigtimes_{x\in U} A_x$ such that $uh = v$. For $y \in U$, let i_y be any index such that $y \in U_{i_y}$. Let $h_y : B \to A_y$ be the composition

$$B \xrightarrow{v} \bigtimes_{i\in I}\Big(\bigtimes_{x\in U_i} A_x\Big) \to \bigtimes_{x\in U_{i_y}} A_x \to A_y.$$

It follows from the equality $fv = gv$ that h_y is independent of the choice of i_y, and from this it is easy to verify that the morphism h induced by the family $\{h_y\}$ is such that $uh = v$. It is also easy to see that u is a monomorphism. Hence u is the equalizer of f and g, and so $\bar{R}_X A$ is a sheaf. ∎

In particular, if P is a presheaf, then the family of stalks P_x give rise to a sheaf $\bar{R}_X P$. If $\alpha : P \to P'$ is a morphism of presheaves, then define

$$\bar{R}_X(\alpha) : \bar{R}_X P \to \bar{R}_X P'$$

by the rule

$$\bar{R}_X(\alpha)_U = \bigtimes_{x\in U} \alpha_x.$$

In this way $\bar{R}_X : \mathscr{P}(X, \mathscr{A}) \to \mathscr{F}(X, \mathscr{A})$ becomes a covariant functor.

Let $(\mu_P)_U : P(U) \to \bigtimes_{x\in U} P_x$ be the morphism whose xth coordinate is P_{Ux}.

Then for $V \subset U$ the diagram

$$\begin{array}{ccc} P(U) & \longrightarrow & \underset{x \in U}{\times} P_x \\ \downarrow & & \downarrow \\ P(V) & \longrightarrow & \underset{x \in V}{\times} P_x \end{array}$$

is obviously commutative, and so μ_P is a morphism of presheaves. Furthermore given a morphism $\alpha : P \to P'$ of presheaves, for each open set U we have a commutative diagram

$$\begin{array}{ccc} P(U) & \longrightarrow & \underset{x \in U}{\times} P_x \\ \downarrow & & \downarrow \\ P'(U) & \longrightarrow & \underset{x \in U}{\times} P'_x \end{array}$$

In other words μ is a natural transformation from the identity functor on $\mathscr{P}(X, \mathscr{A})$ to the functor $\bar{R}_X$.

A **cosheaf** in a category $\mathscr{A}$ over a topological space X is a contravariant functor $\mathscr{U}_X \to \mathscr{A}$ such that the associated covariant functor $\mathscr{U}_X \to \mathscr{A}^*$ is a sheaf. For the theory of cosheaves, the underlying hypothesis on the category $\mathscr{A}$ is that it be cocomplete with inverse limits.

2. $\mathscr{F}$-Categories

A category satisfying the blanket hypothesis of the chapter will be called an $\mathscr{F}$**-category** if it satisfies the following additional conditions:

$\mathscr{F}_1$: Let $I = \bigcup_{\lambda \in \Lambda} I_\lambda$ be a disjoint union of sets, and for each λ let $\{A_i^\lambda\}_{i \in I_\lambda}$ be a naturally directed system of subobjects of some fixed object A. Then

$$\bigcap_{\lambda \in \Lambda} \left(\bigcup_{i \in I_\lambda} A_i^\lambda \right) = \bigcup_{\tau} \left(\bigcap_{\lambda \in \Lambda} A_{\tau(\lambda)}^\lambda \right) \tag{1}$$

where the union on the right side is over all functions $\tau : \Lambda \to I$ such that $\tau(\lambda) \in I_\lambda$ for all $\lambda \in \Lambda$.

$\mathscr{F}_2$: Let $\{A_i, \pi\}$ be a direct system in $\mathscr{A}$, and let $\{\pi_i : A_i \to A\}$ be the direct limit. For some index k let $f, g : B \to A_k$ be such that $\pi_k f = \pi_k g$, and denote $f_i = \pi_{ki} f$, $g_i = \pi_{ki} g$. Then we have

$$B = \bigcup_{i \geqslant k} \operatorname{Equ}(f_i, g_i).$$

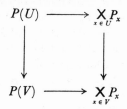

In the case where Λ is a set of two elements and one of the two direct systems is the trivial one consisting of a single subobject B, then (1) becomes

$$B \cap \bigcup_{i \in I} A_i = \bigcup_{i \in I} (B \cap A_i).$$

Therefore a cocomplete abelian category satisfying $\mathscr{F}_1$ is a C_3 category. In this case it follows from III, 1.8, that $\mathscr{F}_2$ is also satisfied. We shall call a cocomplete abelian category satisfying axiom $\mathscr{F}_1$ a C_4**-category**.

Lemma 2.1. *Let $\mathscr{A}$ be an $\mathscr{F}$-category and let P be a monopresheaf in $\mathscr{A}$ over X. Then $\mu_P : P \to \bar{R}_X P$ is a pointwise monomorphism (that is, $(\mu_P)_U$ is a monomorphism in $\mathscr{A}$ for each open U).*

Proof. Suppose that we have two morphisms $f, g : A \to P(U)$ such that

$$A \xrightarrow{f} P(U) \to \bigtimes_{x \in U} P_x = A \xrightarrow{g} P(U) \to \bigtimes_{x \in U} P_x.$$

Then for each $x \in U$ we have

$$A \xrightarrow{f} P(U) \to P_x = A \xrightarrow{g} P(U) \to P_x.$$

Therefore by $\mathscr{F}_2$ we can write

$$A = \bigcup_{x \in V \subset U} \operatorname{Equ}(f_V, g_V)$$

where $f_V = P_{UV} f$, $g_V = P_{UV} g$. Hence by $\mathscr{F}_1$ we have

$$A = \bigcap_{x \in U} \left(\bigcup_{x \in V \subset U} \operatorname{Equ}(f_V, g_V) \right) = \bigcup_{\tau} \left(\bigcap_{x \in U} \operatorname{Equ}(f_{\tau(x)}, g_{\tau(x)}) \right)$$

where the union on the right side is over all functions $\tau : U \to \mathscr{U}_X$ such that $\tau(x)$ contains x and is contained in U. Hence to show that $f = g$, it suffices to show that for each τ the restrictions of f and g to $\bigcap_{x \in U} \operatorname{Equ}(f_{\tau(x)}, g_{\tau(x)})$ are the same (I, 9.1). Now for each τ, $\{\tau(x)\}_{x \in U}$ is an open cover for U, and the composition

$$\bigcap_{x \in U} \operatorname{Equ}(f_{\tau(x)}, g_{\tau(x)}) \to A \to P(U) \to \bigtimes_{x \in U} P(\tau(x))$$

is the same whether $A \to P(U)$ is f or g. Therefore the conclusion follows since P is a monopresheaf. ▮

Corollary 2.2. *Let $\mathscr{A}$ be an $\mathscr{F}$-category and let P be a monopresheaf in $\mathscr{A}$ over X such that $P_x = 0$ for all $x \in X$. Then $P = 0$.*

Proof. $P_x = 0$ for all x implies $\bar{R}_X P = 0$. But then P, being a subsheaf of 0, is also 0. ▮

3. Associated Sheaves

It follows from the fact that limits in $\mathscr{P}(X, \mathscr{A})$ are computed pointwise that inverse images and intersections of pointwise monomorphisms are again pointwise monomorphisms, and that all equalizers in $\mathscr{P}(X, \mathscr{A})$ are pointwise monomorphisms. Also, since $\mathscr{A}$ is locally small, each object of $\mathscr{P}(X, \mathscr{A})$ has only a set of (equivalence classes of) pointwise subobjects. We use these remarks in the following theorem.

Theorem 3.1. *If $\mathscr{A}$ is an $\mathscr{F}$-category, then $\mathscr{F}(X, \mathscr{A})$ is a coreflective subcategory of $\mathscr{P}(X, \mathscr{A})$, and for each $P \in \mathscr{P}(X, \mathscr{A})$ the coreflection $R_X P$ is pointwise a subobject of $\bar{R}_X P$. If $\mathscr{A}$ is cocomplete then so is $\mathscr{F}(X, \mathscr{A})$. If $\mathscr{A}$ is cocomplete with a generator, then $\mathscr{F}(X, \mathscr{A})$ has a generator.*

Proof. Consider a presheaf morphism $\alpha : P \to F$ where F is a sheaf. Form the diagram

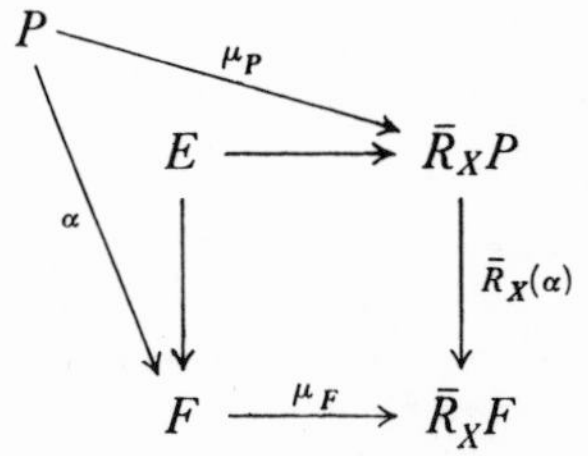

where the inner square is a pullback diagram and the outer square is commutative since μ is a natural transformation. By the definition of pullback, we obtain a morphism $P \to E$ keeping the diagram commutative. Now E, being the pullback of a diagram of sheaves, is also a sheaf. Since μ_F is a monomorphism (2.1), so is $E \to \bar{R}_X P$ (I, 7.1). Let $R_X P$ be the intersection of all pointwise subsheaves of $\bar{R}_X P$ through which μ_P factors. Then $R_X P$ is again a pointwise subsheaf of $\bar{R}_X P$, and α factors through $P \to R_X P$. Furthermore, if there were two distinct such factorizations, then the equalizer of the two factorizations would provide us with a proper pointwise subsheaf of $R_X P$ through which μ_P factors, contradicting the definition of $R_X P$. Hence, the factorization is unique, and so $P \to R_X P$ is the coreflection of P in $\mathscr{F}(X, \mathscr{A})$.

From V, 5.2, it now follows that if $\mathscr{A}$ is cocomplete then so is $\mathscr{F}(X, \mathscr{A})$. If $\mathscr{A}$ has a generator as well, then by VI, 4.3, $\mathscr{P}(X, \mathscr{A})$ has a generator. Consequently, by V, 1.5, $\mathscr{F}(X, \mathscr{A})$ has a generator. ▌

The coreflection $R_X P$ of a presheaf P in the category of sheaves $\mathscr{F}(X, \mathscr{A})$ is called **the associated sheaf of** P. If X is an indiscrete space (i.e. X has two open sets, X and $\emptyset$) then it is easily seen that a presheaf F is a sheaf if and only if $F(\emptyset) = 0$. From this it follows that the associated sheaf $R_X P$ of a presheaf P is such that $R_X P(X) = P(X)$ and $R_X P(\emptyset) = 0$.

4. Direct Images of Sheaves

Let $f : X \to Y$ be a continuous map of topological spaces (i.e., if V is open in Y, then $f^{-1}(V)$ is open in X). If $V' \subset V$, then $f^{-1}(V') \subset f^{-1}(V)$, so that f^{-1} can be regarded as a functor from $\mathscr{U}_Y$ to $\mathscr{U}_X$. Given a presheaf P in $\mathscr{A}$ over X, we obtain a presheaf f_*P in $\mathscr{A}$ over Y (called the **direct image** of P with respect to f) by taking the composition $Pf^{-1} : \mathscr{U}_Y \to \mathscr{A}$. Thus

$$f_*P(V) = P(f^{-1}(V)).$$

A morphism $\alpha : P \to P'$ of presheaves induces an obvious morphism $f_*(\alpha)$ $f_*P \to f_*P'$, and this makes $f_* : \mathscr{P}(X, \mathscr{A}) \to \mathscr{P}(Y, \mathscr{A})$ into a covariant functor. Since limits in $\mathscr{P}(X, \mathscr{A})$ and $\mathscr{P}(Y, \mathscr{A})$ are computed pointwise, it follows that f_* preserves limits. If $\mathscr{A}$ is cocomplete then f_* also preserves colimits.

Let $\{V_i\}$ be an open cover for V in Y. Then $\{f^{-1}(V_i)\}$ is an open cover for $f^{-1}(V)$ in X. From this it is trivial to verify that if F is a sheaf in $\mathscr{A}$ over X, then f_*F is a sheaf in $\mathscr{A}$ over Y. Observe that

$$f_* : \mathscr{F}(X, \mathscr{A}) \to \mathscr{F}(Y, \mathscr{A})$$

preserves limits, but does not in general preserve colimits.

If $g : Y \to Z$ is another continuous map, then it follows from the relation $(gf)^{-1}(W) = f^{-1}(g^{-1}(W))$ that $(gf)_* = g_*f_*$. Also if $f : X \to X$ is the identity map, then $f_* : \mathscr{P}(X, \mathscr{A}) \to \mathscr{P}(X, \mathscr{A})$ is the identity functor.

Theorem 4.1. *Let $\mathscr{A}$ be any category and let $f : X \to Y$ be any continuous map of topological spaces. Then the functor $f_* : \mathscr{P}(X, \mathscr{A}) \to \mathscr{P}(Y, \mathscr{A})$ has a coadjoint f^0. If $\mathscr{A}$ is a C_3 category then f^0 is exact.*

Proof. Let $Q \in \mathscr{P}(Y, \mathscr{A})$. For U an open set in X define

$$f^0Q(U) = \varinjlim_{f(U) \subset V} Q(V).$$

(Thus, if $f(U)$ happens to be a single point y in Y, then $f^0Q(U) = Q_y$.) If $U' \subset U$, then $f(U') \subset f(U)$, and so the open sets in Y containing $f(U)$ form a subfamily of the open sets in Y containing $f(U')$. There results an obvious morphism

$$f^0Q(U) \to f^0Q(U')$$

and this makes f^0Q a presheaf over X. Likewise, a morphism $\beta : Q \to Q'$ of presheaves gives rise to a morphism

$$(f^0\beta)_U : f^0Q(U) \to f^0Q'(U)$$

and $f^0\beta$ is clearly a morphism of presheaves. In this way f^0 becomes a covariant functor from $\mathscr{P}(Y, \mathscr{A})$ to $\mathscr{P}(X, \mathscr{A})$. We wish to show that f^0 is the coadjoint of f_*.

Given $P \in \mathscr{P}(X, \mathscr{A})$ and $Q \in \mathscr{P}(Y, \mathscr{A})$ we define a function

$$\eta_{Q,P} : [f^0Q, P] \to [Q, f_*P]$$

as follows. For $\alpha : f^0Q \to P$, define

$$\eta_{Q,P}(\alpha)_V : Q(V) \to f_*P(V) = P(f^{-1}(V))$$

as the composition

$$Q(V) \to f^0Q(f^{-1}(V)) \to P(f^{-1}(V)).$$

The first morphism arises from the fact that $f(f^{-1}(V) \subset V$ and so $Q(V)$ is one of the objects in the direct system defining $f^0Q(f^{-1}(V))$. The second morphism is just $\alpha_{f^{-1}(V)}$. It is then straightforward to show that $\eta_{Q,P}(\alpha)$ is a morphism of presheaves.

Now we define a function

$$\eta'_{Q,P} : [Q, f_*P] \to [f^0Q, P].$$

Given $\beta : Q \to f_*P$, an open set $U \subset X$, and an open set $V \subset Y$ containing $f(U)$, we have the composition

$$Q(V) \xrightarrow{\beta_V} f_*P(V) = P(f^{-1}(V)) \to P(U). \tag{1_V}$$

It follows from the fact that β is a morphism of presheaves that $\{(1_V)\}_{f(U) \subset V}$ is a cocompatible family, and thus we get an induced morphism

$$\eta'_{Q,P}(\beta)_U : f^0Q(U) \to P(U).$$

Again it is straightforward to show that $\eta'_{Q,P}(\beta)$ is a morphism of presheaves.

One then checks without difficulty that $\eta_{Q,P}$ and $\eta'_{Q,P}$ are inverses of each other, and finally that η is natural in Q and P. This establishes that f^0 is the coadjoint of f_*.

Now suppose that $\mathscr{A}$ is C_3. Then corresponding to an exact sequence of presheaves in $\mathscr{P}(Y, \mathscr{A})$

$$0 \to Q' \to Q \to Q'' \to 0$$

and an open set U in X, we have an exact direct limit sequence

$$0 \to \varinjlim_{f(U) \subset V} Q'(V) \to \varinjlim_{f(U) \subset V} Q(V) \to \varinjlim_{f(U) \subset V} Q''(V) \to 0$$

by III, 1.9. Hence f^0 is an exact functor. ∎

5. Inverse Images of Sheaves

Theorem 5.1. *Let $\mathscr{A}$ be an $\mathscr{F}$-category. Then for any continuous map $f: X \to Y$ the functor $f_*: \mathscr{F}(X, \mathscr{A}) \to \mathscr{P}(Y, \mathscr{A})$ has a coadjoint $f^* = R_X f^0: \mathscr{P}(Y, \mathscr{A}) \to \mathscr{F}(X, \mathscr{A})$. Furthermore, f^* has the following properties:*

(i) *$f^*|\mathscr{F}(Y, \mathscr{A})$ is the coadjoint of $f_*: \mathscr{F}(X, \mathscr{A}) \to \mathscr{F}(Y, \mathscr{A})$.*
(ii) *$f^* R_Y = f^*$.*
(iii) *If $g: Y \to Z$ is another continuous map, then $(gf)^* = f^* g^*$.*
(iv) *For any presheaf $Q \in \mathscr{P}(Y, \mathscr{A})$ and $x \in X$ we have $(f^*Q)_x \approx Q_{f(x)}$ and this isomorphism is natural with respect to morphisms in $\mathscr{P}(Y, \mathscr{A})$.*
(v) *For all $x \in X$ and all presheaves $P \in P(X, \mathscr{A})$ the coreflection $\varphi: P \to R_X P$ induces an isomorphism $\varphi_x: P_x \to (R_X P)_x$.*
(vi) *$R_X P = 0$ if and only if $P_x = 0$ for all x.*

Proof. The functor $f_*: \mathscr{F}(X, \mathscr{A}) \to \mathscr{P}(Y, \mathscr{A})$ can be regarded as the composition of the inclusion of $\mathscr{F}(X, \mathscr{A})$ into $\mathscr{P}(X, \mathscr{A})$ with the functor

$$f_*: \mathscr{P}(X, \mathscr{A}) \to \mathscr{P}(Y, \mathscr{A}).$$

By 3.1 the former has a coadjoint R_X, and by 4.1 the latter has a coadjoint f^0. Hence $f^* = R_X f^0$ is the required adjoint (V, §1).

(i) It follows trivially from the definition of adjoint functor and the fact that $\mathscr{F}(Y, \mathscr{A})$ is a full subcategory of $\mathscr{P}(Y, \mathscr{A})$ that $f^*|\mathscr{F}(Y, \mathscr{A})$ is the coadjoint of $f_*: \mathscr{F}(X, \mathscr{A}) \to \mathscr{F}(Y, \mathscr{A})$.

(ii) Regarding $f_*: \mathscr{F}(X, \mathscr{A}) \to \mathscr{P}(Y, \mathscr{A})$ as the composition of

$$f_*: \mathscr{F}(X, \mathscr{A}) \to \mathscr{F}(Y, \mathscr{A})$$

with the inclusion of $\mathscr{F}(Y, \mathscr{A})$ into $\mathscr{P}(Y, \mathscr{A})$ and using (i), we see that $f^* R_Y$ is a coadjoint for $f_*: \mathscr{F}(X, \mathscr{A}) \to \mathscr{P}(Y, \mathscr{A})$. Hence, by uniqueness of coadjoints (V, 2.2) we have $f^* = f^* R_Y$ as required.

(iii) By definition, $(gf)^*$ is the coadjoint of

$$(gf)_* = g_* f_*: \mathscr{F}(X, \mathscr{A}) \to \mathscr{P}(Z, \mathscr{A}).$$

Considering this last as the composition of $f_*: \mathscr{F}(X, \mathscr{A}) \to \mathscr{F}(Y, \mathscr{A})$ and $g_*: \mathscr{F}(Y, \mathscr{A}) \to \mathscr{P}(Z, \mathscr{A})$, and again using part (i), we see that $(gf)^* = f^* g^*$

(iv) Consider a point $x \in X$, and let $g_x: \{p\} \to X$ be the map from a one point topological space to X such that $g_x(p) = x$. If P is a presheaf over X, then it follows from the description of g_x^* as the composition of g_x^0 with the coreflection $R_{\{p\}}$ that $(g_x^* P)_p = P_x$ (see the remark at the end of §3 concerning the coreflection of a sheaf over an indiscrete space). Now for $f: X \to Y$, we have $f g_x = g_{f(x)}$, and so for a presheaf Q over Y we have, using (iii),

$$Q_{f(x)} = (g_{f(x)}^* Q)_p = ((f g_x)^* Q)_p = (g_x^*(f^* Q))_p = (f^* Q)_x.$$

Since each of the above identifications is natural, the proof of (iv) is complete.

(v) Consider the following commutative diagram which the morphism $\varphi_P : P \to R_X P$ induces on coreflections:

$$\begin{array}{ccc} P & \xrightarrow{\varphi_P} & R_X P \\ {\scriptstyle \varphi_P}\downarrow & & \downarrow{\scriptstyle R_X \varphi_P} \\ R_X P & \xrightarrow{\varphi_{R_X P}} & R_X R_X P \end{array}$$

Since every sheaf is its own associated sheaf via the identity morphism, we see that $\varphi_{R_X P} = 1$. Hence we have $R_X \varphi_P = 1$. Using the natural equivalence established in (iv), consider the commutative diagram

$$\begin{array}{ccc} P_x & \approx & (R_X P)_x \\ {\scriptstyle (\varphi_P)_x}\downarrow & & \downarrow{\scriptstyle (R_X \varphi_P)_x} \\ (R_X P)_x & \approx & (R_X R_X P)_x \end{array}$$

Since $(R_X \varphi_P)_x = 1$, it follows that $(\varphi_P)_x$ is an isomorphism as required.

(vi) If $P_x = 0$ for all x, then $\bar{R}_X P = 0$. Hence, by 3.1, $R_X P = 0$. Conversely, suppose that $R_X P = 0$. Then $(R_X P)_x = 0$ for all x, and so by (v), $P_x = 0$ for all x. ▮

Corollary 5.2. *Let $\mathscr{A}$ be a cocomplete $\mathscr{F}$-category and let X be a topological space. Then for each $x \in X$ the restriction of S_x to $\mathscr{F}(X, \mathscr{A})$ is a colimit preserving functor.*

Proof. We have seen in §1 that S_x is colimit preserving on $\mathscr{P}(X, \mathscr{A})$. Now the colimit in $\mathscr{F}(X, \mathscr{A})$ of a diagram in $\mathscr{F}(X, \mathscr{A})$ is obtained by taking the colimit in $\mathscr{P}(X, \mathscr{A})$ and coreflecting in $\mathscr{F}(X, \mathscr{A})$ (V, 5.2). Hence, the conclusion follows from 5.1, (v) which says that coreflections induce isomorphisms on stalks. ▮

6. Sheaves in Abelian Categories

Lemma 6.1. *Let $0 \to P' \to P \to P'' \to 0$ be an exact sequence of presheaves in an abelian category.*

(i) *If P' is a sheaf and P is a monopresheaf, then P'' is a monopresheaf.*
(ii) *If P'' is a monopresheaf and P is a sheaf, then P' is a sheaf* (cf. VI, 6.1).

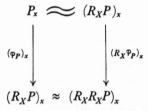

Proof. Let $U = \bigcup_{i \in I} U_i$ be an open covering, and consider the commutative diagram

$$\begin{array}{ccccccc}
 & & 0 & & 0 & & 0 \\
 & & \downarrow & & \downarrow & & \downarrow \\
0 & \longrightarrow & P'(U) & \xrightarrow{u'} & \mathsf{X}_{i \in I} P'(U_i) & \xrightarrow{f'-g'} & \mathsf{X}_{(j,k) \in I \times I} P'(U_{jk}) \\
 & & \downarrow & & \downarrow & & \downarrow \\
0 & \longrightarrow & P(U) & \xrightarrow{u} & \mathsf{X}_{i \in I} P(U_i) & \xrightarrow{f-g} & \mathsf{X}_{(j,k) \in I \times I} P(U_{jk}) \\
 & & \downarrow & & \downarrow & & \downarrow \\
0 & \longrightarrow & P''(U) & \xrightarrow{u''} & \mathsf{X}_{i \in I} P''(U_i) & \xrightarrow{f''-g''} & \mathsf{X}_{(j,k) \in I \times I} P''(U_{jk}). \\
 & & \downarrow & & & & \\
 & & 0 & & & &
\end{array}$$

The left column is exact by assumption and the other two columns are exact since products preserve kernels. Statements (i) and (ii) then follow by elementary diagram chasing. ▌

Lemma 6.2. *Let $\mathscr{A}$ be a C_4 category. Suppose that $\alpha : F \to P$ is a morphism in $\mathscr{P}(X, \mathscr{A})$ where F is a sheaf and P is a monopresheaf. Then α is an isomorphism if and only if α_x is an isomorphism for all $x \in X$.*

Proof. If α is an isomorphism then α_x is an isomorphism by the functorial property of S_x. Conversely, suppose that α_x is an isomorphism for all $x \in X$. Consider the exact sequence in $\mathscr{P}(X, \mathscr{A})$

$$0 \to \operatorname{Ker} \alpha \to F \xrightarrow{\alpha} P \to \operatorname{Coker} \alpha \to 0. \tag{1}$$

For any $x \in X$ we have by C_3 an exact sequence in $\mathscr{A}$

$$0 \to (\operatorname{Ker} \alpha)_x \to F_x \xrightarrow{\alpha_x} P_x \to \operatorname{Coker}(\alpha)_x \to 0.$$

But since α_x is an isomorphism, this means that $(\operatorname{Ker} \alpha)_x$ and $(\operatorname{Coker} \alpha)_x$ are 0 for all $x \in X$. Consider the exact sequence

$$0 \to \operatorname{Ker} \alpha \to F \to \operatorname{Im} \alpha \to 0.$$

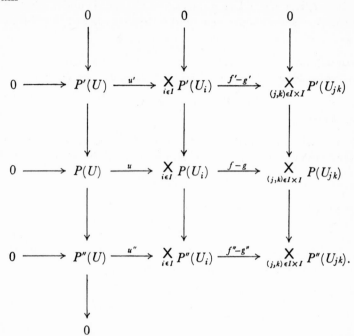

Since Im α is a subpresheaf of the monopresheaf P, it follows that Im α is also a monopresheaf. Hence, by 6.1, (ii), Ker α is a sheaf. But then since $(\text{Ker } \alpha)_x = 0$ for all x, by 2.2, Ker $\alpha = 0$. Using the exact sequence (1) and 6.1,(i), we then see that Coker α is a monopresheaf, and so since $(\text{Coker } \alpha)_x = 0$ for all x we have Coker $\alpha = 0$. Therefore α is an isomorphism. ▌

Theorem 6.3. *Let $\mathscr{A}$ be a C_4 category and let X be any topological space. Then the category of sheaves $\mathscr{F}(X, \mathscr{A})$ is a complete C_3 category and the coreflector*

$$R_X : \mathscr{P}(X, \mathscr{A}) \to \mathscr{F}(X, \mathscr{A})$$

is an exact functor.

Proof. By V, 5.3, it suffices to show that R_X preserves kernels. Let $0 \to P' \to P \to P''$ be an exact sequence in $\mathscr{P}(X, \mathscr{A})$. Then by C_3 for $\mathscr{A}$ the sequence

$$0 \to P'_x \to P_x \to P''_x$$

is exact in $\mathscr{A}$ for all x. Therefore by 5.1, (v) the sequence

$$0 \to (R_X P')_x \to (R_X P)_x \to (R_X P'')_x \tag{2}$$

is exact. Let $K \to R_X P$ be the kernel in $\mathscr{P}(X, \mathscr{A})$ of $R_X P \to R_X P''$. By 6.1, (ii), we know that K is a sheaf. Consider the diagram

$$\begin{array}{ccccc} R_X P' & \longrightarrow & R_X P & \longrightarrow & R_X P'' \\ & & \nearrow & & \\ & K & & & \end{array} \tag{3}$$

Since R_X is an additive functor, the composition in the top row is zero. There results a morphism $\alpha : R_X P' \to K$ making (3) commutative. Passing to stalks, using C_3 for the category $\mathscr{A}$, and using the exactness of (2), we see that α_x is an isomorphism for all x. Hence, by 6.2, α is an isomorphism. Thus $R_X P' \to R_X P$ is the kernel of $R_X P \to R_X P''$, and so R_X preserves kernels. ▌

Proposition 6.4. *Let $\mathscr{A}$ be a C_4 category. Then a sequence*

$$F' \to F \to F'' \tag{4}$$

is exact in $\mathscr{F}(X, \mathscr{A})$ if and only if the induced sequence

$$F'_x \to F_x \to F''_x$$

is exact in $\mathscr{A}$ for all x.

Proof. By 5.2, S_x is a cokernel preserving functor on $\mathscr{F}(X, \mathscr{A})$, and by C_3 for $\mathscr{A}$ it is also kernel preserving. Consequently, it is an exact functor. This proves the proposition in one direction. Now let

$$S(F) = \bigoplus_{x \in X} F_x$$

for a sheaf F over X. Then by what has already been proved and by C_1 for $\mathscr{A}$, S is an exact functor. Also by 2.2, S preserves nonzero objects, and so it follows from II, 7.2, that S is faithful. The proof of the proposition in the other direction now follows from II, 7.1. ∎

Corollary 6.5. *If $\mathscr{A}$ is a C_4 category, then a morphism $\alpha : F \to G$ in $\mathscr{F}(X, \mathscr{A})$ is the zero morphism if and only if $\alpha_x : F_x \to G_x$ is the zero morphism in $\mathscr{A}$ for all $x \in X$.* ∎

Proposition 6.6. *Let $\mathscr{A}$ be a C_4 category and let $f: X \to Y$ be a continuous map of topological spaces. Then the sheaf valued functor f^* is exact on both $P(Y, \mathscr{A})$ and $\mathscr{F}(Y, \mathscr{A})$.*

Proof. On $\mathscr{P}(Y, \mathscr{A})$ we can write $f^* = R_X f^0$. Since f^0 is exact (4.1) and R_X is exact (6.3), we see that f^* is exact.

Now on $\mathscr{F}(Y, \mathscr{A})$, f^* is a coadjoint (5.1, (i)) and consequently it is cokernel preserving. Since the kernel of a morphism in $\mathscr{F}(Y, \mathscr{A})$ is the same as the kernel in $\mathscr{P}(Y, \mathscr{A})$, and since f^* is kernel preserving on $\mathscr{P}(Y, \mathscr{A})$, it follows that f^* is also kernel preserving on $\mathscr{F}(Y, \mathscr{A})$. ∎

7. Injective Sheaves

If the C_4 category $\mathscr{A}$ has a generator, then by 3.1, $\mathscr{F}(X, \mathscr{A})$ also has a generator. But then $\mathscr{F}(X, \mathscr{A})$ being a C_3 category with a generator, has an injective cogenerator (III, 3.4) and so, in particular, $\mathscr{F}(X, \mathscr{A})$ has injectives. We are going to show more generally that if $\mathscr{A}$ has injectives, then so does $\mathscr{F}(X, \mathscr{A})$. The procedure generalizes a method of Godement [18, p. 260].

Lemma 7.1. *For each $x \in X$ let I_x be an object in a category $\mathscr{A}$. Let Q be the sheaf defined by $Q(U) = \bigtimes_{x \in U} I_x$ (i.e., Q is $\bar{R}_X I$ in the notation of §1). Then for any presheaf P we have a one to one correspondence*

$$\theta : [P, Q]_{\mathscr{P}(X,\mathscr{A})} \to \bigtimes_{x \in X} [P_x, I_x]_{\mathscr{A}}$$

which is natural in P.

Proof. For $x_0 \in U \subset X$ we have the projection

$$Q(U) = \bigtimes_{x \in U} I_x \to I_{x_0}$$

giving rise to a direct limit morphism $\bar{p}_{x_0} : Q_{x_0} \to I_{x_0}$. If $\alpha : P \to Q$ is a morphism of presheaves, then the family of morphisms $\bar{p}_{x_0} \alpha_{x_0}$ defines an element $\theta(\alpha)$ in $\bigtimes_{x \in X} [P_x, I_x]_{\mathscr{A}}$. It is clear that θ is natural in P. On the other hand, a family $\{\alpha_x : P_x \to I_x\}_{x \in X}$ defines a morphism of presheaves $\bar{R}_X P \to Q$ which, when composed with $\mu_P : P \to \bar{R}_X P$, gives us a morphism $\theta'(\alpha) \in [P, Q]$. We leave it to the reader to show that θ and θ' are inverses of each other. ∎

Corollary 7.2. *If $\mathscr{A}$ is a C_3 category and I_x is injective in $\mathscr{A}$ for all $x \in X$, then Q is injective in $\mathscr{P}(X, \mathscr{A})$.*

Proof. If $P' \to P$ is a monomorphism in $\mathscr{P}(X, \mathscr{A})$, then we must show that $[P, Q] \to [P', Q]$ is an epimorphism of groups. By C_3 for $\mathscr{A}$, $P'_x \to P_x$ is a monomorphism for all x, hence since I_x is injective in $\mathscr{A}$, $[P_x, I_x] \to [P'_x, I_x]$ is an epimorphism. Therefore by 7.1 and C_1^* for $\mathscr{G}$, $[P, Q] \to [P', Q]$ is an epimorphism. ∎

Theorem 7.3. *If $\mathscr{A}$ is a C_4 category with injectives, then $\mathscr{F}(X, \mathscr{A})$ has injectives.*

Proof. Given $F \in \mathscr{F}(X, \mathscr{A})$, for each $x \in X$ let $F_x \to I_x$ be a monomorphism into an injective. This gives rise to a monomorphism of presheaves $\bar{R}_X F \to Q$ where Q is as in 7.1. Composing this with $\mu_F : F \to \bar{R}_X F$, by 2.1 we obtain a monomorphism from F into Q. Now Q is a sheaf (1.1) and it is injective in $\mathscr{P}(X, \mathscr{A})$ (7.2). Also it follows easily from the fact that a monomorphism in $\mathscr{F}(X, \mathscr{A})$ is necessarily a monomorphism in $\mathscr{P}(X, \mathscr{A})$ that Q is also injective in $\mathscr{F}(X, \mathscr{A})$. This shows that $\mathscr{F}(X, \mathscr{A})$ has injectives. ∎

8. Induced Sheaves

We shall call a map $f: X \to Y$ of topological spaces a **relative** map if the open sets in X are precisely the sets of the form $f^{-1}(V)$ where V is open in Y.

Lemma 8.1. *If $f: X \to Y$ is relative, then for any category $\mathscr{A}$ the functor*

$$f_* : \mathscr{P}(X, \mathscr{A}) \to \mathscr{P}(Y, \mathscr{A})$$

is full. Furthermore, if $\alpha : P_1 \to P_2$ is a morphism in $\mathscr{P}(X, \mathscr{A})$ such that $f_*(\alpha)$ is an isomorphism, then α is an isomorphism.

Proof. Let $\beta : f_* P_1 \to f_* P_2$ be a morphism of presheaves over Y, and let U be an open set in X. Then U is of the form $f^{-1}(V)$ where V is open in Y. Furthermore, if V' is also such that $f^{-1}(V') = U$, then $f^{-1}(V \cap V') = U$, and we have

$$\beta_V = \beta_{V \cap V'} = \beta_{V'} : P_1(U) \to P_2(U).$$

We define $\alpha_U = \beta_V$ where V is any open set such that $f^{-1}(V) = U$. Then α is a morphism of presheaves, and we have $f_*(\alpha) = \beta$. This shows that f_* is full. The assertion about isomorphisms is a trivial consequence of the fact that every open set in X is of the form $f^{-1}(V)$ for some open V in Y. ∎

Let $\mathscr{A}$ be an $\mathscr{F}$-category, so that by 5.1 the functor $f_* : \mathscr{F}(X, \mathscr{A}) \to \mathscr{F}(Y, \mathscr{A})$ has a coadjoint $f^* : \mathscr{F}(Y, \mathscr{A}) \to \mathscr{F}(X, \mathscr{A})$. By V, §1, we have natural transformations $\varphi : 1 \to f_* f^*$ and $\psi : f^* f_* \to 1$.

Proposition 8.2. *Let $\mathscr{A}$ be an $\mathscr{F}$-category, and suppose that $f: X \to Y$ is relative. If F is a sheaf over X, then there is a sheaf G over Y such that $f^* G \approx F$.*

Proof. Consider the morphism

$$\psi_F : f^*f_*F \to F.$$

By 8.1, f_* is full. Consequently, by V, 1.3, $f_*(\psi_F)$ is an isomorphism. Hence, again by 8.1, ψ_F is an isomorphism, and so we may take $G = f_*F$. ▮

Lemma 8.3. *Let $\mathscr{A}$ be a C_4 category and let $f: X \to Y$ be relative. If F is a sheaf over Y and if K and M are the kernel and cokernel, respectively, in $\mathscr{F}(Y, \mathscr{A})$ for the morphism $\varphi_F : F \to f_*f^*F$, then $K_{f(x)}$ and $M_{f(x)}$ are zero for all $x \in X$.*

Proof. Since f_* is full, by V, 1.3* we see that $f^*(\varphi_F)$ is an isomorphism. Consequently, since f^* is exact (6.6) we see that f^*K and f^*M are 0. The result then follows from 5.1, (iv). ▮

Lemma 8.4. *Let $\mathscr{A}$ be a C_4 category, and let $f: X \to Y$ be relative. If F and G are sheaves in $\mathscr{A}$ over Y such that $F_y = G_y = 0$ for all $y \notin f(X)$, and if $\theta : f^*F \to f^*G$ is an isomorphism, then for some isomorphism $\tau : F \to G$ we have $f^*(\tau) = \theta$.*

Proof. Consider the following exact sequences in $\mathscr{F}(Y, \mathscr{A})$

$$\begin{array}{ccccccccc} 0 & \longrightarrow & K & \longrightarrow & F & \xrightarrow{\varphi_F} & f_* f^*F & \xrightarrow{p_F} & M & \longrightarrow & 0 \\ & & & & & & \wr\!\wr\, f_*(\theta) & & & & \\ 0 & \longrightarrow & L & \longrightarrow & G & \xrightarrow{\varphi_G} & f_* f^*G & \xrightarrow{p_G} & N & \longrightarrow & 0 \end{array} \qquad (1)$$

Using 8.3 and the hypothesis on F and G we see that $K_y = L_y = 0$ for all $y \in Y$. Therefore, by 2.2, $K = L = 0$. Now since $N_y = 0$ for $y \in f(X)$ and $F_y = 0$ for $y \notin f(X)$, it follows from 6.5 that the composition $p_G f_*(\theta)\varphi_F$ is zero. Hence, we have an induced morphism $\tau : F \to G$ making (1) commutative. Likewise, there is a morphism $\tau' : G \to F$ and τ and τ' are necessarily inverses of each other. Consider the commutative diagram

$$\begin{array}{ccc} f^*F & \overset{f^*\varphi_F}{\approx} & f^*f_*f^*F \\ \wr\wr\, f^*(\tau) & & \wr\wr\, f^*f_*(\theta) \\ f^*G & \overset{f^*\varphi_G}{\approx} & f^*f_*f^*G \end{array} \qquad (2)$$

Using the fact that the inverse of $f^*\varphi$ is ψf^* (V, 1.3*), we see that if we replace $f^*(\tau)$ by θ in (2) we still have commutativity. This shows that $f^*(\tau) = \theta$, as required. ▮

If f is the inclusion map of a subspace A into a space X and F is a sheaf over X, then we call f^*F the **sheaf induced by** F **over** A, and we denote it by $F|A$. If $A \subset B \subset X$, then it is clear from 5.1, (iii), that $(F|B)|A = F|A$. Also, by 5.1, (iv) and 2.2, we see that $F|A = 0$ if and only if $F_x = 0$ for all $x \in A$. We call $A \subset X$ a **locally closed** subspace if A is the intersection of an open subset and a closed subset of X. Equivalently, A is locally closed if there is a closed subspace B containing A such that A is open in B.

Theorem 8.5. *Let $\mathscr{A}$ be a C_4 category, and let A be a locally closed subspace of X. If F is any sheaf over X, then there is a unique sheaf F_A over X such that $F_A|A \approx F|A$ and such that $F_A|X - A = 0$. If A is closed, then we have an exact sequence*

$$0 \to F_{X-A} \to F \to F_A \to 0$$

in $\mathscr{F}(X, \mathscr{A})$.

Proof. Uniqueness of F_A has been established in 8.4.

If A is closed, define $F_A = f_* f^* F$ where $f: A \to X$ is the inclusion map. Then we have

$$\varphi_F : F \to f_* f^* F = F_A$$

and by V, 1.3*, $f^*(\varphi_F)$ is an isomorphism. In other words, $F_A|A \approx F|A$. We show that F_A induces 0 over $X - A$. For $x \in X - A$ we have

$$(F_A)_x = (f_* f^* F)_x = \varinjlim_{x \in U} f^* F(U \cap A)$$

where U runs through all open sets in X containing x. But since A is closed, one such U is $X - A$, and so since $f^* F(\varnothing) = 0$, we have $(F_A)_x = 0$. This proves the assertion in the case where A is closed.

Still in the case where A is closed, let M denote the cokernel of φ_F in $\mathscr{F}(X, \mathscr{A})$. For $a \in A$ we have $M_a = 0$ by 8.3, and for $x \in X - A$ we have $M_x = 0$ by what we have already proved. Consequently, $M = 0$ and so φ_F is an epimorphism. Let F_{X-A} be defined by the exact sequence

$$0 \to F_{X-A} \to F \xrightarrow{\varphi_F} F_A \to 0. \tag{3}$$

If we apply f^* to (3), we obtain an exact sequence by 6.6. Since $f^*(\varphi_F)$ is an isomorphism, this shows that $0 = f^* F_{X-A} = F_{X-A}|A$. On the other hand, letting $g: X - A \to X$ be the inclusion and applying g^* to (3), we obtain an isomorphism $g^* F_{X-A} \approx g^* F$ since $g^* F_A = F_A|X - A = 0$. Thus we have proved the theorem in the case of an open subspace.

Now suppose that $A \subset B \subset X$ where B is closed in X and A is open in B. By 8.2 we can find a sheaf G over X such that $G|B = (F|B)_A$. Then we may take $F_A = G_B$. ▮

Combining 8.2 and 8.5, we have:

Corollary 8.6. *Let $\mathscr{A}$ be a C_4 category, and let $A \subset X$ be a locally closed subspace. If G is any sheaf in $\mathscr{A}$ over A, then there is a unique sheaf G^X over X which induces G on A and 0 on $X - A$.* ▮

Exercises

1. Relative to a presheaf P and a point $x \in X$, define a morphism $\bar{p}_x : (\bar{R}_X P)_x \to P_x$ such that $\bar{p}_x(\mu_P)_x = 1_{P_x}$. Hence, show that if $\alpha : P \to P'$ is such that $\bar{R}_X(\alpha)$ is an isomorphism, then α_x is an isomorphism for all $x \in X$.

2. If $\mathscr{A}$ has a zero object, then we have product injections $u_x : P_x \to \bar{R}_X P(U)$ for each $x \in U$ and each presheaf P in over X. Passing to the direct limit we obtain a morphism $\bar{u}_x : P_x \to (\bar{R}_X P)_x$. In general $\bar{u}_x \neq (\mu_P)_x$. (Let X be an indiscrete space, and let $P(X) = \mathbf{Z}$. Then $\bar{u}_x$ is the xth injection $\mathbf{Z} \to \mathbf{Z}^X$ whereas $(\mu_P)_x$ is the diagonal morphism $\Delta : \mathbf{Z} \to \mathbf{Z}^X$.)

3. The categories $\mathscr{S}$, $\mathscr{T}$, and $\mathscr{A}_{\mathbf{Z}}$ of sets, topological spaces, and rings, respectively, are $\mathscr{F}$-categories. (For a discussion of the category of rings, see II, exercise 21.)

For any ring $\mathbf{R}$, the category $\mathscr{G}^{\mathbf{R}}$ is a C_4 category.

4. Define an object U to be **very small** if for each direct system $\{A_i\}$ with direct limit A, the induced morphism from the direct limit of the direct system of sets $[U, A_i]$ to the set $[U, A]$ is a monomorphism. Define U to be **quite small** if every morphism from U to the union of a naturally directed system of subobjects factors through one of the subobjects. In a cocomplete abelian category $\mathscr{A}$, a very small object is quite small. (Use III, 1.5.) If $\mathscr{A}$ is C_3, then a quite small object is very small. In a category with coproducts, an object which is quite small is small, and a small projective is quite small.

In 2.1, the assumption that $\mathscr{A}$ be an $\mathscr{F}$-category may be replaced by the condition that $\mathscr{A}$ have a generating class of very small objects. Hence all the numbers in the chapter involving $\mathscr{F}$-categories are valid for categories which have a generating class of very small objects (J. Gray [19]).

If $\mathscr{A}$ is a cocomplete abelian category with a generating class of very small objects, then $\mathscr{A}$ is C_4.

5. We sketch here an alternative treatment of sheaves, due to Freyd [15], in the case where $\mathscr{A}$ is the category of abelian groups $\mathscr{G}$. For an open set U in X let P^U be the presheaf defined as follows:

$$\begin{aligned} P^U(V) &= \mathbf{Z} && \text{if } V \subset U \\ &= 0 && \text{otherwise} \\ P^U_{VW} &= 1 && \text{if } W \subset V \subset U \\ &= 0 && \text{otherwise.} \end{aligned}$$

If $U_1 \subset U_2$ we have an obvious morphism $P^{U_1} \to P^{U_2}$. For any presheaf P we have the one to one correspondence

$$[P^U, P] \to P(U) \tag{1}$$

which assigns to the presheaf morphism $\alpha : P^U \to P$ the element $\alpha_U(1) \in P(U)$.

Also (1) is natural in U. If $U = \bigcup_{i\in I} U_i$ is an open cover, then we have the exact sequence

$$\bigoplus_{(j,k)\in I\times I} P^{U_{jk}} \to \bigoplus_{i\in I} P^{U_i} \to P^U \tag{2}$$

where the first morphism is the difference between the two obvious ones. Let P be any presheaf, and apply the contravariant functor $[\ ,P]$ to the exact sequence (2). Using the identification (1) we obtain the sequence

$$P(U) \to \bigtimes_{i\in I} P(U_i) \to \bigtimes_{(j,k)\in I\times I} P(U_{jk}) \tag{3}$$

where the morphisms are just those defined in §1. If P is injective in $\mathscr{P}(X, \mathscr{G})$, then $[\ ,P]$ is an exact functor and hence (3) is exact. Now $\mathscr{P}(X, \mathscr{G})$ has a generator, and hence injective envelopes. Also from the exact sequence (3) one sees that the injective envelope of a monopresheaf is a sheaf. (Show that an essential extension of a monopresheaf is a monopresheaf.) From this one verifies that $\mathscr{M}(X, \mathscr{G})$ is a monosubcategory of $\mathscr{P}(X, \mathscr{G})$ (V, §6) and that an object in $\mathscr{P}(X, \mathscr{G})$ is pure if and only if it is a sheaf. Consequently, the conclusions of 6.3 follow from V, 6.8.

The remaining exercises serve to relate the classical theory of sheaves as given in [18] *to the present theory.*

6. A presheaf P in the category of sets $\mathscr{S}$ is a monopresheaf if and only if it satisfies the following condition:

Let $U = \bigcup_{i\in I} U_i$ be an open cover, and let s and t be two elements of $P(U)$. If $P_{UU_i}(s) = P_{UU_i}(t)$ for each $i \in I$, then $s = t$.

A monopresheaf P is a sheaf if and only if it satisfies the following additional condition:

Let $U = \bigcup_{i\in I} U_i$ be an open cover, and for each $i \in I$ let s_i be an element of $P(U_i)$. If for each pair $i, j \in I$ we have $P_{U_iU_{ij}}(s_i) = P_{U_jU_{ij}}(s_j)$, then there exists $s \in P(U)$ such that $P_{UU_i}(s) = s_i$ for all $i \in I$.

7. A **sheaf space** (of sets) over a topological space X is a topological space E together with a local homeomorphism $p : E \to X$. (That is, every point $e \in E$ has an open neighborhood which is mapped homeomorphically onto an open neighborhood of $p(e)$ in X. We do not require that p be onto.) If U is an open subset of X, then a function $s : U \to E$ satisfying $p(s(x)) = x$ for all $x \in U$ is continuous if and only if its image is open in E. In this case s is called a **section** in E over U. The class of images of sections in E forms a basis for the topology on E. If two sections agree at a point $x \in X$, then they must agree in some neighborhood of x. If $p' : E' \to X$ is another sheaf space over X, then for a function $f : E \to E'$ satisfying $p'f = p$, the conditions that f be continuous, open, and a local homeomorphism are all equivalent. Taking such functions as morphisms, the class $\overline{\mathscr{F}}(X, \mathscr{S})$ of sheaf spaces over X becomes a category.

8. Let $LE(U)$ denote the family of sections of the sheaf space E over the open set U. If $V \subset U$, then a function $LE(U) \to LE(V)$ is defined by the operation of restriction, and it is easily verified that LE is a sheaf in $\mathscr{S}$ over X (exercise 6). Furthermore, a morphism $f: E \to E'$ of sheaf spaces induces a morphism $Lf: LE \to LE'$ defined by $Lf_U(s) = fs$, and in this way L becomes a covariant functor from $\overline{\mathscr{F}}(X, \mathscr{S})$ to $\mathscr{F}(X, \mathscr{S})$. From exercise 7 it follows that the stalk $(LE)_x = \varinjlim_{x \in U} LE(U)$ is in one to one correspondence with the subset $E_x = p^{-1}(x) \subset E$.

On the other hand, given a presheaf P in $\mathscr{S}$ over X, we let MP be the disjoint union of sets $\bigcup_{x \in X} P_x$ together with the map $p : MP \to X$ which sends each element of P_x into x. Associated with an element $s \in P(U)$ we have the function $\bar{s} : U \to MP$ which assigns to x the image of s under the morphism $P(U) \to P_x$. Thus $p(\bar{s}(x)) = x$ for all $x \in U$. The family $\{\bar{s}(U) | s \in P(U), U \text{ open in } X\}$ forms a basis for a topology on MP, and with respect to this topology p is a local homeomorphism. In this way M becomes a functor from the category $\mathscr{P}(X, \mathscr{S})$ to the category $\overline{\mathscr{F}}(X, \mathscr{S})$. Using exercise 7 we obtain an isomorphism $MLE \approx E$, and this defines a natural equivalence from ML to the identity functor on $\overline{\mathscr{F}}(X, \mathscr{S})$. On the other hand, starting with a presheaf P we have the function

$$\psi_P(U) : P(U) \to LMP(U)$$

which assigns the section $\bar{s}$ to the element $s \in P(U)$ as described above, and ψ is a natural transformation from the identity functor on $\mathscr{P}(X, \mathscr{S})$ to LM. If P is a sheaf, then ψ_P is an isomorphism. (Use exercise 6.) Hence the categories $\mathscr{F}(X, \mathscr{S})$ and $\overline{\mathscr{F}}(X, \mathscr{S})$ are equivalent.

9. For presheaves P and sheaves F in $\mathscr{S}$ over X, establish a natural equivalence of bifunctors

$$[P, F] \approx [LMP, F],$$

thereby showing that $LM = R_X : \mathscr{P}(X, \mathscr{S}) \to \mathscr{F}(X, \mathscr{S})$.

10. Consider a continuous map of topological spaces $f: X \to Y$ and a sheaf $G \in \mathscr{F}(Y, \mathscr{S})$. Let NG be the disjoint union of sets $\bigcup_{x \in X} G_{f(x)}$, and consider the obvious map $p : NG \to X$. A **basic section** over an open set U in X is defined as a function $s : U \to NG$ such that $p(s(x)) = x$ for all $x \in U$, and such that there is a section $t : V \to MG$ with $f(U) \subset V$ and $s(x) = t(f(x))$ for all $x \in X$. The class of images of basic sections forms a basis for a topology on NG, and with respect to this topology NG is a sheaf space over X. In this way

$$N : \mathscr{F}(Y, \mathscr{S}) \to \overline{\mathscr{F}}(X, \mathscr{S})$$

becomes a covariant functor.

Establish a natural equivalence of bifunctors

$$[G, f_*F] \approx [LNG, F]$$

for sheaves F and G over X and Y respectively, thereby showing that

$$LN = f^* : \mathscr{F}(Y, \mathscr{S}) \to \mathscr{F}(X, \mathscr{S}).$$

11. A **sheaf space of abelian groups** over X is a sheaf space $p : E \to X$ together with an abelian group structure for each of the sets $E_x = p^{-1}(x)$, $x \in X$, such that addition is a continuous function from a subset of $E \times E$ to E. (In particular, p must be onto, since each of the sets $p^{-1}(x)$ must consist of at least one element.) A morphism of sheaf spaces of abelian groups is a morphism $f : E \to E'$ of sheaf spaces of sets such that the induced map $E_x \to E'_x$ is a morphism of abelian groups for each $x \in X$. The category of sheaf spaces of abelian groups over X is denoted by $\overline{\mathscr{F}}(X, \mathscr{G})$.

If $E \in \overline{\mathscr{F}}(X, \mathscr{G})$ and s and t are two sections over the open set U, then the function $s + t : U \to E$ defined by $(s + t)(x) = s(x) + t(x)$ is a section over U. The function $X \to E$ which assigns to each $x \in X$ the zero element of the corresponding stalk is a section over X. If s is a section over U, then the function $-s : U \to E$ defined by $(-s)(x) = -s(x)$ is a section over U. Thus the set of sections $LE(U)$ has the structure of an abelian group, and L can be considered as a functor from $\overline{\mathscr{F}}(X, \mathscr{G})$ to $\mathscr{F}(X, \mathscr{G})$.

On the other hand, if P is a presheaf in $\mathscr{P}(X, \mathscr{G})$, then the additive structure of the stalks P_x is continuous with respect to the topology on MP defined in exercise 8, and thus M can be considered as a functor from $\mathscr{P}(X, \mathscr{G})$ to $\overline{\mathscr{F}}(X, \mathscr{G})$. The natural transformations of exercise 8 are valid within the categories $\mathscr{P}(X, \mathscr{G})$ and $\overline{\mathscr{F}}(X, \mathscr{G})$, and it follows again that the categories $\mathscr{F}(X, \mathscr{G})$ and $\overline{\mathscr{F}}(X, \mathscr{G})$ are equivalent. The natural equivalence of exercise 9 still holds, showing that $LM = R_X : \mathscr{P}(X, \mathscr{G}) \to \mathscr{F}(X, \mathscr{G})$. The functor N of exercise 10 can be considered as a functor from $\mathscr{F}(Y, \mathscr{G})$ to $\overline{\mathscr{F}}(X, \mathscr{G})$, and the natural equivalence of that exercise is valid. Thus $LN = f^* : \mathscr{F}(Y, \mathscr{G}) \to \mathscr{F}(X, \mathscr{G})$.

If $p : E \to X$ is a sheaf space and if each of the sets E_x has a ring structure in such a way that both addition and multiplication are continuous, and if further the collection of unit elements forms a section over X, then E is called a **sheaf space of rings**. The results of the exercise are then valid if the category of abelian groups is replaced everywhere by the category of rings.

12. If $f : E \to E'$ is a morphism in $\overline{\mathscr{F}}(X, \mathscr{G})$, then the kernel of f is that subspace of E consisting of all elements which are taken into the zero element of the corresponding stalk of E'. The cokernel of f is stalkwise over x the cokernel of the morphism $E_x \to E'_x$ induced by f. The topology on Coker(f) is defined by taking as a basis the class of images of sections in E' under the obvious map $E' \to \text{Coker}(f)$. The image of f is given by the setwise image.

If $\{E^\lambda\}_{\lambda\in\Lambda}$ is any family of objects in $\overline{\mathscr{F}}(X, \mathscr{G})$, then the coproduct is given stalkwise by the formula

$$\left(\bigoplus_{\lambda\in\Lambda} E^\lambda\right)_x = \bigoplus_{\lambda\in\Lambda} E^\lambda_x.$$

The topology is obtained by taking as a basic family of sections the functions of the form $\sum_{\lambda\in\Lambda} s_\lambda : U \to \bigoplus_{\lambda\in\Lambda} E^\lambda$, where $s_\lambda \in LE^\lambda(U)$ is zero except for a finite number of λ. The product of the above family is given stalkwise over x by the set of all Λ-tuples (s_λ), where s_λ is a section in E_λ defined over a common open set U containing x for all $\lambda \in \Lambda$, modulo the equivalence relation which identifies two tuples (s_λ) and (t_λ) if and only if there is an open set V containing x such that $s_\lambda | V = t_\lambda | V$ for all $\lambda \in \Lambda$.

The intersection of a family of subobjects in $\overline{\mathscr{F}}(X, G)$ is given by the interior of the setwise intersection.

13. Let ω denote the set of positive integers. For $n \in \omega$ let F^n be the sheaf space of abelian groups defined over the closed interval $[0, 1]$, such that $F^n_x = \mathbf{Z}$ for $x \in [0, 1/n)$ and $F^n_x = 0$ for $x \in [1/n, 1]$, where the only sections in F^n are the constant maps. Let $F^{n'}$ be the subsheaf space of F^n such that $F^{n'}_x = F^n_x$ for $x \in (1/2n, 1/n)$ and $F^{n'}_x = 0$ otherwise. Then the product of epimorphisms

$$\mathsf{X}_{n\in\omega} F^n \to \mathsf{X}_{n\in\omega} F^n/F^{n'}$$

is not an epimorphism, and consequently the category $\mathscr{F}([0, 1], \mathscr{G})$ is not C_1^*. (Show that $\left(\mathsf{X}_{n\in\omega} F^n\right)_0 = {}^{\omega}\mathbf{Z}$, whereas $\left(\mathsf{X}_{n\in\omega} F^n/F^{n'}\right)_0 = \mathbf{Z}^{\omega}$.) Hence deduce from III, exercise 2 that this category does not have projectives.

14. Let X be a locally compact Hausdorff space (so that every point has a basic family of compact neighborhoods). Then $\overline{\mathscr{F}}(X, \mathscr{G})$ is a C_4 category, and consequently $\mathscr{F}(X, \mathscr{G})$ is a C_4 category.

Bibliography

[1] Baer, R., *Bull. Am. Math. Soc.* **46** (1940), 800–806.

[2] Baer, R., *Math. Z.* **38** (1934), 375–416.

[3] Buchsbaum, D. A., Exact categories and duality. *Trans. Am. Math. Soc.* **80** (1955), 1–34.

[4] Buchsbaum, D. A., A note on homology in categories. *Ann. of Math.* **69** (1959), 66–74.

[5] Buchsbaum, D. A., Satellites and universal functors. *Ann. of Math.* **71** (1960), 199–209.

[6] Cartan, H., and Eilenberg, S., "Homological Algebra." Princeton Univ. Press, Princeton, New Jersey, 1956.

[7] Deheuvels, R., Homologie des ensembles ordonnés et des espaces topologiques. *Bull. Soc. Math. France* **90** (1962), 261–321.

[8] Eckmann, B., and Schopf, A., Über Injektive Moduln. *Arch. Math.* **4** (1953), 75–78.

[9] Eilenberg, S., Abstract description of some basic functors. *J. Indian Math. Soc.* **24** (1960), 221–234.

[10] Eilenberg, S., and MacLane, S., Natural isomorphisms in group theory. *Proc. Nat. Acad. Sci. U.S.* **28** (1942), 537–543.

[11] Eilenberg, S., and MacLane, S., General theory of natural equivalences. *Trans. Am. Math. Soc.* **58** (1945), 231–294.

[12] Eilenberg, S., and Moore, J., Foundations of relative homological algebra (to appear).

[13] Eilenberg, S., Rosenberg, A., and Zelinsky, D., On the dimension of modules and algebras, VIII. *Nagoya Math. J.* **12** (1957), 71–93.

[14] Freyd, P., Functor Theory (Dissertation). Princeton University, Princeton, New Jersey, 1960.

[15] Freyd, P., Abelian Categories (Mimeographed Notes). Columbia University, New York, 1962.

[16] Freyd, P., Relative homological algebra made absolute. *Proc. Nat. Acad. Sci. U.S.* **49** (1963), 19–20.

[17] Gabriel, P., Des Catégories Abéliennes. *Bull. Soc. Math. France* **90** (1962), 323–448.

[18] Godement, R., "Théorie des Faisceaux." Hermann, Paris, 1958.

[19] Gray, J. S., Sheaves with values in a Category (Mimeographed Notes, Revised Edition), Columbia University, New York, 1962.

[20] Grothendieck, A., Sur quelques points d'Algèbre homologique. *Tôhoku Math. J.* **9** (1957). 119–221.

[21] Hilbert, D., Über die Theorie der Algebraischen Formen. *Math. Ann.* **36** (1890), 473–539.

[22] Hochschild, G., Relative homological algebra. *Trans. Am. Math. Soc.* **82** (1956), 246–269.

[23] Hochschild, G., Note on relative homological dimension. *Nagoya Math. J.* **13** (1958), 89–94.

[24] Kan, D., Adjoint functors. *Trans. Am. Math. Soc.* **87** (1958), 294–329.

[25] Kelley, J. L., "General Topology." Van Nostrand, Princeton, New Jersey, 1955.

[26] Lawvere, F. W., Functorial Semantics of Algebraic Theories (Dissertation). Columbia University, New York, 1963.

[27] Lubkin, S., Imbedding of abelian categories. *Trans. Am. Math. Soc.* **97** (1960), 410–417.

[28] MacLane, S., Groups, categories, and duality. *Proc. Nat. Acad. Sci. U.S.* **34** (1948), 263–267

[29] MacLane, S., Duality for groups. *Bull. Am. Math. Soc.* **50** (1950), 485–516.

[30] MacLane, S., Locally small categories and the foundations of set theory. *Proc. Symp. Foundations Math., Warsaw* (1959).

[31] MacLane, S., "Homology." Springer, Berlin, 1963.

[32] Mitchell, B., Homological Tic Tac Toe (Dissertation). Brown University, Providence. Rhode Island, 1960.

[33] Mitchell, B., The Full Imbedding Theorem (Mimeographed Notes). Columbia University, New York, 1963.

[34] Watts, C., Intrinsic characterizations of some additive functors. *Proc. Am. Math. Soc.* **11** (1960), 5–8.

[35] Yoneda, N., On the homology theory of modules. *J. Fac. Sci. Univ. Tokyo Sect. I* (1954), 193–227.

[36] Yoneda, N., Note on products in ext. *Proc. Am. Math. Soc.* **9** (1958), 873–875.

Subject Index